Psychoanalysis:
Education, Research, Science, and Profession

Psychoanalysis: Education, Research, Science, and Profession

ROBERT S. WALLERSTEIN, M.D.

INTERNATIONAL UNIVERSITIES PRESS, INC.
MADISON   CONNECTICUT

INTERNATIONAL UNIVERSITIES PRESS ® AND IUP (& design) ® are registered trademarks of International Universities Press, Inc.

Library of Congress Cataloging-in-Publication Data

Wallerstein, Robert S.
    Psychoanalysis: education, research, science, and profession/Robert S. Wallerstein.
        p. cm.
    Includes bibliographical references and indexes.
    ISBN 0-8236-5218-1
    1. Psychoanalysis—Study and teaching. 2. Psychoanalysis—Philosophy. 3. Psychoanalysts. I. Title.

RC502 .W35 2004
616.89′17—dc21

                                                        2002032820

Manufactured in the United States of America

TO JUDY

who has given inspiration and pleasure
to this lifelong journey

Table of Contents

Acknowledgments

Acknowledgment is gratefully made to the following journals and book publishers for permission to reprint chapters in this volume: the *International Journal of Psycho-Analysis* for chapter 1 from the *International Journal* and chapter 2 from the *International Review*, the *Journal of the American Psychoanalytic Association* for chapter 4; the *Psychoanalytic Quarterly* for chapters 7 and 9; *The Psychoanalytic Study of the Child* for chapter 8; the *Bulletin of the Menninger Clinic* for chapter 10 and 11; Grune and Stratton for chapter 3; the American Psychiatric Association for chapter 5; International Universities Press for chapter 6.

Preface

In 1975, International Universities Press published a collection of sixteen of my papers from that first twenty-five years of my life in psychoanalysis under the title *Psychotherapy and Psychoanalysis: Theory, Practice, Research.* In the late 1990s, this same press undertook to publish a widened collection of my papers from the succeeding twenty-five years, papers that would reflect the fuller development of the themes represented a quarter-century earlier.

This proved a more formidable undertaking, and has become—even with the drastic curtailment necessitated by the current economics of the book publishing business, and by the limits of book length that could attract willing, but busy, readers—two separate volumes. The first, published in 1999, *Psychoanalysis: Clinical and Theoretical,* comprised a collection of papers that crystallized in two directions: (1) the exposition of the ever shifting and evolving relationship between psychoanalysis and the range of psychoanalytically based and informed psychotherapies, in both theory and in practice; and (2) the burgeoning of psychoanalytic theoretical and clinical diversity or pluralism—partly under the influence of current postmodernist intellectual trends—and its implications for the maintenance of a defining psychoanalytic common ground.

Deferred for the second volume of this turn-of-the-century twosome was the range of considerations of my evolved and now crystallized stances on psychoanalytic education and research, on psychoanalysis as a science and a profession, now published as a series of eleven papers in this volume. These papers stem from my lifetime of involvement in empirical psychoanalytic research in the Psychotherapy Research Project (PRP) of The Menninger Foundation—of which I gave a final clinical accounting in my 1986 book, *Forty-Two Lives in Treatment: A Study of Psychoanalysis and Psychotherapy*—and in a currently ongoing successor project, dubbed PRP-II, and my simultaneous lifelong preoccupation in organized psychoanalysis with the issues and the problems of psychoanalytic education. Related to the issues of psychoanalytic research, of course, are concerns with the nature of psychoanalysis as a science, and what kind of science, and with what conceptual parameters and methods it can aspire to operate. And related to the issues of psychoanalytic education are concerns with the identity of psychoanalysis as a discipline, and its productive place within our contemporary sociopolitical world. These are collectively the issues addressed in the papers within the present volume, representing my psychoanalytic posture after more than half a century of psychoanalytic work, beginning with my entry in 1949 into psychiatric training within a psychoanalytically guided department of psychiatry.

What have had to be omitted from this current two-volume set of papers, for reasons of length and hence of cost and attractiveness, have been a sequence of papers reflecting my concerns with the relationship of psychoanalysis to the whole world of outer reality, the least developed of the interfaces of Freud's structural model. These are both theoretical papers on the conceptualization of the interplay of inner (psychic) reality and external (material) reality in psychic development and functioning, and what can be called "applied" papers on the capacity of psychoanalysis to function under adverse external circumstance—in the extremes within repressive and totalitarian regimes, Communist and Fascist—as well as the capacity, and willingness, of psychoanalysis to play a role in addressing the major social and political pressures and dangers of our twentieth and early twenty-first century world. These are such issues as human conflict and its control, the once awesome and still existent nuclear threat, all the way to the less frightful but still very real issues of psychoanalytic survival as a viable professional enterprise within a world of limited economic resources, faced with the issue of setting priorities that provide economic sustenance for ever growing populations. Partly to make up for these omissions, this volume concludes with a listing of my entire scientific bibliography to which readers can turn to find access to these and any of the other issues covered in the range of articles in this collection of three volumes of my selected papers, on each of which I have written more extensively elsewhere.

I end this preface with the customary, but never routine, thanks: To the late Martin Azarian and to Margaret Emery of International Universities Press for their willing support in publishing, over the years, three successive volumes of my selected papers, spanning the decades from 1951 to 1996; to Barbara Lehman who has faithfully and diligently prepared my manuscripts over so many years.

Robert S. Wallerstein

Part I

Psychoanalytic Education and Research

I have had a long-abiding concern with the issues and problems of both psychoanalytic education and psychoanalytic research (and also in their potential impact on each other). Concerning psychoanalytic education, in a prior book of my selected papers (1975), I published my first paper specifically devoted to this topic, entitled "The Futures of Psychoanalytic Education" (1972). The occasion was a 1971 panel at the American Psychoanalytic Association celebrating the tenth anniversary of COPE, the American's Committee on Psychoanalytic Education. This was a study group devoted to the exploration of all aspects of the tripartite psychoanalytic educational structure devised originally by Max Eitingon and his colleagues with the creation of the first organized psychoanalytic institute in Berlin in 1920. This model had persisted basically unaltered throughout the psychoanalytic world over the half-century until the 1971 panel.

The heady post-World War II decades of ebullient psychoanalytic expansion, the 1950s and the 1960s, were marked among other things by the rise in America of university-based psychoanalytic institutes established as autonomous units within psychoanalytically friendly medical school departments of psychiatry. My call on the 1971 panel was for the closer integration of our psychoanalytic institutes within the overall university educational enterprise, not only

in terms of the further development of the university-based institutes as we knew them then, but more sweepingly in the (perhaps
Utopian) direction of autonomous psychoanalytic institutes within
universities, independent from, but affiliated with, both the medical
school and the graduate faculties in the behavioral sciences and the
humanities. At the time, I saw this idealistically as the logical and
vitally necessary developmental trajectory for psychoanalytic education which would ineluctably lead to the breakdown, finally, of the
relative isolation from the wider scientific and intellectual world
that psychoanalysis had historically endured, by dint of its particular
developmental history. This could eventuate in a true flowering of
psychoanalytic scholarship and research, and also of interactively
rewarding discourse with all the cognate disciplines of human intelligence that the university structure is uniquely designed to ensure.

This initial interest in the structure of psychoanalytic education
within the particular circumstances of organized psychoanalysis in
America three decades ago developed into a more intense preoccupation with psychoanalytic education worldwide. From 1975, I became increasingly involved in the educational issues confronting
the International Psychoanalytical Association (IPA) in its widely
varying geographic, sociocultural, and linguistic settings. All of
these issues of psychoanalytic education, which I have dealt with
over the intervening years, have been the subject of continuing intense (and quite unresolved) dialogue within organized psychoanalysis in America and worldwide. The discussion of these issues is just
as timely today as when they were first raised, which adds warrant
to my decision to include two of the most salient of my papers in
this collection.

The first of the two papers I have selected for inclusion in
this volume is "Perspectives on Psychoanalytic Training Around the
World," the main presentation and discussion paper for the seventh
Pre-Congress Conference on Training, held in conjunction with the
thirtieth biannual IPA Congress in Jerusalem in August 1977. The
paper was based on a questionnaire survey of the fifty-seven-member
psychoanalytic institutes, to which twenty-eight responded, some in
astonishingly full and thoughtful detail. The questionnaire was built
around three groups of interrelated questions: (1) How had the
institute attempted to encompass the dual goals of training competent practitioners for the profession of psychoanalysis, and of educating people to comprehensively understand and advance our
knowledge of the science of psychoanalysis? (2) What was the kind

and degree of personality alteration that psychoanalytic training is expected to achieve with candidates? (3) How did the training sequence organized in relation to these educational goals and these expectations for personality alteration foster or impede these goals and expectations? What emerged from analysis of the questionnaire responses was (1) a detailed overview of the identifying commonality that makes psychoanalytic training, at least in its structuralization, seem everywhere pretty much the same; (2) but that within this basic framework there was at the same time an enormous degree of variation, at some points to actual polar opposites, around many of the major pedagogical, scientific, and even verging on the philosophical, issues that beset our professional educational enterprise.

The second article, chapter 2, "The Mental Health Professions: Conceptualization and Reconsideration of a New Discipline," is a conceptual offshoot of psychoanalysis, an effort to create, by fiat, an entirely new mental health professional education, a Doctor of Mental Health (DMH) degree. This degree was to be based on the amalgam of the preparatory educational experiences most relevant to clinical mental health practice from the training for the three major mental health professional disciplines, psychiatry, clinical psychology, and psychiatric social work. This experimental program in mental health professional education, conceived out of a particular set of historical circumstances and opportunities, was established in 1973 within the University of California system and first formally presented, in its conceptualization and its operation, to a psychiatric–psychoanalytic audience in this paper as the invited fourth annual Gustav Bychowski Lecture at the Mount Sinai School of Medicine, Department of Psychiatry, New York, coincidentally the institution in which I had received my own initial psychiatric residency training almost three decades earlier.

At the time of that presentation (April 1977), the DMH program had become formally established within the University of California system, had been in operation four years, with four classes, the first two with six in each class, and the next two with twelve in each class, and was looking forward, a year later, to its first DMH graduates from the five-year program. It was, however, still very much a program in formation, with its necessary doctorate degree not yet approved in the university's academic and administrative hierarchy, and licensure for a career of future professional practice in only the embryonic stage of progression through the State of

California legislative process. Actually, the DMH degree was subsequently officially approved in time to be awarded to the first graduates a year later, and though separate licensure was never approved, the graduates did become eligible for licensure as clinical psychologists. Nonetheless, because of increasing financial pressures within the university at that time, combined with professional pressures from medical and psychiatric interests both within and outside the university, the DMH program was closed out in 1986 after thirteen years of operation after having graduated about seventy-five students in nine successive five-year classes (see Wallerstein, 1991, for a full discussion of this program). The program itself no longer exists but the idea, psychoanalytically conceived and sponsored, lives on in the literature, to be revived some day one hopes under more propitious circumstances. Certainly the soundness of the conception as a felicitous road to mental health professional practice is amply attested by the successful practice careers established by almost the entire cadre of graduates, a high number of whom continued with full psychoanalytic training and practice, some with distinguished scholarly careers as psychoanalytic contributors.

One last orienting statement about psychoanalytic education: Though Freud wrote very little specifically about psychoanalytic education, here, as almost everywhere else in things psychoanalytic, he nonetheless did spell out and grapple with the central issues that have subsequently concerned psychoanalysis, as they have evolved over all the years since. For this reason, I have felt it central to my account to cite the same few, but very salient, passages about psychoanalytic education embedded in *The Question of Lay Analysis* (1926b) and the 1928 letter to Pfister (Freud and Pfister, 1963), in both of the articles in this section. I ask forgiveness for this minor redundancy; it would have disrupted the fabric of each of those articles had I tried to eliminate these quotations.

To turn now to psychoanalytic research: My involvement in this arena has been the distinguishing mark of my entire psychoanalytic career spanning a half-century. The centerpiece of this has been the Psychotherapy Research Project (PRP) of The Menninger Foundation, of which I was the Principal Investigator from the inception of the project in 1954 until the publication of my final clinical accounting of its work and findings in my 1986 book, *Forty-Two Lives in Treatment: A Study of Psychoanalysis and Psychotherapy*. Over a more than thirty-year time span the project published six other books and monographs as part of a total of over seventy publications, of which I was author or coauthor of about twenty-five. Of the sixteen chapters in my 1975 book of selected papers (*Psychotherapy and Psychoanalysis: Theory, Practice, Research*), four were direct publications from PRP. Another four chapters were more general reflections on the relationship between psychotherapy and psychoanalysis that were based to a very considerable degree on my experiences within PRP.

In the present section of this volume, I am including only three further papers from my overall corpus in PRP and other research-based publications, two of them directly from PRP and one, a more general statement about psychotherapy research, which clearly incorporates perspectives gained from work within PRP. Chapter 3, "Psychotherapy Research: One Paradigm," was written originally for a Festschrift honoring Jurgen Ruesch (Ostwald, 1977). Of the several articles I wrote for different purposes and occasions, which have presented an overview of the construction of PRP, its aims and objectives, its form and scope, its working procedures and instruments, and its methods of data analysis, this paper is the most comprehensive, and yet succinct, such statement. I feel it gives a very clear view of the nature of PRP, what it set out to investigate, and how it went about that task. Each of the content areas and themes presented in it have of course been the subject of other much more detailed articles on that particular aspect of the project.

A companion article to chapter 3 appeared in Wallerstein (1999, chapter 12) because, though it summarizes the main findings and conclusions of PRP, a formal and systematic study of the processes and outcomes of psychoanalytic psychotherapies, its overall content made it fit better with a cluster of articles considering the relationship of psychoanalysis to the derived psychoanalytic psychotherapies published over a number of years from a variety of perspectives.

The second in this trio of research articles, chapter 4, "Assessment of Structural Change in Psychoanalytic Therapy and Research," is rather a programmatic statement for a successor psychotherapy project (dubbed PRP-II), started at the Langley Porter Institute, University of California, San Francisco, in 1985. This program, still ongoing, is an effort to take one of the main issues dealt with in PRP, the degree to which structural change in personality organization—beyond just symptom relief and altered manifest behavior patterns—occurs differentially in exploratory–expressive psychoanalytic psychotherapy and psychoanalysis as compared with the psychoanalytically informed supportive psychotherapies that are more explicitly designed to restore the ego's faltering equilibrium rather than to achieve basic conflict resolution and character change. The somewhat surprising and quite compelling findings in PRP in this regard (1999, chapter 12) would need confirmation in a subsequent study built on the use of a reliable and valid metric to assess psychic structure and measure structural change. Our group feels that it has created such an instrument in our Scales of Psychological Capacities (SPC). The urgent need for such an instrument, the rationale for its construction in the particular form that we used, and an outline of its original array of descriptors, subsequently added to and developed further in later, more detailed publications, is the substance of chapter 4. Research studies employing the SPC are currently underway within our group in San Francisco and also in a half-dozen European countries using translations into German, Swedish, Finnish, Italian, and French.

The third article in this group on psychoanalytic research, chapter 5, "Outcomes of Psychoanalysis and Psychotherapy at Termination and at Follow-Up," is not about either PRP or PRP-II, but is rather a comprehensive overview of several "generations" now of psychoanalytic therapy research in which PRP is summarized within the frame of the entire field of formal and systematic psychotherapy research as it has developed from as early in 1917 until the present. In this chapter, I arrange this story across four "generations" of psychoanalytic therapy research, each succeeding generation starting at a chronologically later time, but also conceived with a more sophisticated and state-of-the-art design, both conceptually and methodologically. The generations overlap, with the first-generation studies that I describe covering a range of half a century, from 1917 to 1968; the second-generation studies beginning already in the 1950s; and PRP, started in 1954, is placed as a third-generation study. Overall, chapter 5 surveys, and hierarchically orders, the whole array of formal and systematic studies of psychoanalytic therapy processes and outcomes as judged at both termination and follow-up points, over this eighty-year time span until the present, within which the specific work of PRP and the ongoing and still planned work of PRP-II finds its proper context.

1.

Perspectives on Psychoanalytic Training Around the World

The topic of this seventh Pre-Congress Conference on Training of the International Psychoanalytical Association is "The Principles, the Aims and the Procedures of Psychoanalytic Training as Represented in our Member Institutes." It is not the first time that a Pre-Congress has set for itself so far-reaching and comprehensive a canvas; the fourth Pre-Congress held in Vienna in 1971, reported by Calef (1972), though given the much narrower title, "The Assessment of Student Progress," ranged broadly, far beyond its declared title, over (surprisingly) much the same issues to which this paper (and this coming Pre-Congress) will address themselves. That Pre-Congress and Calef's summary covered such diverse areas as the fit of the philosophical goals of the training to the educational methods employed to realize them; the need for and the value of the maintenance of rigorous training standards as against the humility that needs be necessarily exercised in our assessments of students in view of our all too human fallibilities and ignorances; the various qualities we hope to develop or evoke in our candidates upon a successful passage through our training institutes; the proper role of the training analyst in regard to assessment and progression issues, together with the degree of imbrication with or separateness from the training sequence that the training analysis should maintain;

7

the role of the formalization and institutionalization of training in fostering, or conversely, in hampering, the fullest realization of creative analytic potential in our students; and the role of evaluation per se in the training process, as well as the specification of the criteria for that evaluation at each step in the training progression. To this whole array of issues Calef declared the spirit of that Pre-Congress as follows: "At least by implication, every facet of training (including the training analysis) was questioned as to its purpose and necessity" (p. 39).

This coming seventh Pre-Congress is to follow in this same ambitious and broad scope with the added conviction conveyed in the charge from Serge Lebovici, president of the International, that we have collectively as an organization now matured to the point where we can be beyond a sharing body, and can begin to be a shaping body. Our Pre-Congress can be a symposium that will try, through the vehicle of intensive study prior to the Pre-Congress and intensive interchange during the Pre-Congress, to see what broad—even worldwide—consensus can be *forged* and *subscribed to* around the vital training principles, aims, and procedures that will give greater coherence and cohesion to the nature of the training, no matter what the ecological, cultural, and historical diversity represented in our worldwide training centers.

To initiate this dialogue and at the same time to gather a comprehensive database of the perspectives upon and the practices of psychoanalytic training round the world, the Pre-Congress Organizing Committee devised an open-ended letter of inquiry sent to all directors of education and chairpersons of education/training committees of all the member institutes of the International Psychoanalytical Association around the world. This letter invited responses (as full as the respondents were willing to make them and representing as much as possible the consensus or the range of viewpoints within each responding group) to three main sets of questions, or questions under three main headings. These are repeated here verbatim from the original letter.

> 1. How do you attempt to encompass the dual goals of training competent practitioners for the *profession* of psychoanalysis, and of educating people to comprehensively understand and advance our knowledge of the *science* of psychoanalysis? Are these completely compatible at all steps in the training progression, or are there different points depending on the differing interests and talents of the students

and faculty, or do these dual goals partially conflict with each other? Do you have similar training goals for all candidates, or do you have differing goals (at least in emphases) for different candidates, either individually, or in groups along specialized tracks?

2. What is the kind and degree of personality alteration that you expect psychoanalytic training to achieve with your candidates? How does this influence your criteria for selection, for progression, and for graduation (qualification) as a psychoanalyst? Are there any absolute or relative barriers in the personality and the psychopathology of the candidate that determine your position relative to progression and graduation? If so, what are they? Are there any requirements of demonstrated personality alteration for progression and graduation? If so, what are they? (And how do you determine the existence of these?—e.g., examinations, papers, classwork, supervision, reports of training analysts?)

3. How does the training sequence (of personal analysis, formal curriculum, and supervised analytic work) organized in relation to these educational goals and these expectations for personality alteration foster these goals and expectations? How may your organization of the training sequence at times hamper these goals and expectations? Do you have formal postgraduate educational programs, and how do they serve to consolidate or to further the goals and expectations of the training experience?

It is with the answers received to this letter of inquiry, built around current training concepts, attitudes, and procedures (and dilemmas), that this statement of "Perspectives on Psychoanalytic Training Around the World" takes its point of departure. In so doing, I will bypass the considerable literature on training issues and problems that has accumulated unevenly in our scientific journals around the world (which is anyway, much of it, familiar to most of us) except for reference, where apposite, to Freud's rather sparse statements scattered in just a few places and mostly in *The Question of Lay Analysis* (Freud, 1926b), on training issues and training requirements. These statements of Freud's will be referred to in part to indicate our historical continuity and development and how far along this road we have come, and also, paradoxically, as is often so true with Freud, via in many instances the very same quotations, Freud's essential modernity, and how little we are beyond his positions.

I should, however, before beginning a systematic survey and exposition of the facts and opinions reported in all the letters (and appended documents) of response, state both some ground rules I am following and some caveats the reader ought to bear in mind. As for the ground rules:

1. First, I make no pretense of quantifications or meaningful statistics, except in the roughest sense of giving a feeling for the degree or preponderance or intensity of sentiment expressed. Of the fifty-seven Institutes on five continents, we received replies from twenty-eight (or half)—in four languages. They varied in length and fullness of information from rather brief letters with staccato responses to quite lengthy and detailed documents written after considerable internal discussion within the originating institute and reflecting a thoughtful consensus on these issues within the training body, often accompanied as well by position papers, reprints, as well as official training brochures. In view, however, of both the incompleteness of the sample, and the great spread in the amount and detail of the data in the various responses, any effort at any truly quantitative presentation of observations and conclusions could well be misleading—and, equally important, often beside the point.

2. A second, self-imposed ground rule has to do with the particularity of reference and quotation: I will use verbatim quotations liberally because of the often cogent and quite idiosyncratic language with which views are expressed. In order, however, to foster the most candid and yet tactful dialogue, I will not identify these by author but rather by institute, and the latter not in all instances. Since I do feel that the country and region and language of origin may often be critical to the understanding of the viewpoint and its historical and social context, I wanted to avoid the opposite extreme of anonymous attribution, with the leveling and hampering effect that this could have on the liveliness of the discourse.[1]

3. The third ground rule is at the same time a caveat. I have made no effort to accord equal discussion space to each of the questions raised under the three main headings of the letter of inquiry or to each of the issues dealt with in the replies from the various institutes. Nor have I accorded space in terms of any judgment of my own or expression by colleagues of the objective importance of the particular issue within the total fabric of the

[1] Since the actual respondents from the twenty-eight institutes are not identified by name, I do want to take this opportunity to thank them very sincerely for their efforts—either as individuals or expressing a group consensus—that have been the main labor that has made my collating task possible and rendered it pleasurable. I also want to thank Dr. Edward Burke and Ms. Lisa Dunkel for translation help with the many replies that came in languages other than English.

psychoanalytic training structure. Rather, the space accorded, and the relative emphasis of topics, will reflect the dynamic interplay between the preoccupation of the Organizing Committee in framing the questions in the letter of inquiry the way we did, and even more the preoccupation of the respondents as they responded differentially to the initiating stimuli. In this way, it will be at least a statement of the chief verbalized *concerns* of psychoanalytic educators, circa 1977.

4. And lastly, a major caveat in the reading both of the questions and the answers. Despite the care with which the questions were chosen and constructed, and the clarity of meaning that they had for us who devised them, it became evident from the nature of the responses that in some ways, particularly with the first set of headings, the questions were insufficiently informative, probably oversimplified and skewed in what they connoted, and thus lent themselves to what we felt at times to be a misreading of our intent. For example, a number of respondents saw (incorrectly from our viewpoint) the distinction drawn between psychoanalysis as a profession and psychoanalysis as a science as that between the technique and the theory of psychoanalysis and then rightly contended that technique and theory are indissolubly linked and do not stand in conflict either conceptually or in practice. Also, to set up as one of the nodal goals of psychoanalytic training, education for *science,* bypasses for many people the issue of the extent to which psychoanalysis *is* a science, as against being another species of enterprise altogether (humanistic and artistic), and that therefore setting up the dichotomy the way the question has it, does violence to the nature of the psychoanalytic enterprise to begin with—and may pull then for distorted and noncomparable responses, which is what did happen to some extent. And lastly, when research is invoked and spoken to in the questionnaire replies (especially by those negatively minded about it), it is at times equated with systematization into formal designs with specific attention to issues of sampling, control, and movement toward quantification. To us this is but one kind and line of psychoanalytic research, of research into the nature of psychoanalytic propositions and processes; another, equally valid kind of research, and indeed with a longer tradition in our science, is that which derives from the intensive individual case study method innovated by Freud, and still the fundament of most of what we know and practice in psychoanalysis. Some people have trouble

seeing the potential for *research* in the intensive case study method—except in Freud's case.

With these ground rules and caveats fairly in mind, let us turn now to the collective voice of psychoanalysis on the many issues raised explicitly (and implicitly) in the letter of inquiry to our member institutes. First, to the first expressed question, and the one that drew the largest volume of concerned and detailed response, that of somehow encompassing dual and perhaps not always compatible goals, of training for a helping profession and educating for a science. That this was an issue from the start of psychoanalysis is attested by Freud's (1926b) statement in *The Question of Lay Analysis*: "I have never really been a doctor in the proper sense . . . I have no knowledge of having had any craving in my early childhood to help suffering humanity. . . . In my youth I felt an overpowering need to understand something of the riddles of the world in which we live and perhaps even to contribute something to their solution" (p. 253). A page later, he cautions, "I only want to feel assured that the therapy will not destroy the science" (p. 254).

Yet, in some half-dozen of the institute responses from both Europe and Latin America (perhaps in part due to the possible misreading already alluded to), no issue or problem was discerned in this stated duality of goal. There are statements to the effect that there is really only one valid training goal, or that the practice and the science cannot be separated. A most detailed and optimistic statement in this regard comes from the Brazilian Society of Rio de Janeiro.

> [T]he dual goals of personal analysis and didactic follow-up became a single goal in the sense of training clinically competent candidates, promoting a harmonious union between the private work that the candidate carries out with his personal analyst and, on the other hand, his performance in the courses given for the purpose of improving his understanding, development and utilization of such scientific knowledge as he may be acquiring.

These are clearly seen as completely compatible activities, leading not surprisingly then to the declaration that "the good psychoanalytic clinicians are simultaneously, sooner or later, creative persons who are going to contribute to the development of our theories." To this can be added such briefer supporting statements as that of Colombia, that there is no distinction between the professional and scientific aims, that compatibility is achieved by *not* differentiating them, but by constantly integrating them throughout the training; that of France, that all teaching worthy of the name is indissociably training *and* research; and that of Paris, that there is no difference in goals and methods between the concern to form professionals and the concern to form theoreticians. Corollary to all these statements, of course, is the declaration that the identical training is the most appropriate for all candidates—and this quite aside from the separate issue of whether or not the particular institute trains nonmedical analysts. A few additional institutes (three more, India, Canada, and Downstate) spoke of no inherent conflict in goals, only apparent conflict, or some perceived conflict (when applied psychoanalysis is improperly looked upon as a dilution of orthodox analytic principles), with all of these stressing mutual interdependence of goals and methods.

On the other side, an equal total number (ten institutes on four continents) spoke eloquently of the dilemmas they experienced in carrying out this syncretic task posed for psychoanalytic training. Finland, in fact, multiplied it to a fourfold task of training for the profession of analysis, the science of analysis, the teaching of analysis, and the applications of analysis (to psychotherapy, to psychological research, to psychiatry, to behavioral science, etc.) and spoke then of the appropriateness of differential selection criteria for those emphasizing one or another of these pathways as a primary career goal. For most of these institutes, a hard choice is made with the according of the dominant priority in each instance to the clinical training of the practitioner. Israel expressed this as well as any, stating that it encompasses the dual goals of training by, in effect, opting for one, that of training competent practitioners for the profession of psychoanalysis—but this at considerable expense to the other goal.

> The general feeling among the group is that the way of thinking of a practitioner of psychoanalysis is in conflict with the more secondary process way of thinking which a research student would develop. It is felt, therefore, that a research orientation would better be offered only after the analytic way of thinking and responding has been surely established . . . [But] one price we pay for this attitude of ours is that there is a minimum of psychoanalytic research going on, and that we do not sufficiently teach our students to further their independent thinking.

Another, briefer statement in the same vein is quoted from Porto Alegre. "We have not been able to achieve the double purpose which we have set as a goal. . . . We have only been able to form analysts reasonably competent for the performance of the profession, as well as to try, through suggestive means, to stimulate the spirit of research." Or, last in this vein, from Boston, that they attempt to encompass the dual goals and feel that they are generally successful in achieving the first, but are less successful with the second. 'We do not offer as comprehensive a view of human behavior and total human psychology as we believe necessary. We try to teach a scientific attitude and scientific activity. However, none of this is developed to the same degree in our program as is our approach to training competent practitioners.'

Others see some possible resolutions of this dilemma through proper training (and dosing). For example, Baltimore sees no basic incompatibility but, 'We do think, however, that during the *early phase* of training—the first two years—the major task is to master the fundamentals of analytic theory and practice. An emphasis on advancing our science during this early period might well be incompatible with concentrating on getting a firm grasp of the principles,' and they add the statement that anyway, 'As far as the advance of science is concerned, we think that this depends far more on the particular gifts and interests of individuals than on the training *per se*.' This is echoed by Barcelona in the statement that, 'theoretical and clinical training are essential and complementary and must each be introduced at the *appropriate moment* . . . we feel that at the beginning not only are they not compatible, but they may also interfere with and hamper each other. It is important, therefore, to determine the appropriate moment in which to begin these stages.'

The British Society clearly calls attention to the Scylla and Charybdis dangers in this issue. 'We are very much aware of the danger on the on hand of training technicians—on the other hand, allowing theory to become empty theorizing . . . Our bias is in favour of a good professional performance . . . the practical training takes precedence . . . the future analyst will take responsibility for patients, and, therefore, our responsibility in this area is of the foremost importance.' Despite the growing attention to this specific issue in recent years within psychoanalysis (particularly in the United States), Seattle opines that it is no closer today to resolution, 'In summary, I must say that the imbalance in favor of training practitioners is just as marked today as it was ten years ago and may even be becoming more marked.' And Belgium sounds a distinct alarm if this state of affairs is allowed to continue. They too talk of 'the emphasis on the training of practitioners rather than on the formation of theoreticians' and declare that this threatens our future as a discipline. They point to the large number of competent practitioners who do not seek further qualifications, do not seek to qualify as training analysts, and indicate that the Institute in its dissatisfaction with this state of affairs has decided to reinforce its demands for theoretical study.

Given this degree and range of serious concern with these educational issues, what are the various plans advanced for addressing them in ways which would more comprehensively encompass these dual aims of the training? Pittsburgh is an example of a multifaceted and serious approach to training with these dual goals explicitly in mind, though they ruefully begin the statement with, 'Various measures have been utilized; our success in these and overall has only been incomplete'. The measures include (1) a *spiral curriculum*, 'by alternating emphasis on psychoanalytic theory and psychoanalytic practicum on an annual basis, we have attempted to heighten the explicit awareness of the differences between training and education and to bring the student into reiterated contact with these alternations' (Downstate essays somewhat of the same by a deliberate repetition of curriculum content at more and more complex levels of integration in successive years); (2) an *elective curriculum*, focused around the methods and content of psychoanalytic research, applied psychoanalysis, and the writing of psychoanalytic papers; (3) an effort to establish a *research section*, akin to the section for child analysis, and headed by a research analyst; (4) *cross disciplinary workshops* on such topics as Models of the Mind, or Studies in Cerebral Lateralization, in which the teaching and learning is shared by analysts with researchers in psychology and in neurophysiology; and (5) a formal *follow-up study* of the course and outcome of Institute-supervised cases.

San Francisco, on the other hand, is an example of an Institute likewise concerned about these issues, but less explicitly and formally organized to systematically address them. It rather points to such signs (much more commonplace than in the Pittsburgh example, and also less specifically focused and effective) as (1) the examples held of faculty members who are contributing scholars in the field; (2) the effort at "critical teaching" in the seminars; (3) the preceptorship as an advanced course in the curriculum requiring an individual scientific presentation or paper; (4) the training of nonmedical candidates alongside of and in the same manner as the medical candidates, taking that to underscore the importance of research and of interdisciplinary scientific exchange; (5) specific research electives; (6) study groups on important current issues; and (7) vigorous encouragement of participation in scientific meetings, both locally and nationally. In St. Louis, the faculty as a whole meets on a regular basis to enhance faculty development and scientific life, and beyond that, there is specific encouragement to individual students and members to make research contact with individual members of the faculty of the institute and also faculty members of the local universities who are engaged in analytic or cognate research. In connection with this last suggestion, see Freud's (1919) little known and curiously ambivalent paper, "On the Teaching of Psycho-Analysis in Universities," in which he explores the advantages, but also the cautions, both ways, that would devolve from a closer involvement of psychoanalysis within the university structure. It foreshadows the same arguments that we have so heatedly amongst ourselves on this selfsame issue today. And maybe most telling in the search to meaningfully encompass the twin goals of preparing for the profession and for the science through the educational activities of the institute is the report from Boston of actual support funds from which direct subsidies (albeit modest ones) can be made available to researchers for the purposes of carrying out scientific studies—in effect, small research grants from institute monies.

Almost always linked to the issue of pursuit of the dual goals of training for a profession and educating for a science is the not fully congruent issue of the mix of students in analytic training, the extent and circumstances of training of nonmedical alongside the medical candidates, or put most extremely and polemically, *The Question of Lay Analysis.* On this Freud had much to say in his book of just that title and his views upon the matter are very well known amongst us and equally well known outside our ranks in the wider intellectual world. Freud (1926b), in his call for full equality of access to training, even objects to the use of the somewhat pejorative phrase "lay analysis" though he uses it in his title. He (Freud, 1926b) takes this stand after a surprisingly modern statement on the fundamentals of training.

> At these Institutes the candidates themselves are taken into analysis, receive theoretical instruction by lectures on all the subjects that are important for them, and enjoy the supervision of older and more

experienced analysts when they are allowed to make their first trials with comparatively slight cases. A period of some two years is calculated for this training [p. 228].

Only that last sentence betrays the noncurrent fifty-year-old origin of the statement. Of this then, Freud said: "anyone who has accomplished all this *is no longer a layman in the field of psychoanalysis*" (p. 228). In fact, Freud only allowed two specific roles to the physician qua physician in analytic practice. The first was in initial diagnosis, to wit, "I allow—no, I insist—that in every case which is under consideration for analysis the diagnosis shall be established first by a doctor" (p. 243). And the second was in the handling of intercurrent somatic symptoms with all the attendant issues of differential diagnosis, but in these instances he urged a medical consultation whether the analysis itself was being conducted by a medical or a lay analyst.

Both during and since Freud's day, passions have run high amongst us on these complex issues treated perhaps oversimply by Freud in the few quotations here given. I will deal with them here only as they touch upon the question of how we can best encompass the dual goals stated for our analytic training and how this was reflected in the questionnaire responses. Some institutes, but very few, seem to limit training available to members of allied disciplines, or academics, for the most part to what is called in the United States "partial training," usually consisting in those instances of a personal analysis with a training analyst and participation in the full sequence of theoretical courses and seminars, but usually not the clinical courses, and specifically excluding the carrying out of supervised psychoanalytic treatments. The ostensible purpose is to provide this "partial training" to scholars from related or allied fields who will not become psychoanalytic clinicians but will become trained to carry out psychoanalytically informed research within their own primary discipline or even research on or within psychoanalysis itself, whether singly or in conjunction with analytic colleagues. The experiences reported from this partial training have been mixed; Germany reports a bad experience with what they call "informational training" for members of other disciplines, while Seattle, contrarily, reports a good experience, what they call the "salutory effect" upon all of them, of their "Academic Training Program," partial training for people particularly from the humanities and the social sciences.

Much more common, though far from universal, is the willingness of institutes to offer full analytic training to qualified nonmedical applicants. In the United States this is done on a very limited basis and under the specific banner of "research candidacy" with individual approval for each instance from the American Psychoanalytic Association's Board on Professional Standards (thus linking nonmedical training specifically to research and the furtherance of scholarship and scientific advance in our field). In the rest of the world, in those institutes that offer nonmedical training, it is much more open, and specifically on the same clinical basis as the training offered to medical candidates. That is, in the United States, the nonmedical training, whether partial or full (and many institutes do both depending on the perceived needs of the individual student) is drawn into the service of the "furtherance of our science" issue—in some cases almost as if to imply that *they* (the nonmedical analysts) are our primary research resource enabling the rest of us (the medical analysts) to be reconciled more easily to the fact that, for the most part, we are "only clinicians," since we have ensured that our research progress is in the good hands of those we have trained from nonmedical, more research-oriented disciplines. In the rest of the world, nonmedical training, where it is offered, is (again for the most part) declared a virtue, or at least proper in its own terms without need for a research or science rationale and without therefore promoting (even if unwittingly) the comforting illusion that the problem of research and science is on the road to being solved for us.

To illustrate the extremes of opposed viewpoints about this issue, I will quote from two institutes, neither in the United States. India, for example, declares in its letter (and it is but one of many) that it makes no distinction whatsoever between medical analysts and lay analysts, "psychoanalysts are psychoanalysts" (harkening back in effect to the 1926b statement quoted here from Freud). They accept as qualification for analytic training a degree in medicine or from a university and, in fact, "The Board of the Institute has the power to admit in exceptional circumstances a candidate who may not possess any degree or medical qualification." Diametrically opposed to this position is that of the Brazilian Society of Rio de Janeiro which articulates the view of a whole group (mainly from Latin America and the United States) that:

> [I]t is the prevailing view in our Society that psychoanalysis constitutes a medical specialty. . . . I am one of those who believe that it is

very difficult for professionals outside the medical area (and not all within it) to possess the personality characteristics of interesting themselves basically in the sufferings inherent in human beings, who are the fundamental field of psychoanalytic activity. . . . I judge that a nonmedical professional will be, under the best circumstances, a theoretician in the sense of being intellectualized, an individual who will see only intellectual processes. Neither do I believe in the psychoanalytic scientist, or scientific psychoanalyst, that is, a psychoanalyst doing analysis as a science and solely for purposes of scientific research.

A few of the letters spoke specifically of the experience with full training for nonmedical candidates and this was uniformly viewed as favorable. And it was stated by several to carry specific dividends in the research and science area. San Francisco, for example, declared it a way of underscoring the importance to the whole institute of research and of interdisciplinary scientific exchange, while Pittsburgh called it "a lively leaven" for the rest, forcing or seducing both teachers and fellow candidates into sampling a research stance in looking at psychoanalysis. Canada additionally pointed to it as a bridge to and liaison with university academic life. The array of nonmedical disciplines involved in the training activity varies considerably from place to place. A number of institutes in both hemispheres limit it to clinical psychology; others specifically name the range of behavioral sciences, psychology, anthropology, and sociology; at least one sets the qualification at a Ph.D. in any of the social or biological sciences; and others, again from diverse places around the world, do not necessarily require a Ph.D. with training having become available to social workers, educators, and in rare instances lawyers, business administrators, and one actress. The letter quoted from India makes this total openness a matter of declared policy.

Lastly, under this major heading of the encompassing of the dual goals of training for a profession and educating for a science, and the linked issues of the conditions and qualifications for medical and nonmedical training in psychoanalysis, which as we have seen, are related but not completely congruent issues, we do need also to consider, at least briefly, some of the specific curriculum implications that derive from these particular considerations (in addition to the particular kinds of curriculum ventures that have already been used as examples of specific points, for example the so-called spiral curriculum at Pittsburgh and at Downstate). Though the concept of the lockstep curriculum, the same training sequence for all, is decried in many thoughtful writings on this issue, most institutes, it is clear from the questionnaire responses, whether they limit their training to medical candidates, or offer it to nonmedical candidates from various allied disciplines as well, nonetheless do adhere to the single uniform training sequence. It is not always clear whether they do this on principle or out of expediency. On the other hand, though many talk (often wistfully) of individualized training and tailormade curriculum tracks, whether for individual candidates or for different kinds of candidates, few do carry this out. Specific examples of such, however, will be given from three.

The British Society, since its curriculum revision of a number of years ago, has a curriculum offering some forty different "curriculum events" from which each candidate (medical or nonmedical) must choose a minimum of twenty-six. Thus each candidate has an individually tailored course sequence worked out in concert with a progress adviser, each sequence consisting of both required and elective courses. This curriculum innovation, which apparently has been very well received, was a careful and considered response to a number of years of increasing complaints about the training and teaching, the familiar charges of teaching that was considered rigid, uncreative, not relevant, or infantilizing. The institute of France goes even further and leaves the students absolutely free in their choice of courses, and in fact, the students need not even take all their courses under the auspices of the French Psychoanalytic Association. They can take courses in other institutes, or in other institutions, university departments, or hospitals. The only requirement is that at the end of the training period, the candidate must have his entire (individualized) curriculum sequence "validated" by the faculty and at this time he must give a full account of the training sequence that he has followed. And lastly, a third variation, there is the less far-reaching position of the Paris Institute where, in fact, there is a significant division in faculty opinion on the curriculum between the "directivists" and the "laxists"; that is, between those who favor a more uniformly organized body of teaching and those who favor a more individual and personal course of study. The majority there may agree, however, that specialization, which is "premature" and pushed too far, ought not to be looked upon with favor but should be regarded rather as a personal limitation.

Before leaving this whole area of the first main set of headings in the original letter of inquiry to the institutes, we can turn to

Freud's statements on what kind of profession psychoanalysis should be and what kind of training would be required to fulfill the goals of that kind of profession, because they are probably more radically far-reaching than anything yet proposed or carried out within any of our training institutions around the world. In a 1928 letter to Pfister, his minister analytic colleague, the physician Freud declared his credo:

> I do not know if you have detected the secret link between [The Question of] Lay Analysis and the [Future of an] Illusion. In the former I wish to protect analysis from the doctors and in the latter from the priests. I should like to hand it over to a profession which does not yet exist, a profession of lay curers of souls who need not be doctors and should not be priests [Freud and Pfister, 1963, p. 126].

For this new profession he says (Freud, 1926b): "A scheme of training for analysts has still to be created. It must include elements from the mental sciences, from psychology, the history of civilization and sociology, as well as from anatomy, biology and the study of evolution" (p. 252). At another place in the same work he develops these curriculum ideas more fully:

> If—which may sound fantastic to-day—one had to found a college of psycho-analysis, much would have to be taught in it which is also taught by the medical faculty: alongside of depth-psychology, which would always remain the principal subject, there would be an introduction to biology, as much as possible of the science of sexual life, and familiarity with the symptomatology of psychiatry. On the other hand, analytic instruction would include branches of knowledge which are remote from medicine and which the doctor does not come across in his practice: the history of civilization, mythology, the psychology of religion and the science of literature. Unless he is well at home in these subjects, an analyst can make nothing of a large amount of his material [p. 246].

Such a curriculum combined with the student mixture (medical and nonmedical) that would be drawn to it, would go far to protect psychoanalysis *as a science,* as part of the concert of disciplines advancing the knowledge of man.

As a "depth-psychology," a theory of the mental unconscious, it [psychoanalysis] can become indispensable to all the sciences which are concerned with the evolution of human civilization and its major institutions such as art, religion, and the social order. It has already, in my opinion, afforded these sciences considerable help in solving their problems. But these are only small contributions compared with what might be achieved if historians of civilization, psychologists of religion, philologists and so on would agree themselves to handle the new instrument of research which is at their service. The use of analysis for the treatment of the neuroses is only one of its applications; the future will perhaps show that it is not the most important one. In any case, it would be wrong to sacrifice all the other applications to this single one, just because it touches on the circle of medical interests [p. 248].

I turn now to the second major grouping of questions in the letter of inquiry to the institutes, those having to do with the personal changes that the analytic training process can be expected to effect, how one can assess them, and how they are brought about. The logical starting place under this heading is the process of selection for candidacy itself. On the efficacy of this, Freud, as we know, was most obvious, trusting rather on the trial of analysis itself. "The analysis, to which all the candidates in an analytic training institute have to submit, is at the same time the best means of forming an opinion of their personal aptitude for carrying out their exacting occupation" (Freud, 1926b, p. 245). Though we all concur in this, we all at the same time put a considerable (and some say, a disproportionate) effort into the selection process for candidacy and into the refinement of the selection criteria—both positive and negative—perhaps out of our real awareness that collectively we do not find it easy to terminate candidacies that have advanced to the trial analysis stage and that are felt to be irremediably deficient. Many statements were made in the letters of response of the kinds of positive (and negative) selection criteria that guide these selection efforts. A typically good statement of the positive selection criteria is that from Sweden, which looks for:

Good character, self-observation (and self-knowledge), sensibility for unconscious processes, flexibility in defense, balance between activity and passivity, interest in people and ability to create good interpersonal relationships (not just with patients), ability to verbally express experiences and feelings, creativity, and width of interest.

Various other statements, though each phrased differently, were quite similar in thrust, though often with a special additional emphasis. Among such other additional concerns that were specifically mentioned were motivation (elaborated by Belgium as "motivation that is not conformist, desire to rely on group norms, or narcissistic, seeking magical omnipotence"), integrity (which the Brazilian Society of Rio de Janeiro specified as "an integrity of character that permits him to love and defend the truth even when this seems to pay no dividends"), analyzability (called by Uruguay, "a degree of openness to the unconscious and a disposition of the candidate to analyze himself"), talent and intellectual endowment, curiosity ("always susceptible of renewal, concerning human and mental phenomena"—Brazilian Society of Rio de Janeiro), "adequate" culture and sophistication, workable kinds of anxiety ("possess a quantity of floating anxiety capable of making him uncomfortable enough"—Brazilian Society of Rio de Janeiro), and helpful kinds of psychopathology (according to Israel," some narcissistic psychopathology, after analysis, makes for positive sensitivity; the same holds for some tendency to depression, when worked through").

Clearly, few candidates are such encompassing paragons and we do settle for less than the optimal. As St. Louis says, "we seek individuals who have demonstrated intellectual or other forms of creativity but recognize that not all possess this." The statement from Finland admonishes us in addition not to have just one set of all-purpose (and overly idealistic) criteria looking to select for one goal, one outcome. In keeping with the concept of diverse uses and applications of analysis, and different training tracks within the institute, they have selected candidates "who showed exceptional theoretical or teaching capacities about whom we knew that they would never become practicing analysts . . . became high-level university teachers. So far we have been fortunate in these choices for those people's interest in analysis has remained lively and their cooperation with the Psychoanalytic Society has been close and permanent."

Running through all these statements on positive selection criteria has been the underlying debate between the "hard" and "easy" admissions policies, linked of course both to the nature of our expectations of change from the training process itself, as well as to our realistic assessment of our own difficulties in dealing with the difficult candidate, once admitted to training. Israel for example calls for higher (more rigid?) selection criteria just because we cannot expect that much basic change in character or in capacity from

the analytic training process. Canada states that its admission policies have "oscillated between difficult admission and easy admission
with stricter surveillance." They now tend toward the latter but ruefully acknowledge that very few are ever asked to leave the course.
Institutes that have a predominantly Kleinian orientation (for example, here, Argentina and Barcelona) seem willing to take sicker candidates because they concomitantly expect more (or have more
illusions about?) personality change in personal analysis. The Barcelona group seems willing to take otherwise gifted or potentially creative students who touch on the borderline, the psychotic, the
psychopathic, or the perverse, to see if these structures prove to be
"rigid and immobile" in (lengthy) analysis.

These various issues and uncertainties in the selection process
are given additional voice in a variety of cautions and fears expressed over the ways we select and the problems we thereby have
(or create). Israel, for example, cautioned over the danger that we
(the selectors) will look to our own pathologies as being a good
basis for the selection of future analysts. Paris asks about our own
cautious leveling tendencies. Are we too much "playing it safe" and
increasingly accepting more "average" personalities as our candidates, the perennial cry over quantity at the expense of quality? In
the most general such statement and caution over criteria from
every stage from selection through finally to graduation, Finland
states that "it would be convenient to have certain clearly conceptualized knowledge, working ability, and personality requirements
which would represent generally accepted standards. However, such
agreements could easily make some current prejudices into pseudo-
objective laws which would rob analysis of much of its inner freedom
and still unknown potentialities." Here clearly is a circling back to
Freud's own views on the limitations of the selection process with
which I began this section.

The obverse side of this coin to which I now turn, consists of
the many statements on negative or disqualifying selection criteria.
In some sense they are the opposite of the stated positive criteria
and I can begin then in similar manner by again quoting the general
statement from Sweden (on this side now) which rejects on the
basis of:

[I]nability to see manifold dimensions in behavior and in the statements of himself and others, inability to endure anxiety and frustra-
tion without acting out, inability to use theoretic knowledge, inability

to create object relationships on an adult level (individuals who are too narcissistic).

The negative selection criteria advanced clearly fall into two major categories, those that reflect too much psychopathology, and those that represent deficiencies in regard to the positive indicators. Of most widespread concern (in sheer counting of responses) are the evidences of pathology, and here the three main ones, regularly repeated, are psychosis, perversion, and psychopathy. Eleven institutes specifically mentioned psychosis, using such additional phrases as manifest psychotic symptoms, psychotic core, gross psychiatric illness, primitive ego mechanisms and regressive states, psychotic process or tendencies. Ten specifically mentioned perversions, in some instances qualifying this with such words as major or manifest and fixed perversions, and in at least two instances reminding us that this could only be disqualifying for selection "if known to us at the time of selection." In nine instances, psychopathy was specifically mentioned, by that name or variously sociopathy or pronounced delinquency. For the rest, there were too many others indeed mentioned by smaller scatterings of institutes, some of them really subheadings under these three main contraindications. In that category we can place negative concerns with regressive or borderline states, frank and lasting predominance of manic defenses, predominantly pregenital problems, character disorders, severe personality problems or character distortions which are based on developmental arrests, open homosexuality, unsublimated sadomasochism, toxicomania, or severe addictions. Two institutes speak in general of unanalyzable psychopathology. Of this Finland states, "the experience seems to be that persisting character anomalies are more harmful than psychoneurotic symptoms which have defied personal analysis," though San Francisco inserts a somewhat opposed viewpoint that we overall have not systematically addressed the question as to whether our overall criteria for analyzability of candidates ought to be broadened to encompass the more severe disorders that we have expanded our theoretical and technical knowledge bases to deal with. On this question, I have already indicated the greater willingness of at least some predominantly Kleinian institutes to take chances on such sicker candidates, at least where gift and potential are present, in the light of their perhaps much greater optimism concerning the achievable alterations in analysis and in training.

With the major surge of interest and knowledge in recent years into the narcissistic disorders, it is no surprise to find this theme recurrently mentioned. For six institutes these are still mentioned as a major barrier, but usually qualified in a quantitative sense as "excessively massive narcissistic defenses," or "pure" narcissistic personalities, or "severely unbalanced narcissism" or "such severe narcissistic disorders as to result in an inability to be object-related." Turning now more to deficiencies of necessary positive indicators, perhaps the transition ought to be by way of one concern that bridges both realms of severe pathology and of deficiency of needed capacity, one institute's statement of explicit negative view of "major ethical disturbances particularly in the area of professional relations with patients" (St. Louis). For the rest, there are the expected statements of absence of the usual positive criteria, lack of psychological mindedness, insufficient talent or inadequate intellectual endowment, lack of sufficient motivation, "inability to develop an autonomous work ego," and inadequate tolerance for anxiety. A statement from Germany covers this array in general, looking negatively at those "psychic disturbances which impair the ability for empathy, personal reliability, scientific flexibility, and thirst for knowledge of the candidates. These cannot be reduced to a general formula." Two last points should be mentioned here (that perhaps are somewhat more formulalike), the stated policy of three of the respondent institutes that applicants over the age of 40 are accepted only under the most exceptional circumstances; and the concern of two other of the respondents over somatic (or psychosomatic) health issues, indicating severe physical deformity or progressive psychosomatic involvement or "epileptic personality" to be barriers to admission.

Before leaving the topic of positive and negative selection indicators, cautions advanced in regard to considering the negative side ought also to be mentioned just as on the positive side. The first has to do with quantitative considerations of degree, the concept of absolute and serious, as against only relative, contraindications to acceptance and a number of institutes made sure to differentiate their statements in this matter. Second, with negative indications much more than with positive, there is the obvious self-interest of the applicant in concealment so that the statements made have in some instances been qualified with "we have not knowingly accepted anyone with. . . ."

The logical next issue to be discussed following that of selection is the degree and kind of change, of alteration in personality structure and functioning, that can be expected from the personal analysis, and more broadly, from the totality of the analytic training process. On this too, we know Freud's familiar, very cautious, position stated at the very end of his active working lifetime in "Analysis Terminable and Interminable" (1937). Freud speaks there of the expectations one ought reasonably to have of an analytic practitioner. "It is therefore reasonable to expect of an analyst, as part of his qualifications, a considerable degree of mental normality and correctness" (p. 248). But he is not at all convinced on how much this can or ought even to be achieved during the training period itself. Speaking then specifically of the personal analysis itself, stated to be the beginning of preparation for future activity as an analyst, Freud says: "For practical reasons this analysis can only be short and incomplete. . . . It has accomplished its purpose if it gives the learner a firm conviction of the existence of the unconscious" (p. 248). To supplement then the inevitable shortcomings of such an analytic endeavor, Freud called on both after-analysis and reanalysis. Of the first he said: "We reckon on . . . the processes of remodelling the ego continuing spontaneously in the analysed subject" (p. 249) and then on reanalysis he made his famous statement:

> Every analyst should periodically—at intervals of five years or so—submit himself to analysis once more, without feeling ashamed of taking this step. This would mean, then, that not only the therapeutic analysis of patients but his own analysis would change from a terminable into an interminable task [p. 249].

Perhaps because this last injunction is honored so much more in the breach than in the observance, our focus since the time of Freud has become much more upon the changes to be achieved within the analysis and the training procedure—and both our analyses and our total training sequence have concomitantly increased vastly in intensity and duration. But, as has already been made clear at earlier points in this paper, we are collectively by no means all of one mind on this issue. Quite the contrary—our divisions here run as deep as they do on any of the issues here under consideration. Let me begin the discussion of these issues with a brief cautionary statement from the Finnish Institute on both our assessment method and our assessment criteria: they ask on the one hand that the *same* criteria be used in the evaluation of the analytic progress of students as with the evaluation of patients and suggest the possible usefulness of Anna Freud's metapsychological profile in this regard. They give as example a listing of indicated changes to be sought in the various psychic instances; in the id, drive sublimation, and drive discharge into private life; in the superego, an accession of conscientiousness, dependability, and moral courage; in the ego, achievement of a relatively autonomous work ego with all of the functions that go into the work ego and an emergent consolidation of the sense of identity as an analyst. On the other hand, and this is already acknowledged in the kinds of changes they seek in the functioning of the psychic instances, the total task of the training analysis is both different from and more than the task of the therapeutic analysis:

> We know that a wide variety of personality constellations can be considered "healthy" or "normal" without being suitable for a practicing analyst. We also know that there are rather disturbed analysts who still are able to do good analytic work ... It seems to be more important for an analyst to know where and in which way he is sick than to be ideally healthy.

Within the many nuances implicit in this overall statement of the issues from Finland, we can place the varying viewpoints on expectable change. The greater weight of numbers is on the side of more limited change. St. Louis talks of goals that are relatively modest:

> We do hope that the total experience will eventuate in greater emotional and intellectual openness, in greater capacity for empathy and sensitivity to psychological issues, in greater freedom in their personal lives and relationships and in a generalized psychological maturation and independence of professional motivation.

Israel, after a good statement of the goals of the analysis (1) to solve one's personal problems to a reasonable degree and understand better the motivations and genetic antecedents of one's behavior; (2) to improve one's ability to understand the language of unconscious processes; (3) to remove major obstacles to communicating with the patient so that the analytic process can be optimally utilized; (4) to acquire a reasonable ability at self-analysis as an ongoing process; and (5) to crystallize one's identity as an analyst, says however: "we expect too much and only little is achieved ... we attempt to define more clearly the narrow range between the possible and the optimal." That statement goes on to talk of changes in integrity, ethical standards, curiosity about oneself and the unconscious, and a mitigating of extreme attitudes in interpersonal relationships where these had existed. Of the last, they wryly opine that the interpersonal relationships that exist in psychoanalytic communities around the world can be seen as indication that, often, personal problems "had not been solved to a reasonable degree." The Dutch caution that especially with seemingly:

[I]deally gifted persons . . . of more than usually differentiated emotional development, maturity of personality, and capacity for introspection and empathy we can easily have unrealistic expectations of our training. If an applicant in his practical work has given evidence of having a special feeling for the various aspects of the emotional world of the child in adult patients we are quite happy . . . personality alterations are expectably to be expressed in degree rather than in kind.

Baltimore inserts a special caution into this discussion, noting that achieved changes may be more internal, than open or visible.

On the other hand, some candidates may show little overt change in personality. In those with stable, mature personalities and psychological giftedness, the changes may be more internal. The changes described should result in the capacity for empathy, the free availability of one's imagination, the ability for transient identifications and regressions in the service of the ego, and the ability to synthesize and construct from the patient's productions.

In assessing all this (especially "internal" changes) we may of course have severe limitations if, as in Holland, the only assessment tool they allow, the supervision, is declared "only suitable [or better, most capable] for establishing and assessing not personality alteration but changes in work attitude." (Further on in this paper, I will deal at length with the controversy alluded to here between "reporting" and "nonreporting" training analysts).

Other institutes that are less guarded (less pessimistic) take a position, which I will call a more "average" stand for expectable changes with personal analysis and analytic training. These can be viewed along several general dimensions. The first is in the adequate resolution of the presenting psychopathology. Typical statements under this heading include (1) "To whatever degree is necessary to function adequately as a psychoanalytic clinician" (San Francisco); or (2) "resolution of personal problems with sufficient solidity that the postgraduate functioning as an analyst is not expected to be significantly impaired" (New York). There were a number of others similar enough to these. A second dimension is in the consolidation of certain capacities and intellectual abilities. Typical statements under this heading include (1) "to contribute to the development of personal resources that we think we discovered upon admission . . . to train abilities already found in the candidate" (Sweden); or (2) "to expect some intellectual growth beyond successful psychoanalytic treatment of neurotic difficulties and tend to be disappointed when this is not achieved . . . [though] I can think of instances where intellectual growth and development of increased breadth of interest were certainly minimal and the candidate went on to graduation" (Seattle). A third dimension is in the achievement of certain work-necessary abilities. And typical statements under this heading include (1) "Changes sought in personality are not those that would occur in terms of classical psychopathology but rather have to do with degree of development that is accomplished toward one's work as a psychoanalyst" (Colombia); or (2) "Competence to conduct a psychoanalysis independently is the primary consideration in deciding upon a readiness for graduation. But theoretical talent has often led us to persist with a candidate whose clinical weakness would otherwise have led us to give up" (Downstate).

In addition to these general dimensions of common concern in relation to achievable or expectable change, a number of institutes pointed to quite specific change goals to which they accorded particular importance or value. Canada, for example, spoke specifically to the issue of narcissism and stated that how much narcissism is relinquished and how much object relations are resolved becomes a crucial problem in graduation to membership. Canada likewise makes a specific point of attention to the development of the ability for self-analysis. Porto Alegre struck an idiosyncratic note of special concern with the quality of one's zest for the work of analysis. "The candidate is expected to show interest and dedication for the study and to take from it some kind of personal gratification, that is, that he is not limited only to perform his 'school duties.' " Downstate mentioned an obviously important issue, that no other institute noted, the absence or overcoming of serious reading or learning inhibitions.

In passing now to those institutes that expect much more, a lot of personality change through the analytic and the training process, we have the now familiar constellation of the more Kleinian institutes, the willingness to take chances with "sicker" candidates, and the requirement of far longer analytic and training experiences. An example among these, Barcelona, stated that it is difficult to evaluate the degree of personality alteration to be achieved: "it is our hope that by analyzing the most primitive mechanisms and anxieties" and they specifically talked of long training analyses, at least five years, with a frequency of up to six times a week. The Brazilian Society of Rio de Janeiro developed this theme in more detail. They talk of achieving a greater integration of the psychotic elements of the personality, a greater capacity to tolerate transferences, develop a creative therapeutic alliance and an enriching symbiosis, and a greater capacity to tolerate separations, frustrations, guilt, and depression, to repair one's internal objects and have consideration for them—the latter based on the approach of the candidate to the depressive level as a criterion of analytic progress and maturation, with a consequent better elaboration of remorse and the ability to bear suffering. In the light of this seemingly major personality reconstruction, it is a little hard to comprehend precisely what is stated at another place in the response from that institute that there are no established expectations of personality alteration. "We attach importance to the fact that each candidate will present and develop his own personality in harmony with his own particular endowments. From this premise flows our conviction that psychoanalysis does not directly alter a personality."

As a final statement under this topic of expectable changes from analytic training, I would like to quote the perhaps Utopian statement from the Paris Institute about the ongoing process nature of the analytic enterprise. In the analytic training, the candidate is expected to integrate this analytic process into his personal life, to "interiorize" it into his experience of others (his analysands), and to integrate the essentials of the psychoanalytic culture into his own life. This can set up conflicts between long- and short-term effects, between the wish "to cure" instead of "to analyze," to "succeed" professionally instead of experiencing the necessity for the incessant pursuit of knowledge. It is suggested that the best thing one can undergo is not just a "slice of analysis," but a reanalysis. Again, we have circled back to Freud's position.

Among all the topics that have polarized opinion within psychoanalytic training institutions, none has been more vigorously or contentiously argued in recent years than that of the proper role of the training analyst in monitoring and assessing the analytic progression (both therapeutic and educational) of his analysand. In most of the recently burgeoning literature in this area in the United States, the lines have been sharply and simply drawn, and perhaps misleadingly so because it has tended to load the controversy pejoratively between reporting (RTA) and nonreporting training analysts (NRTA). The arguments on the two sides in the United States literature seem to carry about an equal weight of numbers, and this has been comparably reflected in the worldwide responses to our letter of inquiry with exactly twelve taking their stand on each side of this issue, and among each twelve, there was representation of each of the three major regional groupings of analytic institutes, the European Federation, the American Association, and COPAL.

Those twelve who take a stand against any species of assessing and reporting have the most categorical position. The training analyst is never involved in any discussion about or report upon his or her candidate, the candidate always being judged at each step in the educational progression (matriculation decision for entering into the didactic curriculum, readiness to start the first and subsequent supervised cases, permission to analyze without supervision, the graduation decision, etc.) by people to whom the candidate is, in the language of the Swedish Institute, an "adult autonomous person." The assessment burden, apart from the ongoing reports of course instructors and analytic supervisors, and as sole source before the candidate enters into these sequences, falls upon repetitive interviewing, often in considerable depth, at times by several members of a panel, with constant comparison of interviews before and after the stated progression intervals. At times there are rather elaborate systems for having the interview panel at a subsequent stage or decision point consist of at least one interviewer who took part in the preceding stage and thus can compare and contrast the emergence of issues at the two points in time and at least one interviewer fresh to the assessment who can produce a relatively uncontaminated cross-sectional assessment as of this particular stage in the educational progression. Where the training analyst fits into this whole assessment process is then usually carefully stated and sharply circumscribed, as, for example, by the Dutch Institute: the duty of the training analyst is to report to the training committee only the dates of the beginning and of the ending of the analysis and whether the ending was decided upon by mutual consent, or not.

The two institutes in France seem to have carried the logical consequences of this position to the utmost and have tried to explain its philosophical and pedagogical basis most fully in their letters of response and so serve well for a detailed exposition of the logic of this extreme within the context of this presentation. The Institute of France states that the personal analysis, the fundament of training, has been disengaged as much as possible from all a priori control by the institution, so that analysis can take place without being subject to any external requirements. Toward this end, all interviewing and selecting prior to analysis is eliminated—the only interviews by the institute committee are at the time of the candidate's request for matriculation. Concomitantly, the roster (even the title) of training analysts has been eliminated and the aspiring candidate can seek analysis with anyone qualified to do unsupervised analysis (even an advanced student). At whatever point the analysand feels it appropriate, he or she can request the matriculation interviews. The interview committee in turn only decides yes or no on the matriculation request; it does not give reasons or make any recommendations in relation to the ongoing analysis. At no point is the opinion of the analyst ever sought. The institute states that the evolution into this structure goes back prior to 1968, and is not just a response to the student events of that year.

The Paris Institute takes a like stance starting from the similar position that the didactic purpose of the designated training analysis will provide a source for and a reinforcement of inevitable burdensome resistances in personal analysis. Preselection interviews, prior to the acceptance into analysis, have therefore been abandoned because a favorable selection by a committee, however neutral, might seem in the mind of the candidate to prejudge the outcome of a process which had not yet even started. Even the term *didactic analysis* has been abandoned as has the term and notion of a *training analyst*. The title now for teaching faculty is *titular member*. Similarly, the terms *candidate* and *student* are reluctantly and ambivalently used. Thus the analytic process is safeguarded by the total noninvolvement of the personal analyst in the training sequence.

On the other side of this whole issue, among the twelve institutes reporting that they provide for some degree of participation of the training analyst in the training progression of the candidate, there is a far greater range of permissive and required practice in regard to reporting and control. Among some, this seems totally discretionary. San Francisco talks of "reports from the training analyst, which can at his discretion, be specifically and meaningfully informative or not, and may or may not be helpful to the ongoing evaluation." Downstate requests a report from the training analyst if he chooses to give one. They state that "most do report, at least on the presence or absence of a working analysis . . . [And] we expect those training analysts who do not report to *themselves* confront directly with the candidate the issue of unsuitability on the basis of unanalyzable pathology." When candidates are discussed by the Education Committee at Downstate the training analyst excuses himself from the room and no training analyst ever participates in an educational decision or in an administrative action involving his candidate.

Other institutes require reporting, but only in extreme cases. For example, Mexico states: "the training analyst may only break his training confidentiality in highly severe cases where the intake procedure failed to detect dangerous or severe pathology." Similarly, from Finland, "Although we know that the person best informed about the changes and growth in the student's personality is his analyst, we do not use his knowledge unless he himself has exceptional reasons to intervene in evaluation or decision concerning a particular student." The respondent from Finland then went on to state: "I personally share the opinion of those analysts who feel that the very fact that the candidate's analysis is part of the formal training is a serious hindrance to its becoming for him a 'real' and maximally growth-promoting experience."

Going a little further along the reporting spectrum is the Australia Institute, which does not ask for any regular reports except for indication from the training analyst that he does not disapprove of the analysand's applying for progression into the educational training sequence. In that institute two kinds of communication are requested from the training analyst: (1) response to the question whether acceptance for training progression will seriously prejudice the analysis; and (2) notice of discontinuance of the analysis, for whatever reason (if the discontinuance is considered premature, the training is automatically suspended pending review and decision by the Education Committee). Again, this institute feels that the training always poses a threat to the personal analysis of the candidate, and they want as much as possible for the training analyst to be neither an assessor nor an examiner of the candidate.

A good half of the institutes in this assessing and reporting group take a stand for a more routine approval and/or disapproval by the training analyst of various vital steps in the training progression on the ground that no one else is as well qualified to judge.

The way this is done varies in detail but only a few will be quoted. For example, the British Institute states:

> As to personality changes, I think we put the main burden of assessment onto the training analyst; a candidate is accepted only provisionally and it is the training analyst who has to recommend registration. Equally, he has to give his agreement to various steps in training, such as taking the first case, and qualification.

A quite comparable overview comes from New York. That institute states that the beginning of courses is to be determined individually on the basis of mutual agreement between the student and the analyzing instructor; so is the decision to start the first supervised case. Unto the ultimate graduation decision: "Both the training analyst's view and the experience of the students' supervisors are applicable to this judgment." In the extreme decision, "The Student Committee's recommendation that a student be asked to resign is based on *all* information available—from the analyst, supervisors, course teachers and discussions with the student." As a last statement from New York, the mutual influence of training and of analysis upon progression on the other can go both ways. "In some instances graduation is conditional on the analysis and/or the supervision continuing afterwards."

A very strong statement of this position, stronger than any other, is that of the Brazilian Society of Rio de Janeiro. In evaluating the degree of personality alteration attained, they state: "We are firmly of the opinion that the inquiry involved in the candidate's personal analysis can answer this item more satisfactorily than any other." All other views are "complementary." In such steps as even "the second case under supervision is recommended by the first supervisor and accepted (or not) by the training analyst . . . the supervisor will discuss with the candidate's analyst the appropriate time for beginning the second case under discussion." Finally, in evaluating "progression and graduation, as regards achievement in the courses and social attitude, the opinion of the candidate's training analyst does not prevail over the appraisal of the training committee, although it is a factor of exceptional value and often decisive."

At the other end of the spectrum and the polar opposite of the position of the two French institutes, is that of India which requires the fullest possible mutual exchange of information between training analyst and Institute Board, within of course the limits deemed by them necessary and appropriate to the most thoroughly informed training decisions. To quote in detail from their letter:

> On receiving a satisfactory report from the training analyst (after 200 sessions or so) in respect of the personality structure of the candidate, the Board decides to admit him to the Institute as a trainee . . . the personal analysis is deemed to be complete *by the Board* only when it is satisfied from the reports of both Training and Control Analysts that he has acquired a deep insight into his own mental mechanisms and that his personal complexes have been adequately resolved and that he is able to tackle the problems of his patients. . . . His control analysis is deemed to be complete only when the Board is satisfied from the reports of both the Control Analyst and the Training Analyst on the overall competence of the student.

The Board, that is, rather than the training analyst or any individual teacher or supervisor, exercises final responsibility for both the training analysis and all other aspects of training equally, one not more than the other. It is stated, for example, that upon submission of final reports by the training analyst and the control analysts, the Board will decide by majority vote whether the student's analysis and his control analysis will be deemed complete in all respects. In the exercise of this judgment the Board may demand from the training analyst and the control analyst records of the training and control analyses or other details pertaining to the student. In fact, the control analyst may refer a student to the Board for consideration of a further course of personal analysis, or the Board may consider this on its own, notwithstanding the completion report of such a student's personal analysis by the training analyst. Here, in this most extreme position, not only are reports from within the analytic process fed by the training analyst into the educational progression decision-making process, with all its potential for repercussion upon the analytic process, but additionally, reports and opinions from outside the analysis (supervisors, instructors, the Board of the Institute) are fed back into or imposed as requirements upon the training analysis importantly influencing its course and duration. In this sense, the training analyst is, like all others, an instrument of the Board in implementing the responsibilities that it undertakes for the entire training process, training analysis included.

With this total spread of divergent viewpoints within our constituent institutes on this most vital training issue, it is no wonder that one particular institute (Israel) can report a three-way split within its ranks. The majority there opt for allowing and requiring the training analyst to veto steps in the candidate's educational progression if he or she deems them inappropriate or the candidate unsuitable for them. It is expected in such instances that the meaning and impact of this intervention within the candidate's analysis would be worked out in that arena, and that nothing else but the fact of the veto would be divulged to the Education Committee by the analyst. A minority within that training group, however, opts for expecting regular explicit verbal reports on the therapeutic progression of the candidate and the readiness for the various stages of the educational progression. Another minority opt to ask nothing, since any transfer of information from the analysis is declared to be fundamentally incompatible with the therapeutic role of the training analyst. It is fair to speculate, I think, that this same range of opinion (probably in these same relative proportions) exists within many or most of our institutes around the world, even where a unified position was presented in response to the Pre-Congress letter of inquiry, and also that the Israeli three-way division of viewpoint reflects fairly accurately (again in maybe these same relative proportions) the overall worldwide analytic division on this issue.

I turn now to the last of the sequence of issues to be discussed under the general heading of the alterations to be expected or hoped for from psychoanalytic training, the discussion of the variations in the attributes of the training sequences as these potentially influence the training's ability to achieve the goals set for it. The data here are somewhat more straightforwardly numerical and many of them could no doubt be culled at least equally well from a study of the training catalogs and brochures prepared for potential candidates and interested others by almost all of the institutes in the world. Nevertheless, I will discuss various aspects of the whole sequence of training here, but with less emphasis on numerical counts and more on exposing the diversity of intent and expression that at least some of the respondents' letters reveal to exist in actual institute practices.

In regard to selection, this is done through multiple interviews in the vast majority of institutes, with up to seven interviewers in at least one institute, and with at least one other (which used three interviewers) making the point that the decision to accept must be unanimous. Several emphasize that these are, nonetheless, provisional acceptances for a trial analysis. A fair number, as has already been made clear in connection with other issues, wanting to separate the personal analysis as much as possible from the whole educational training progression, require that the personal analysis start and be under way often for at least a specific predetermined period of time (up to three years in one case) before formal application for interviews leading to acceptance as a candidate will be permitted. In one quite special variation (Sweden), two sets of admissions interviews, one to two years apart, are required so that the interviewers can ascertain the degree to which the intervening analysis has effected a positive analytic unfolding and development (with the personal analyst himself outside this decision-making process). In this way, the Swedish Institute tries to keep the personal analysis clearly outside the training sequence, and yet allows interviewers to draw upon data from it as basic to their making proper judgments of suitability for official candidacy.

The analysis itself is also subject to many variations in conditions. Official minimum lengths (in hours) are for the most part meaningless since they are almost uniformly far exceeded. In one institute the declared "usual" length rises to truly severe heights, fifteen hundred hours. Whatever the length, there are also often specifications about concurrent training sequences. Some (like Australia) require personal analysis for at least a year prior to and then *throughout* the rest of the total educational sequence. A number (like San Francisco) imply that all three major training arms (the training analysis, the formal curriculum, and the conduct of supervised analyses) should all be concurrent, that there are often difficulties if the personal analysis is largely prior to formal acceptance for training and does not overlap the supervision, or if the supervisions are delayed for whatever reason so that the seminars are completed before the supervisions are begun. Baltimore says this emphatically: "We feel that it is important that the personal analysis extend *far into* the period of supervision in order to give the widest possibility for particular problems that arise in the analysis to be dealt with in the candidate's own analysis." Many institutes also stipulate that if problems do arise within the supervisions, after the candidate is no longer in analysis, that they do count on self-analytic work or a return to personal analysis, either on the candidate's own or with various degrees of encouragement from the institute.

For matriculation as a candidate officially into the formal educational sequence (course and seminars) almost all institutes rely either upon the signification of the training analyst or an interview process or some combination thereof, weighted varyingly toward one pole or the other. Those institutes that rely heavily upon the interview process are quite mindful, nonetheless, of its many limitations. In this latter regard, Baltimore states that:

> [They have] some question as to the best method of eliciting the necessary information in the matriculation interviews. Some interviewers bend over backwards not to intrude and thus disturb the individual's analysis. Yet if the interview is too superficial, the necessary information will not emerge. This is an area in which we feel more work needs to be done. Possibly if these interviews were more sensitive to the candidate's situation, the "problem" candidate at a later stage could be prevented.

St. Louis describes its method of constituting the interview team. At least one member is from the group of initial selection interviewers and is thus able to evaluate personal progress through the intervening period in analysis; and at least one member is new to the candidate and thus better able to evaluate the current level of functioning in a more absolute sense. The institute adds that acceptance for progression at this step is not meant to imply that troubling personal difficulties have been adequately resolved but only that the potential for such resolution exists more strongly at this point than it did at the selection time. Paris, where the personal analysis is kept entirely outside the training arrangements, describes the process whereby the matriculation interviews (held with a committee of Titular Members) are initiated entirely by the candidate. But this cannot be before a minimum of three years of analysis and the committee is constantly watchful for whatever in the request may constitute an acting out in relation to the personal analyst. The decision by the committee may be (1) refusal, based on serious questions either of the capacity or the analyzability of the applicant; (2) postponement for at least a year on the basis that "premature" approval would risk undue interference with the ongoing analysis; or (3) acceptance into the training sequence, probationary or full. As a single counterpoint to this focus on the interview process, its reach and also its limitation, there is the statement from Finland that they do *not* use interviews and examination as assessment techniques, "because they tend to perpetuate an infantile atmosphere in the training situation."

The seminar sequence, once entered upon, shows some considerable degree of common form around the world. It is usually from three to five years in length. It is most often a common curriculum, pursued lockstep fashion by all candidates; mention has already been made of those of the responding institutes that have the will and the ability to individualize the curriculum (the British and the two French). A few experiment with a co-instructor system, usually one of the two from the more junior faculty; some very few have course coordinators for the major curriculum areas—theory, psychopathology, development, technique—responsible for vertically integrating the course sequence and coordinating the recommended reading lists. Mostly, it is clear that formal curriculum is the least emphasized of the three major components (personal analysis, didactic curriculum, and analytic supervision) of the tripartite training structure. A typical statement is: "This area is of relatively minor use in evaluating the candidates." The statements of a few of the institutes stand out against this trend, however. For example, St. Louis specifies a significant emphasis upon the role of the classroom teacher, and "we pay a higher faculty fee for preparation and teaching of a class than we do for supervision." They further state that it "has been explicitly announced that satisfactory classroom performance is a requirement for progression in the institute." This is a statement that is conspicuously absent from either the letters or the training catalog of most institutes. Only Downstate emphasizes the formal curriculum to a comparable extent. "Courses and seminars *are* of great value as a method of teaching psychoanlysis and have an *equal partnership* and an intersecting relationship with the other two divisions in the tripartite structure of analytic education."

A few of the institutes made a special note of the way they introduce material from child development and child analysis into the regular (adult) training sequence. The British and Australian require a year-long course of observation into aspects of normal infant and child development of all first-year candidates. In Pittsburgh, they interlard courses on child observation and child development into all levels of the adult curriculum and feel that this has had a strong and appropriate impact on both faculty and students. Barcelona is among those that hold it advisable even for nonchild analysts to actually take a child into analysis. It does need to be said that this scatter of observations on the relationship of the child and adult training curricula reflects only the lack of focus on this issue in the original letter of inquiry to the institutes. It in no way speaks to the actual richness and diversity of program development in this vital interface in the various institutes around the world.

Also, again because of lack of question focus in this area, relatively little was said in the letters of response about supervision, its procedures, and its problems. Institutes generally require three or four supervised cases, and often stipulate that at least one be carried to termination under supervision. They often set minimum numbers of required supervision hours, but as with the training analysis, the minimum is almost always far exceeded. It is held desirable almost everywhere that each case have a different supervisor and in some places supervision evaluations are done jointly by the several supervisors. Almost nowhere that we know of is it held proper for the training analyst to be one of the supervisors, though in some (usually smaller) institutes this is at times acceded to on the basis of expediency in an advanced (third or fourth) case. Some institutes (Sweden) emphasize that the (annual) formal supervision evaluation is a two-way street with open dialogue and free exchange of viewpoint. Sometimes, of course, the supervision evaluations seriously threaten the training progression, leading at times to reanalysis, to training interruption, or even to expulsion from candidacy. Depending on when this happens, there are varying kinds of problems. For example, St. Louis calls for a full-scale reevaluation of the total training progression at the time of approval for the candidate's third analytic case. But they confess that it is extremely awkward for both the faculty and the candidate if the latter is deemed unfit for advancement at this late stage. They say that they would much rather hold the candidate back at the matriculation point into courses or at the start of the first supervised analytic case.

There is real variability in examination and thesis requirements among our member institutes. Many have several kinds of oral examination proceedings, most often focused around the matriculation point into courses and therefore formally into the "school" aspect of the analytic training process. Many, especially those that more rigorously as a matter of principle block any kind of formal assessing and reporting by the training analyst, necessarily rely most heavily then on a repetitive interviewing (examination) process. Yet not all agree to do this. Sweden is an example of an institute that has no formal examinations because they "assume that every candidate wishes to acquire knowledge." What makes this particular question hard to assess is that no clear distinction was called for in the letters of response between interviews as examinations, which I think almost all use in some form or another, and actual formal declared examinations, which probably only a few subscribe to as such. About the issue of a thesis or graduation paper, opinion again seems to be evenly divided between requiring it or not, with some institutes actually reversing themselves in each direction and, in some instances, with more than one reversal. Of comments in favor of the requirement, I will quote St. Louis which has "hopes and expectations that this will permit us to observe how effectively the educational and personality changes have been integrated during the course of the candidate's experience and development." On the other side, I will quote Seattle, which dropped the thesis requirement because "many candidates did their thesis in a fairly perfunctory way—usually reporting a case study demonstrating their capacity to conduct a psychoanalytic treatment—rather than attempting a searching inquiry into theoretical issues with attempts at any kind of innovation."

Moving on to the final formal step, graduation, this of course is the ultimate assessment or examination. Those institutes that have allowed maximum freedom from requirements and self-direction in the training progression, often with almost no assessment or examination process throughout all that time, necessarily pose the most rigorous terminal examination procedures. One example of such is the Paris Institute where the "validation" of the training consists of a detailed examination procedure together with case discussions of the cases treated before the whole training committee assembled together. This collective inquiry and collective discussion seems preferable to that institute to the older method of simply adding up the separately arrived at positive and negative opinions of the various supervising and teaching members of the training committee. They feel that this reliance on group interaction and collective judgment makes the whole process less personalized and capricious. The decision at this point is only to graduate, reject, or defer. A number of institutes have explicitly come to the policy often called in the United States "compassionate graduation." This was put rather delicately by one on referring to "candidates about whom one might say that the Committee has more reasons for not rejecting them than reasons for actually accepting them." As a last comment about graduation, it should go without saying that most institutes do allow for the possibility that a candidate may be graduated as capable of doing satisfactory independent analytic work while still not terminated in his personal analysis and continuing it with the original training analyst even into the postgraduation period. However, most of these would at the same time share in the caveat expressed by one that "the training analysis need not be completed, but there must have been some indication that progress is proceeding and that a natural termination is anticipated."

For requirements into the postgraduate period and formal postgraduate educational programs, there are some diverse efforts, but a general feeling that this is done too little and too unsystematically. Some do have specific requirements into this immediate postgraduate period, of which two somewhat typical ones will stand in illustration. Finland, for example, requires that for advancement from graduated associate member status to that of full member in the analytic society, the neophyte member must have gone on (post graduation) to complete at least two analytic cases under supervision. They feel that so many are graduated (by themselves and elsewhere) without having successfully brought a single analysis to a natural termination and that "we do not know how they will deal with such a situation with its particular problems and difficulties. Also, we know that the young analyst often gets rid of his remaining ambivalence toward analysis only after his first successfully treated and terminated case." In like vein, the British require a Membership Course in which the young analyst continues with two cases in monthly consultation with a senior analyst of his choice. This is not supervision, but the consultant will help if asked. The evaluation from this Membership Course then becomes the final report on the capability of the analyst to do truly independent analytic work. Concerning specific postgraduate programs (study groups, workshops, etc.) for graduated analysts in groups, or in continuations of their classes, they are more often felt desirable than actually implemented. As one letter said, they are "both absent and needed." Nonetheless, there are such group developments of which probably the best known are the Kris Study Groups of the New York Institute participated in by both very senior analysts and usually the best of the recent graduates. These groups have adhered to systematic courses of study of various advanced technical and theoretical topics that have eventuated in a variety of published papers, as well as a specific published Monograph series. At least one Institute noted that it has a special program for aspiring training analysts.

Aside from these regular developmental stages in the training sequence participated in, in some fashion, by all institutes, our letter of inquiry also elicited responses of a variety of particular additional aspects of training as specific concerns of particularly interested or involved institutes. For example, some make very specific provision for extra clinical training for those nonmedical candidates who come to training with no or with insufficient clinical background and experience. Several (Australia, Britain, Canada, Israel), for example, indicate some requirement of exposure to severe psychopathology through work in a psychiatric hospital, supplemented in one of these by an additional year in a psychiatric outpatient clinic. Finland carries this concept even further by requiring the nonmedical candidate not only to work for at least a year in a hospital department of psychiatry, but to then demonstrate "psychiatric mastery" through passing an appropriate examination. Other institutes make a point (for all candidates, medical and nonmedical) of a widened curriculum expanded beyond the specific psychoanalytic subject matter. Here again, Finland teaches both psychotherapy and also behavioral science. India carries the broadest total curriculum requirement with added courses (for all candidates) in biology, neurology, and genetics, through the varieties of psychology to anthropology, sexology, and psychotherapies other than psychoanalysis. India likewise requires of each candidate at least eight case studies done in a mental hospital or a clinic either maintained or recognized by the analytic society.

Not quite coordinate with these many stipulations concerning analytic training and the training sequence, but nevertheless belonging more here than elsewhere, are some statements by a few institutes dealing with the role of the students in regard to the privileges and governance of the educational sequence and the whole school structure. These go two ways. Some, sounding curiously old-fashioned in today's world, still do not permit students to attend the scientific meetings of the parent society until they have achieved some specified degree of advanced standing, in Australia not before starting the second supervised case. Finland, going a step further, has decided that the recent loosening with invitation to all candidates to attend society meetings has been detrimental to the society functioning, restricting free discussion and lowering the standards of debate. They plan to reverse the policy and admit students to meetings on an individual basis and only when such effects are not to be expected. More in keeping with what seems to be the increasingly "modern" trend is the Dutch Institute in which widespread student involvement in the total life of the Institute includes even participation in the governing structure. The candidate's society has a board which is an equal discussion partner in governance with the training committee, the board of the society, and the board of the institute. The Institute letter says: "The candidates have their own organization to participate in a constructive interplay between cooperation and opposition in the negotiations to improve psycho-analytic training." Along with this the Institute has a committee of appeal, for recourse from adverse selection and progression decisions. Any aggrieved student can appeal to the committee, which is made up of widely respected senior analysts who have no direct tie to the training committee, and apparently this mechanism is used in about one out of ten instances of rejection (Holland is not the only institute to have such an appeal mechanism).

I will now turn to the third major grouping of questions in the letter of inquiry to the institutes, those having to do with the ways in which the organization and the conduct of the training act to foster or, conversely, to hamper, the achievement of all the adumbrated training goals. This section will be very brief because its major content has mostly already been covered in the pro and con discussion around each of the training issues reviewed. A few additional points will, however, be detailed here as they were specified by individual institutes, all of them really direct consequences of the ways in which the various training issues discussed in this survey have been dealt with by individual institutes. Perhaps not surprisingly, most of the comments that belong under this heading are in the negative, hampering range. For instance, India talks of the problems created by improper initial selection, of "someone with too rigid an ego structure," compounded when the wrong selection is followed by a stubborn persistence by the institute in pursuing the training in the fond hope that somehow more prolonged analysis will yet alter the basic ego structure. They feel especially prone to this error (for all concerned) when they "are carried away by an apparently clear intellectual understanding on the part of the candidate of the emotional processes." Other institutes (the Brazilian Society of Rio de Janeiro is a typical example of such) feel that a major source of difficulty in training comes rather at the landmark progression points, starting courses too early, starting supervisions too early. To counteract these potential dangers, they are quite willing to stretch out the total analytic training sequence to lengths that other institutes, more concerned with the potential adverse effects of long training and the advanced age of most candidates, would feel border on the unconscionable. Many institutes decry the lock-step rather than individually monitored progression of the training that they feel caught up in, but one (Seattle) specifically faults it as a major way in which training goals are hampered—"the fairly automatic progression of candidates into their course work and first supervisory case on the basis of the absence of negative criteria rather than the presence of positive areas."

The British put forth two major hindrances to the achievement of the training goals that reside in the training situation. The one is a universal aspect of the training structure, one taken so for granted as an inherent given of the situation, that no other institute thought even to devote any attention to it at all in their letters of response—and that is that analytic training is postgraduate training, on top of the full-time work by which the candidates earn their livelihood and "this often hampers us in giving as thorough a theoretical training as we would wish to do." The other hindrance that concerns the British stems from the assessing functions of the training analyst, functions that as a "reporting" institute they feel vital to the proper conduct of training, and yet that they do acknowledge can pose serious difficulties to the training process. "The role of the training analyst in the training sequence is sometimes unavoidably an interference in the psychoanalytic situation in which the analyst should be completely neutral, in that, giving permission for the training puts the analyst in a judging position."

On the other side, of factors conducive to the facilitation of training goals, there was an almost total absence of direct response. Perhaps it was because we for the most part take our training structure and the ways in which it works effectively very much for granted, nothing to be specifically noticed or commented on. One institute however (Downstate) chose to go on record with a specific ringing endorsement of the concept of the traditional tripartite educational format within our institutes. They consider the three aspects of the training program as interlocking and essential elements of the whole. "We feel that the tripartite system fosters the development of a psychoanalyst and strengthens the psychoanalytic identification in a candidate." If this is a widely shared educational conviction within our ranks, and there is every evidence that this is properly the case, then one can ask what the implications of this educational philosophy are for the many concepts discussed in this manuscript of partial training, of multiple tracks, or individualization and specialization of training—all of them advanced as ideas helpful and even necessary to the differential maximization of the several purposes of psychoanalytic training that we do agree our training and education are (or should be) ideally about.

Before turning to an effort at an overview of what the collated responses to the Pre-Congress Organizing Committee's letter of inquiry to the institutes around the world reveal about the nature and health of our overall psychoanalytic training enterprise, I will draw this ordered rendering of the array of responses to the letter of inquiry to a close with a scattering of statements of cautions, hopes, and fears expressed by some of the institutes as special concerns upon the future of psychoanalysis. Some institutes (Israel and Paris) expressed dismay over the advanced age, coupled with the often lengthy training period, of our candidates, with the Paris Institute emphasizing that it is not unusual for individuals to be graduated from the institute and enter upon fully independent practice as late as age 50. This same theme has received considerable emphasis in the United States, was the designated topic area of one of the nine preparatory commissions for the Conference on Psychoanalytic Education and Research (COPER) held by the American Psychoanalytic Association in 1974, and surfaced at that conference in the reports of several other of the preparatory commissions as well. Another concern shared by a number and voiced especially by Sweden is the counterpart of the "widening scope" of involvement of psychoanalysis into the psychotherapies more broadly and into shared inquiry with the cognate behavioral sciences in the understanding of the mind of man, and that is the concern then to, at the same time, be able to effectively safeguard the core of psychoanalysis from dilution in a general psychodynamic sea.

Somewhat related to this last point is a concern voiced by the Dutch that in a world of such expanding kinds of activities properly drawing the allegiance (and the time) of psychoanalysts, that there are less and less full-time analysts in the old-fashioned sense, less even half-time analysts, and that this poses a particular problem in regard to the renewal of the pool of training analysts from individuals who have devoted themselves centrally just to psychoanalysis. In an effort to cope with this and their concerns about the analytic experience of even senior practitioners, the Dutch among others have instituted a new procedure for prospective training analysts, including obligatory consultation on their work with at least three different patients and extending over a period of at least eighteen months.

In this array of concerns is one that relates to a worldwide growing external pressure upon professional practice, through the expansion of coverage under private and governmental health insurance programs. In Canada, where psychoanalysis is now covered as a reimbursable benefit under the national health insurance system, many supervisors are refusing to take cases into supervision unless they are private patients "outside the system." This is declared to stem from "traditional attitudes" concerning motivation and dependency and the institute says regretfully that among many, "attitudes remain fixed regarding this issue."

Thus, a survey of the principles, the aims, and the procedures of psychoanalytic training around the world as revealed in the letters of response and of appended material sent by our member institutes in reply to the questionnaire inquiry of the Pre-Congress Organizing Committee. On the chief structures as embodied in the tripartite training model and the fundamental, logical and sequential relationships of these components to one another, there is a basic concurrence that as we have seen stems essentially unaltered from the time of Freud's statement about those first training institutes of his day. In that sense, there is an identifying commonality that makes psychoanalytic training—at least in its structuralization—seem everywhere pretty much the same. At the same time, it is clear that within this basic framework there is an enormous range of variation, at some points to actual polar opposites, around many of the major pedagogical, scientific, and even verging on the philosophical, issues that beset our professional educational enterprise, and that these variations and oppositions are with few exceptions not along any natural geographical, linguistic, cultural, or ideological cleavage lines. Rather, on almost each issue adumbrated, the worldwide variability can be seen duplicated within almost each region of our association, no matter how seemingly homogeneous the culture and history of the area.

What are these major training issues around which we diverge, and often vigorously and fundamentally? Six major ones have clearly emerged in the letters of response to the Pre-Congress questionnaire that have been quoted from to this point. Let me restate them as sharply as possible in order to highlight the arenas of disagreement and controversy. They are:

1. The extent to which a real problem of training incompatibility is posed by our simultaneous intent to encompass two not necessarily congruent educational goals for our candidates in training, that is, educating for a science and training for a profession. About half our institutes see no meaningful distinction between the two

goals and therefore no problem, though one can wonder, as has been made clear, to what extent this reflects a different reading and a different conceptualization of the distinction posed, between the nature of psychoanalysis as a profession, and its nature as a science. The other half of the institutes see a real and thorny problem in this, another of our syncretic dilemmas in psychoanalysis, and no one of this group really feels that the training issues posed by this adherence to our professed dual goals have been solved, or even been adequately conceptualized in terms of their reach and the logical implications for training that flow from the dichotomy. Mostly, they ruefully acknowledge that in their training practices training for professional skill and expertise necessarily takes primacy to the detriment of our overall advance as a science.

2. The issue of proper training prerequisites for psychoanalytic education, stated variously as the issue of medical and nonmedical training, or the proper mixture of the potential student pool from which psychoanalysis should seek its renewal, or, in Freud's language, the *Question of Lay Analysis*. Here the debate has persisted unchecked during the more than fifty years since Freud's publication of the book of that name, with the only shifts, the gradual erosion of the once sharp geographic cleavage line, and perhaps also the significant softening of the militant anti-lay training stance of previous monolithic centers of opposition. But today there are still institutes on the two extremes; those which hold that psychoanalysis is a branch of the medical healing arts, a medical subspecialty, no more and no less, and those which hold that psychoanalysis is a completely separate discipline in itself, and that it is only enriched by students coming to it from a diversity of backgrounds, medical and nonmedical, clinical and academic. Most institutes are at neither extreme, and in this majority there is still a real, but less sharp hemispheric cleavage line. In Europe for the most part, the training of nonmedical candidates is exactly on the same basis as the training of medical candidates, though not at all in equal numbers, while in the United States the training of nonmedical candidates is restricted to research and scholarly career purposes with built-in control mechanisms that have served to sharply limit its scope to a relative handful. Subsidiary to this set of issues are the varieties of in-between training, partial training or specialized tracks of training that are related partly (but not only) to this issue of special purposes of training other than for clinical practice, for candidates from different disciplines, medicine and other.

3. The issue of the kind of curriculum that is best suited to our training institutes, that which has been more traditional in professional school education, the uniform or essentially lockstep curriculum in which the total student body is held responsible for mastering satisfactorily a common body of professional knowledge, skill, and attitude, so that they can each be "good enough," competent, independent practitioners as against the more traditional graduate academic education in the university, individualized or tailor-made sequences geared to the very specific differentiated interests and career goals of each different student. In part, of course, this does relate, as was stated in the preceding paragraph, to the medical/nonmedical issue, or again, the issue of training all for purposes of clinical practice as against other career purposes; in part it is a question in its own right, of tracks and specialization as desiderata even within the confines of the single goal of full training for clinical practice purpose, the same for all, and quite apart, incidentally, from the question then of whether medical monopoly is necessary or appropriate or beneficial in this realm. Since this set of issues has to do only with the formal curriculum, which, despite the lip-service that we pay to its equal importance in the training trinity, is, nonetheless, actually held to be of lesser import and in less esteem as a vehicle of training than either the training analysis or the supervisions, there has in consequence been less intensity surrounding these curriculum struggles. By the same token, it is easier to alter principle and practice in this area than in, say, that just discussed, of the proper conditions and proper scope of training of nonmedical candidates.

4. The issues of selection for training, and of the place of selection criteria, both positive and negative. Here we also have polar extremes between the effort, on the one hand, of total abolition of preselection as a process with anybody who is qualified being free to go into analysis with any practitioner (in some instances, even with advanced students) and able then to apply for admission to the institute curriculum after some suitable (often lengthy) period of analysis, as against the effort, on the other hand, at the most rigorous screening and preselection before admission to the training analysis under institute auspices. Embedded here are the issues of open versus restricted admission, of "easy" versus "hard" admission standards, and the related issues, of course, of the real willingness to look at the initial period in analysis as a "trial analysis" in the sense meant by Freud and the will then to screen out those that

on trial prove to be unsuitable by dint of deficiency of talents or irremediability of psychopathology. On this issue, one can discern the closest to an ideological cleavage line with the Kleinian-oriented institute being more willing to gamble on far sicker candidates if there seems to be a redeeming creative potential—with the expectation anyway that all analyses should regularly plumb to the psychotic and depressive core of the personality and bring even severe degrees of psychopathology to successful resolution.

5. Inextricably linked, of course, to the stance on the selection issue is that of the expectable kind of degree of personality alteration to be achieved in the personal analysis and in the overall training sequence. Here there seems to be a fairly reliable correlation with the position on the selection issue, and that is, again, that the Kleinian-oriented institutes that tend to have the freer admission processes with a willingness to take gambles on candidates who might be deemed too disturbed by other institutes, tend concomitantly to engage in much longer analyses and to count on achieving more far-reaching personality changes. Actually though, here again there was a whole spectrum of convictions concerning the degree of expectable change from the most pessimistically minimal through the realistically "average" to the most ambitiously far-reaching, and there was far from a constant correlation with any ideological or any other cleavage line. There was some evidence that the larger (and older) institutes tended to a more conservative stance in this regard and that the smaller (and newer) institutes tend to be somewhat more ebulliently optimistic. Mostly, it is clear that there is a wide spectrum of viewpoint, and very far from anything approaching agreement on what or how much change we have a right to expect from the training analysis or from any other so-called ordinary or therapeutic analysis for that matter. It is equally clear that one's personal position in this regard colors strongly one's stance on selection criteria, how rigorous and how careful they should be. Nor have we uniformly faced, as one institute reminded us, the implications for the treatment of our candidates of the recent years of widening scope of both theoretical understanding and therapeutic efficacy in relation, for example, to the narcissistic characters or the borderline characters. Logically, this might be thought to push us toward wider (more optimistic) selection criteria, but it is clear that this has not necessarily followed.

6. Last in this listing, but probably first in heated and controversial attention in our current literature, is the issue of the role of

the training analyst in the assessment of his and her candidate and in the monitoring of the candidate's progression through the institute. This is the issue condensed, simplistically and maybe misleadingly, into the distinction between reporting and nonreporting training analysts. Here again we found an equal division of voices, with representatives in both of the camps from each of the regional, linguistic, and ideological areas. And, again, there were not just two polar positions, but a full spectrum from absolute interdiction and as absolute as possible removal of the personal analysis from the training progression through a range to totally discretionary reporting, to then a minimal requirement for reporting in various kinds of defined extreme instances, on to routine involvement at the level of giving approval to progression sequences, or at least not disapproving (not exercising a veto); to full participation as a key figure in the administrative decision-making process and onto the extreme where the training analyst is only the instrument of the training committee which collectively makes all definitive decisions about the training progression based on the fullest input from all sources, including from the training analyst. Embedded within this, and at times almost lost in the controversy, are all the scientific and pedagogical issues of differentiated reporting, in regard to the achievement of the ego capacities necessary for proper work functioning at each stage of the training progression as against achievements in resolution of personal problems, or in regard to judgments on levels of integration reached—in either the work ego or the personal ego—as against the confidential material from the inner life of the analysand upon which such judgment are based. This level of discourse is not uniformly reached in all discussions of the currently explosive issue, which of all of these is the one that is most vitally agitating our candidate groups at this time.

There are, in short, major differences amongst us on vital aspects of the training experience, with their wide ramifications into the total structural fabric and the total psychological climate within which the training is conducted. To what extent can we respond to the charge from our president, Serge Lebovici, to ascertain, through the deliberations of the Pre-Congress and in the further dialogues that will ensue as we each carry on these discussions in our own member institutes, the extent to which we can collectively be a shaping body for psychoanalytic education worldwide, and not only an information sharing body I think that it is reasonable to conclude on the basis of this survey that our expectations in this regard need to be somewhat modest at this point in time. In its training philosophy and practices, psychoanalysis worldwide is clearly a most richly variegated, always vigorously opinionated, and often sharply disputatious body. We can wholeheartedly agree on certain fundaments, the structural framework bequeathed to us from the time of Freud, our tripartite training model, and within that we have worked out the great variety of training destinies and training psychologies that I hope have been delineated with new clarity by our joint endeavors in thinking about the many training issues raised explicitly and implicitly in the original letter of inquiry from the Pre-Congress Organizing Committee. We have in full view now a range of experiments in training. Perhaps we can use the Pre-Congress itself to further our dialogue on these issues, to push the comparison and contrast between these various perspectives into a fuller understanding of all the logical scientific and pedagogical implications of each, and for each in terms of their advantages and also their off-setting disadvantages. If we can begin that process at this seventh Pre-Congress in Jerusalem and continue it then in our member institutes around the world, and bring it back for increasingly focused discussion and perhaps some resolutions at successive Pre-Congresses, we will, I think, have amply furthered our intents in this endeavor, and have aided both our training organizations and our discipline that they serve, to better integrations of principles, aims, and procedures. In that process we can be confident that our rich variety will not be lost.

2.

The Mental Health Professions: Conceptualization and Reconceptualization of a New Discipline

It is a great privilege to be invited to present the annual Gustav Bychowski Memorial Lecture honoring one of the major figures in that pioneering generation of psychoanalysts who brought this new psychology and new psychotherapy to America, planting it firmly as a basic science underpinning American psychiatry (to an extent achieved incidentally in no other part of the world) and permeating it far beyond the mental health enterprise throughout the whole of the academic and intellectual life of this New World. It is at the same time a great pleasure that this invitation comes under the auspices of the Mt. Sinai School of Medicine and the Mt. Sinai

Acknowledgments. I want to thank my many coworkers, of all the mental health disciplines who have participated together in the creation and the implementation of the program that I am describing in this paper; and to record special thanks to my fellow members of the Executive Committee of the program, the group that has met weekly over these years to guide this development through all its vicissitudes, academic, bureaucratic, fiscal, legislative, political, even educational and scientific: Martel Bryant, M.D., Bernard Diamond, M.D., Ron Elson, M.D., Marjorie Lozoff, M.S.W., and Leon Wanerman, M.D.

Hospital where I began my own clinical career as intern and resident, first in internal medicine and then in psychiatry, the intersect
thus of my interests and training in both somatic and psychological
medicine—and the soil as well in which grew my own inspirations
toward psychoanalysis.

I therefore do regard it as peculiarly fitting to be able to choose
for this presentation the accounting of an experiment in mental
health education, the effort to create a new profession thoroughly
linked to psychoanalysis, but rooted more broadly as well in the
whole range of biological science, psychological science, and social
science knowledge necessary to the fullest ranging autonomous
functioning of the professional mental health practitioner. This is
an experiment that has been evolving progressively over six years
now since the initial planning group convened in 1971. It has been
spurred by the pressures and opportunities of that particular moment in historic time which I will elaborate in some detail somewhat
further on. I do not mean this talk to be primarily a statement of
our historical development, or more grandly our saga, of which we
do feel proud. That description of our developmental history in its
vicissitudes from the originating exciting idea to a now functioning
program established, albeit still provisionally, within all the complexities of a university and medical school and professional world
bureaucracy is a talk I have given on numerous occasions and in
different places around the country and I expect that some in this
audience have heard it elsewhere. I want rather to take advantage
of this more special occasion to focus more on the philosophical
and heuristic bases of this enterprise as a series of evolving conceptualizations and reconceptualizations over time. I want to think self-
consciously of what the nature of training and practice should ideally be in our field of therapeutic and ameliorative concern with
mental and emotional disorders, as this concern gets (or should get)
optimally expressed in relation both to the incrementally accruing
knowledge in our field of endeavor and the simultaneous and constantly altering psychosocial and also economic–political surround.

In its modern form, the plan to establish, self-consciously, an
ideal training program for mental health professionals was first articulated over twenty years ago by Lawrence Kubie, a distinguished
psychoanalyst and psychiatrist, himself connected with the psychiatric history of this hospital. But as with so much of our knowledge
in the realms of psychology and psychological treatment, clear roots

can be found in the writings of Sigmund Freud, though Freud actually wrote very little directly in relation to training issues per se. Within that small number of Freud's statements that do bear on training concerns, however, I would like to quote from two because I do think that in a very brief compass and in very simple language they set the framework within which the whole subsequent development that I want to describe can be unfolded. The first is from a relatively little known source, the collection of letters to his minister colleague, Oskar Pfister. In a letter of 1928 Freud states:

> I do not know if you have detected the secret link between [The Question of] Lay Analysis and the [Future of an] Illusion. In the former, I wish to protect analysis from the doctors and in the latter from the priests. I should like to hand it over to a profession which *does not yet exist*, a profession of lay curers of souls who need not be doctors and should not be priests [Freud and Pfister, 1963, p. 126; emphasis added].

The second quotation is from Freud's best known statement on training issues, the just mentioned *The Question of Lay Analysis* (1926b) in which he states his prescription, *as of that time,* for the ideal curriculum for this profession as follows:

> If—which may sound fantastic today—one had to found a *college* of *psycho-analysis,* much would have to be taught in it which is also taught by the medical faculty: alongside of depth-psychology, which would always remain the principal subject, there would be an introduction to biology, as much as possible of the science of sexual life, and familiarity with the symptomatology of psychiatry. On the other hand, analytic instruction would include branches of knowledge which are remote from medicine and which the doctor does not come across in his practice: the history of civilization, mythology, the psychology of religion and the science of literature. Unless he is well at home in these subjects, an analyst can make nothing of a large amount of his material. By way of compensation, the great mass of what is taught in medical schools is of no use to him for his purposes [p. 246].

A few pages further on Freud restates this even more tersely: "A scheme of training for analysts has still to be created. It must include elements from the mental sciences, from psychology, the history of civilization and sociology, as well as from anatomy, biology and the study of evolution" (p. 252).

These were Freud's prescriptions as of the 1920s for what he considered the requisite or the best possible training in the theory and practice of the new profession of psychoanalysis that he had single-handedly created. They were stated within the scientific–intellectual context of the Vienna of those decades between the two World Wars, with the kind of medical training background with its very organic emphases in psychiatry that characterized the majority of psychoanalysts, and the greatly diversified, more humanistic backgrounds, not even in all instances academic, that characterized the significant minority of nonmedical psychoanalysts.

The more modern restatement of this call for a new mental health profession, one that Freud rightly said did not yet exist, was made by Kubie in this country in a series of papers beginning in the early 1950s and reiterated tirelessly in varying guises and in varying settings until his recent death. The important herald paper that first comprehensively articulated Kubie's concept, proclaimed its need and its relevance, and established its defining parameters was published in 1954 in a journal not usually remarked by psychoanalytic or other mental health practitioners, the *Texas Reports on Biology and Medicine*. The title was "The Pros and Cons of a New Profession: A Doctorate in Medical Psychology."

In one sense the concept was breathtakingly simple. Kubie started from the premise, true at the time, that the main mental health professional activity, absorbing the overall energy of the vast majority of the varied practitioners in the field, was outpatient psychotherapy. Certainly, there were the many hundred thousand severely ill, for the most part chronically psychotic patients in the public mental hospitals whose numbers in fact seemed inexorably, and to our collective despair, to grow each year. But they were taken care of by a small handful of psychiatrists, still called alienists in some places, sequestered for the most part in remote state hospitals, away from the major population centers and away from the major university academic and medical school centers. It should be borne in mind that this was in the era prior to the advent of the psychoactive drugs which have since their coming made such a difference in the possibilities for therapeutic management of just those severely ill psychotic patients cared for in those hospitals. But for the most part, for the overwhelming number of the mental health practitioners, the main activity, the real action, was in the outpatient psychotherapeutic enterprise, increasingly psychoanalytically based, which took place in private consulting rooms, in social agencies, private and public, in child guidance clinics and in outpatient psychiatric departments. To some extent, these activities also flourished in academic departments of psychiatry in medical schools, just coming into their period of phenomenal post-World War II and National Institute of Mental Health (NIMH) supported growth, and also in the rapidly burgeoning departments of psychiatry in acute general hospitals, the latter almost totally a post-World War II development.

To this outpatient psychotherapeutic enterprise in these various settings came practitioners of varying professional disciplinary backgrounds, converging onto the common practice arena, most centrally of course from the so-called major mental health professional disciplines, psychiatry, clinical psychology, and psychiatric social work. Kubie's thesis simply was that whatever the avenue of background and training access to work in this shared field, that training was grossly skewed and only haphazardly relevant to the tasks of the field. In each instance, from each discipline, one would come trained in some respects, very relevantly and appropriately, but in some other respects grossly overtrained, having acquired bodies of knowledge along the way in one's own professional schooling that for the central purpose at hand were clearly unnecessary or redundant or irrelevant. Indeed, in some instances this was knowledge representing capacities, attitudes, or manners of working that would have to be *un*learned—at times painfully and slowly—in order to work with maximum effectiveness in the mental health arena. At the same time, whatever one's training route, one would have major gaps in critical and essential knowledge and skills, things that perhaps others coming to the work via a different disciplinary channel would have learned (or maybe even also overlearned) at the price, of course, of different gaps from the knowledge areas that their training experience did not adequately encompass.

For example, the physician become psychiatrist through the eight years of his graduate and postgraduate education as medical student, intern, and resident would, for the purposes of work as a psychiatrist and at a time when the field was for most practitioners almost totally coextensive with outpatient psychotherapeutic work, for these purposes be exquisitely trained in the biological sciences, in fact grossly overtrained—to an M.D. degree qualifying him after all to specialty training and practice in any branch of medicine or surgery. At the same time, depending very much on the particular medical school which he happened to have attended and the particular psychiatric residency program in which he happened to have been trained, he would be more or less adequately equipped in psychological science. But in almost every instance, no matter which medical school or residency program he was taught in, his social science (not to speak of humanistic) background could be taken for granted to be grossly deficient to the requirements of the psychotherapeutic task. By the same token, training programs for doctorates in clinical psychology did vary more widely from one university setting to another, in scope, content, focus, and practicum experience, than did medical training, for example. Nonetheless, they fell uniformly short of the biological science base adequate to comprehensive functioning in work with the gamut of the mentally disordered. The psychology that the clinical psychologist was taught within an academic setting granted him a research-oriented doctoral degree with the skewing pressures of the hard science and the quantitative–statistical requirements to which the thesis would often need be oriented in order to pass muster before an academic review committee. The psychology thus taught might often be, much of it, the wrong kind of psychology. Similarly, of course, psychiatric social workers, for all their focus on interviewing skills and on understanding the total psychosocial (and larger socioeconomic and political) surround, were totally without biological science training, and had only varying and often grossly inadequate psychological science training, in the sense of the intrapsychic life.

In the face of this situation, Kubie's bold proposal, which I have called in one sense breathtakingly simple, was simply to start wholly afresh, to take college graduates and to fashion a wholly new graduate *professional* curriculum leading to a new graduate professional degree—he called it a doctorate in medical psychology—built on a new amalgam, a more appropriate and more equal mixture of studies in the three main knowledge areas, biological science, psychological science, and social science. These would be welded together into a preclinical curriculum that would be the most relevant knowledge base for the succeeding clinical years of training in mental health professional work; that is, of application from the relevant knowledge within these three realms of basic science to the clinical problems of patients with mental and emotional disorders. It should be clear from the outset that Kubie's was not meant to be a quickie solution to the manpower needs in the mental health field. His concern was not for shorter but for better, more relevant training. He was actually thinking, in fact, in terms of up to seven to eight years postcollege to final qualification. Since the graduates of such new programs would not be trained in the fullness of biological science knowledge requisite to careers in medicine and surgery, they would not be physicians, would not obtain a medical degree. Since, however, they would be health, or rather mental health professionals, offering professional services to a defined category of people with mental and emotional disorders, it would be a professional degree granted on time and as a group to all in each class who had successfully mastered the required body of knowledge and sets of skills and attitudes. By contrast it would not be a Ph.D., that is, not a research or academic degree built as that is on individual scholarship and creativity demonstrated ultimately in the dissertation, a significant accrual of new knowledge and insight in the particular area chosen for study. For reasons of logical appropriateness, Kubie called it a Doctorate in Medical Psychology.

Kubie foresaw that simple and logical as the conceptualization might be, that such a proposal would not be easy of adoption. The obstacles are many and obvious. It is after all nothing less than a revolutionary call for the creation by fiat of a wholly new profession, an amalgam to be sure of the best and most appropriate in the training backgrounds and experiences of each of the different professions currently sharing in the field of mental health practice. A new profession would be born overnight, without history or tradition or established practice or ethic, or established adherents, practitioners, or willing clients, or ready public acknowledgment or understanding, or license or other legal protection, or access yet to reimbursement formulas or third-party payers.

Historically, new professions do not usually come into being this way; witness rather, how it took some hundreds of years for some barbers to evolve into surgeons. No wonder Kubie said even in this early and beginning paper that it is "difficult to win a dispassionate and objective hearing for my essentially moderate and realistic plan" (p. 693). Nonetheless, he issued his call for some university (or universities) with the vision and with the resources, including a strong, established medical school, with equally strong, established graduate departments in the social and behavioral sciences and school of social work, to undertake the task as its response to the inherent challenge of the times. Kubie spent a large part of the 1954 article in a detailed documentation of the social need for and the logic of just such a development. Such a university with such resources could and should bring together the pioneering faculty drawn from these collaborating schools and departments to essay this experiment, this new form of education proposed for our field.

Such was the 1954 statement of a position. Over the succeeding decades Kubie repeated the statement many times and in many different ways. The idea was strikingly appealing to many, carrying for some the ring of an authentic logic, and at least, for the others less solidly convinced but nonetheless receptive, the form of an important and worthwhile experiment in mental health education. It was an idea that ought to be given its comparative trial alongside the existing mental health professional training programs and activities. Nonetheless this idea for long found no one or no group, certainly no university, ready to undertake the arduous task of trying to translate the dream into a functioning reality.

However, intellectual interest there was as the idea gained currency, as people compared the simple clarity of Kubie's central vision to the existing confusions in the amorphous and unregulated psychotherapy marketplace. All ideologies, all degrees of professionalism and professional commitment, all kinds and levels of training, and all degrees of seriousness or frivolousness vied clamorously for attention—and for their share of the public purse. In 1963 a conference, sparked by Kubie, was called by a group of supporters of the Kubie idea, bringing together at Gould House, the Conference Center up the Hudson owned by New York University, some thirty-two educators from the fields of psychiatry, psychoanalysis, psychiatric social work, and clinical psychology to discuss over several days "An Ideal Training Program for Psychotherapists." I was invited to participate and to present one of the position papers, on the place of research training in the proposed ideal training curriculum for the psychotherapist, whether, how much, when, or where. Not all who were invited to attend were necessarily friendly to the idea, or at least not for the same reasons. Indeed one leading academic figure in personality psychology stated that the proposal for the new profession was one he welcomed because if it took root and succeeded and indeed became a significant professional grouping, it would become a magnet draining off the multitudes of aspiring practitioners devoid of true research and academic interests who currently were cluttering up the clinical psychology graduate training programs, and whose departure would leave psychology able to be properly scientific once again.

Nonetheless, the outcome of the conference was a strong endorsement and a strong impetus given to the idea—out of the excitement of four days of interchange of professionals, practitioners and teachers—from these various mental health disciplines. Participants reached together for their common ground, the ways in which they could complement each other's skills in working in the same arena, and the ways in which they would have liked to have both added to and subtracted from their own training development. They would have preferred to come to their practices more relevantly equipped, rather than having had to, in so many instances, engage in supplemental and on-the-job training, often far less adequately than would be desirable. The book of proceedings of the conference, entitled *New Horizon for Psychotherapy: Autonomy as a Profession* was published eight years after the conference (1971) under the editorship of Robert Holt, the conference organizer. This, psychotherapy, was now declared to be the new and autonomous profession. At this point I want only to highlight by the briefest of quotations from Holt's (1971) introduction to the book, how it reaffirmed in an essentially unaltered way, Kubie's original version of almost two decades earlier. To quote: "the aspirant (*psychotherapist*) must detour through medicine, psychology, or social work, learning substantial parts of *other* disciplines in order to gain access to existing training programs for psychotherapeutic practice (p. 5; emphasis added) . . . a program combining the best of each existing type would probably be preferable to anything that currently exists" (p. 8). And then it states optimistically: "But whether that development comes early or late, I remain convinced that the idea is sound, practicable, and necessary, and that its time is at hand" (p. 3). This was 1971.

Whether its time was actually at hand or not, the idea at least seemed to be gaining some momentum in the literature, because aside from the growing spate of articles dealing with this subject, the same year, 1971, saw the almost simultaneous publication of another book on this matter, *The Fifth Profession: Becoming a Psychotherapist,* by Henry, Sims and Spray. Though this book, unlike the Holt book, was based not on position papers and theory arguments but on empirical studies of socialization and training processes in cohorts of mental health students and practitioners, the overall thrust and conclusions were remarkably similar. In summary: Psychoanalysis was the first theory that offered a rationale for the treatment of mental and emotional disturbances outside institutional settings and in the new psychological therapeutic climate that it created, four training systems gradually grew that have been producing psychotherapists—psychiatry, psychoanalysis, psychiatric social work, and clinical psychology. They have separately trained for this common task, however, through selective emphasis (for the future mental health practitioner) upon those elements from their own disciplinary content matter that they share in common with the other, the allied mental health disciplines.

One quotation will suffice to capture the essence of the book's statement, advancing:

> [T]he proposition that the choices made during the professional training of these men and women are all decided so as to emphasize a limited number of elements that come to represent a common core of mental health ideology and practice. Out of these four early professional routes of marked distinctness, based on four populations of students entering at different ages and from different routes and backgrounds, there emerges at the climax of full professional training, a *fifth profession,* the *psychotherapist.* Through the processes of selective choice, of emphasizing certain experiences in particular subparts of professional training, some common threads of personal belief and conviction grow and develop into a remarkably similar set of professional beliefs and orientations, as well as habits and viewpoints [Henry et al., 1971, p. 6; emphasis added].

Again, that is, there is an emergent *de facto* new profession, an amalgam of common core experiences, skills, and attitudes, and again it is restrictedly (I use the word advisedly) the picture of the full-time psychotherapist with which we are presented.

All of which again brings us to that same year 1971 that marked my own active entry, together with a like-minded group of colleagues drawn from the staff of Mt. Zion Hospital Department of Psychiatry, into the process of planning and implementing the first functioning program for the training of *our* version of the new mental health professional, whom we call D.M.H., Doctor of Mental Health. This is our currently ongoing, considerably modified version of Kubie's dream and, less distinctly perhaps, Freud's dream before him. To fully encompass the nature of our reconceptualization and to therefore make more meaningful the shape of our program construction, I will need to interweave three thematic and descriptive lines: (1) the nature of Mt. Zion Hospital Department of Psychiatry, and its evolving relationships within the professional and academic communities of the San Francisco area; (2) the particular happenstance of timing that, for reasons mostly quite extraneous to the inner developmental logic of the growth of the idea of a new kind of mental health professional, made 1971 the year in which it seemed propitious to essay this undertaking; and (3) the history of psychiatry and psychiatric practice between 1954 and 1971 that we, the group of Mt. Zion planners, felt made our reconceptualization of the assumptions and conditions of the training program necessarily different in many significant (even, depending upon one's point of view, fundamental) ways from Kubie's original, very clear conceptualization of 1954, granting that the Kubie proposal was still persisting in close to unaltered form during the same 1971 in the two landmark books of that year devoted to this subject (Holt, 1971; Henry et al., 1971).

The Mt. Zion Hospital Department of Psychiatry is a well-established, nationally known clinical and training center, dating back to the World War II days which marked the start and rapid spread of this idea, that of a department of psychiatry, training psychiatric residents and allied mental health trainees for essentially outpatient psychotherapy practices within the overall medical and professional community in a training setting weighted more to outpatient than inpatient experiences. All was to be set within a general acute community hospital, which the department of psychiatry would also directly serve via its psychosomatic-consultation-liaison functions. The particular department established at Mt. Zion by its distinguished first chief, Dr. Jascha Kasanin, had from the beginning gradually taken on several distinctive features: it was thoroughly psychoanalytic in ideology; it was for a long time (until 1966 in fact) solely an outpatient clinic dedicated to the individual and relatively long-term treatment of adults and children; and it was multidisciplinary in compass and in training functions, involving as both staff and trainees all three of the traditional mental health disciplines, psychiatry, clinical psychology, and psychiatric social work. When I came to the Department as its first full-time chief, in 1966, there were ongoing established training programs in each of these disciplines, all NIMH supported, which support (for both stipends and some teaching costs) was a very significant part of the total departmental budget. By 1971 the size of the total trainee group had gradually risen to about sixty, residents in both adult and child psychiatry, both pre-doctoral internship years and postdoctoral fellowships in clinical psychology, and in psychiatric social work, field placements for School of Social Welfare master's level students from the University of California at Berkeley, postmaster's clinical fellowships for graduate social workers, and a half-time in-service training program for social work practitioners sent (and paid for) by the social agencies by which they were employed.

It is to this kind of setting repeated manyfold throughout the country that the trends in national mental health policy of the late 1960s and into the beginning of the 1970s posed such a severe threat. Starting with the National Mental Health Act of 1946, which first established NIMH as an organizational entity, it had been national policy to support the specialty training of professional mental health manpower in the three major recognized mental health disciplines via the federal training grant mechanisms. This was in response to the World War II military experience and health manpower inventory which revealed the shocking deficiency of trained personnel in psychiatry and in allied mental health disciplines—only some three thousand trained psychiatrists at the time, coupled at the same time with the unwillingness of the general hospitals in the country to undertake psychiatric residency training programs on the same basis as they did in the medical and surgical specialties, since psychiatry did not have a sufficient inpatient bed base within these general hospitals to either require or be able to support more than the merest handful of residency training positions. It is this breach that it became established governmental policy to fill, and under governmental NIMH aegis, there was the great flowering through the halcyon days of the 1950s and into the mid 1960s of training programs in psychiatry and in allied mental health disciplines leading to large and effective departments of psychiatry in general hospitals like at Mt. Zion, offering training in all the mental health disciplines within a predominantly outpatient clinic setting, uneconomical for the hospital as this otherwise would be.

The big change came in 1968 with the advent of the Nixon administration and the now altered national policies of curtailment of social and human services, especially in the mental health arena where it was now declared that the national purpose had been adequately served in bringing the number of qualified psychiatrists up to the current figure of the high twenty thousands with comparable growth in the other mental health disciplines—and since the gross national shortages of the past were now said to no longer exist, the national training grant support for these training programs in the mental health disciplines could begin to phase down sharply and shortly be scheduled to phase out altogether.

This was of course felt by most of us in the field to be an entirely specious, self-serving argument in the interest of restrictive budget cutting priorities, as witness the still enormous unmet needs of the growing network of mandated community mental health centers, let alone in such other long underserved and neglected areas as organized drug and alcohol programs, geriatric centers, the juvenile justice system, the Prison Bureau, the Bureau of Indian Affairs, and so on. Be that as it may, the national administration each year proposed serious cutbacks in mental health training grant funding to lead over a short span to total termination, and each year Congress was able in partial countervictory to keep the cutback quite small. Bert Brown (1977) the Director of NIMH, in a recent talk describing the successive trends in NIMH support policies, characterized those years as follows:

> At that time (1969) the Administration initiated the phase-out policy (for training programs in the mental health disciplines) and acted on it, budget after budget. . . . Each year it was a real battle; Congress, responding to some constructive prodding, would reinstate a portion of the cut but never enough to offset rising costs and steeper cutbacks. At one point, the Congress restored, the Administration impounded and through our efforts, the courts released [p. 3].

It was quite clear, however, that the Congressional opposition to the Nixon program was being gradually eroded. By 1971, it seemed to many of us that categorical training program support in the so-called traditional mental health disciplines was indeed doomed, with very serious consequences for those many departments of psychiatry in general hospitals across the country that were so heavily dependent for their financial stability on the flow of stipends and teaching support to maintain the entire structure of their clinical services, as well as their training operations. Parenthetically, and again beside the point, the expected demise of categorical training grant support in the established mental health disciplines did not take place, but rather this program support was given an indefinite reprieve as the Nixon administration got swept up into the Watergate debacle that became its total preoccupation and ultimately its downfall.

But it was in that climate of forced reconsideration of the entire future of the psychiatric clinical and training enterprise at Mt. Zion in 1971 that I and a group of colleagues, all central to our training endeavors, wondered if the time was indeed not at hand to propose such bold *new* training ventures, as Kubie's now twenty-year-*old* idea would be. Paradoxically, despite the general aura of gloom over the future of training funds in the usual mental health disciplines, there were some curiously enhanced possibilities for funding this new one. For if NIMH, for whatever reasons, specious or well taken, depending on one's political position, was phasing out of categorical training support in the traditional mental health disciplines, that same NIMH was simultaneously proclaiming its readiness to support new and innovative training ventures in the mental health area—and here we had no doubt that we indeed could qualify. It would be beside the point and a digression from the thread of my conceptual account to detail the subsequent vicissitudes of our funding saga, how the program was developed into a grant proposal, how the experimental mental health manpower program branch of NIMH nonetheless turned it down for support because all their priorities ran counter to our own—where we were a professional training program, they wanted to support paraprofessional training; where we were a long-term (five-year) training program, they wanted to support short-term training; where we required relatively large-scale grant support, they wanted to fund much smaller packages. What we did, of course, in this pluralistic society was to turn to the world of private foundations, and for the period from the fall of 1973, when we actually got under way, through to the coming summer of 1978, we secured a total of five years of support, in smaller amounts from The San Francisco Foundation and the Maurice Falk Medical Fund, and in considerably larger amounts from The Commonwealth Fund and The Henry J. Kaiser Family Foundation, with the understanding that within five years we would either prove ourselves sufficiently to warrant securing of more permanent ongoing hard money funding through the University of California system, as an ongoing university professional training program, or not.

But this is both ahead of the story and apart from it. What is central to my purpose at this point is to discuss those vital changes within our field of professional activity that in our minds required that the program we planned and instituted in the early 1970s would be very sharply (even fundamentally) modified from what Larry Kubie proposed in the early 1950s, relevant as his proposal was to the state of the field at that time. The professional practice situation in the early 1950s, I have already described; for the overwhelming majority of practitioners in all of the mental health disciplines it was an outpatient-oriented activity, whether private or public, solo or through organized group, agency, or department, dealing essentially with the neurotically disordered by psychotherapy, in almost all instances, then, individual psychotherapy.

In the intervening years much had happened, however, both in the accrual of knowledge, particularly the explosion of fundamental biological knowledge in relation to mental illness, mostly of course the more severe mental illness of psychotic proportion, and also in the altered conditions of practice and in the enlarged armamentarium of available therapeutic vehicles. Let me discuss just the two most incisive of these major changes; first, the rise of the community mental health movement firmly came into its own as major governmental policy with the 1963 Kennedy legislation, the Community Mental Health Centers Act, and second, the advent of the psychoactive drugs introduced to America in 1954 by Smith, Kline and French when, by way of Switzerland and then Canada, they brought Largactil to this country and marketed it as Thorazine.

First, however, for the community mental health center movement. The concept was broad and in relation to the prevailing patterns of professional mental health practice, revolutionary. Rather than the clinician operating on the time-honored medical clinical model of acquiring the highest level of clinical skill and competence and then making it available to all who sought or were brought to seek these available services, a reversal was called for in the community mental health concept. A public health model proposed comprehensively reaching out to and blanketing the entire community with a network of educational, diagnostic, preventative, case finding, and early therapeutic intervention services, with special focus on identified and targeted high-risk groups. As part of this whole, all mental health services were to be made available locally, in local population centers where the people were, including not only outpatient care, but also emergency care and partial hospitalization or day care and even full twenty-four-hour hospitalization as needed. This would take place within the local catchment area, and the entire country was to be divided into some two thousand catchment areas, each geographically compact, each serving a defined population of between 75,000 and 200,000 people. All care was thus to be available to all, publicly supported and regardless of ability to pay, and where the people were, as much as possible within public transportation access between patients (in- or outpatient), their families and home settings, and the professional care providers. The large

and usually remote public and state hospitals, which had been growing steadily and inexorably in patient population up to a peak of
about 600,000 in 1956, were now to be used less and less. They
would be used as backup resources for those few patients who could
not be handled fully through early finding and early treatment (including acute hospitalization within the local catchment setting as
needed). They would be for those patients who were so unmanageable, severely disorganized, or so chronically and strikingly unable
to maintain themselves under less than total institutional supervision. And these it was asserted would be few in number, far, far
fewer than the large numbers up into the many hundreds of thousands who had been increasingly populating our state hospitals until
the turnabout of the 1950s occurred. For we had in the meantime
been finding out that the large majority of even those chronically
psychotic who were the overwhelming number of state hospital patients not only did not require their heretofore taken for granted,
long-term, even lifelong confinement—but were actually often
much the worse for it, with all the chronic deteriorating impact of
what came to be known as institutionalism and/or hospitalism.
Partly this new–old insight came out of a revival of the concept of
"moral treatment" that had characterized the most enlightened of
nineteenth-century psychiatry and had then been able to keep quite
sick, chronically sick, psychotic people functioning at least tolerably
well within their outer community (all this now revived under the
banner of milieu treatment and the therapeutic community). The
new view was rendered more possible in part by the already mentioned advent of the psychoactive drugs.

It is the concomitant impact of this second development, the
new possibilities for drug management and drug treatment in relation to mental illness, especially severe mental illness, to which I
now want to turn in this assessment of the drastically altering conditions for the treatment of the mentally ill that took place in the
1950s and 1960s. It is by now universal and commonplace knowledge
in the field that the array of psychoactive drugs, of the several classes,
properly deployed, do make it possible to manage and help large
numbers of severely ill, such as psychotic individuals, in outpatient
settings who would otherwise be too disturbed or too disorganized
or too hurtful to themselves or others, and have to be confined
within institutional settings, often for considerable periods. It is to
me no coincidence that the drugs first became available in this country in 1954 and that the state hospital population finally reached its

peak and then plateaued very shortly thereafter, in 1956, to begin then its consistent and dramatic fall to current levels only a fraction of those that obtained at the height, now twenty years ago. I know that there is some scientific dispute about these time sequences and these figures and that there are zealous claims that even without the drugs, the rising inpatient population in the state hospitals was beginning to respond anyway to the combination of intensified public concern about the conditions being exposed as "snake pits" around the country. There was revived interest in the "moral treatment" of the nineteenth century, and the new thinking about the therapeutic milieu pioneered by Cameron and the Menningers, and the therapeutic community spark plugged by Maxwell Jones, as well as the ideological thrust of the emergent and almost instantly politically powerful community mental health center movement. Perhaps conservatively, I have a feeling that much of this thinking has, to a considerable extent anyway, reversed the cart and the horse, and that it was the availability of the new psychoactive drugs that helped make possible all the successes of the community mental health movement in depopulating the state hospitals. But that is a point of view that receives a very muted reception within the circle of the community mental health enthusiasts.

The point, or at least a major point of all this, however, is that in contrast to the conditions that obtained in 1954 when Kubie issued his clarion call for the new professional undertaking, when the mental health therapeutic enterprise did indeed consist in the main of outpatient psychotherapy for the neurotics, in 1971, when we at Mt. Zion planned our present program undertaking, there were additionally within the mental health treatment system, mostly in the public sector, but also with the help of Medicaid, significantly in the private sector, those hundreds of thousands of chronically psychotic or remitted psychotic ex-state-hospital patients being seen and managed on maintenance psychoactive drug regimes combined with varyingly supportive and expressive concomitant psychotherapeutic contacts. What seemed so clear to us in our planning endeavors was that if we were to prepare comprehensively trained mental health professionals equipped to deal with the whole array of patients out there in the treatment system, and not have our graduates barred from access to large categories of patients, or have access to them only under conditions of limited autonomy, then we would indeed have to take more seriously, even than Kubie in fact did, the

idea that proper training for fully independent and fully comprehensive work in the mental health arena would rest on a serious
mastery of a truly equal tripod, three equal legs in the three basic
science knowledge domains underpinning the understanding of the
disorders of behavior, biological science, psychological science, and
social science.

If we truly believed that our training experience could have
been more appropriately and more relevantly composed by some
more optimal amalgam of the most appropriate and the most relevant from each of our disciplinary paths, filling in gaps and eliminat-
ing tangential or redundant learning, we could devise a curriculum
that would better equip its products to carry out those activities that
characterize therapeutic work with the mentally and emotionally ill.
These are essentially three things that psychiatrists, for example,
basically do, clinically: (1) they do psychotherapy, whether individually or in family or group, whether short or long term, whether
geared to immediate crisis resolution or long-term reconstruction;
(2) they manage and treat patients in hospitals, employing the
whole inpatient setting for its protective, nurturant, and controlling
functions; and (3) they deploy the psychoactive drugs, and, rarely,
other somatic treatment agents.

What is, then, the curriculum that leads most directly, most
comprehensively and most relevantly to this set of clinical compe-
tences? Many psychiatrists feel that much that was learned in the
course of medical education of fundamental biomedical science and
of the clinical applications in the various branches of medicine and
surgery has not been vital or especially useful to our work in the
psychiatric arena, much of it is even clearly irrelevant or even coun-
terproductive to it. It is quite another task, however, given this overall assessment, to then come to properly reasoned and coordinated
decisions about what can and should be left out of, say, the usual
curriculum of the traditional first two preclinical medical school
years, in order to have adequate room for the vastly enlarged psychological science and social science teaching that would together represent the more proper mixture of preclinical studies to undergird
the subsequent clinical learning activities of the would be mental
health practitioner.

This was one of the first tasks to which our curriculum planners
for the new Doctorate of Mental Health program addressed themselves and it proved not to be an easy one. The guiding principle
soon emerged that the comprehensive mental health practitioner

would require some systematic grasp and mastery of the major principles governing each of the basic biomedical sciences. For example, in pathology, that the students understand the differences between tumors and inflammations and infections, what the telltale indicators of each would be, and what significance these distinctions would have for the overall functioning of the human organism. It was not felt, however, that this need would encompass the detailed mastery of the pathology, the various tumors and inflammations and infections of the liver, for example, or of the bones and joints. But certainly some rather full degree of detailed mastery of the pathology of the central nervous system would be very necessary to the proper understanding of all the intricate relationships of brain to behavior, of the organic brain diseases, the dementias and the retardations, and the role of genetic and biological determinants in relation to the major psychotic disorders, the schizophrenias, and the manic–depressive disorders, for example.

None of this would be with the intent that our graduated Doctors of Mental Health would be necessarily involved in the responsibility for management and treatment of the toxic deliria, or the various other acute or chronic brain syndromes (though perhaps they could be). Nor would they treat the various pathologies of the liver or of the bones and joints. But they would, with the curriculum we were devising, be able on the basis of a general knowledge of the main principles of pathology and a more detailed comprehensive knowledge of the pathology of the central nervous system (neuropathology) certainly be in the position to make an adequate differential diagnosis, to refer appropriately to their medical confrères for the management and treatment of the organic mental disorders. They themselves would independently manage and treat the vast bulk of the mentally ill, including those with the functional psychoses, the schizophrenias, and manic–depressive disorders, to manage and treat them with whatever combination of somatic (drug) and psychosocial approaches would be most appropriate to each individual patient.

I think that by now you can well see from this particular example the general approach that our curriculum planners took to the problem of education in the basic biological preclinical sciences of medicine for the students in our new mental health professional training program. Within a two-year basic preclinical framework organized on the campus of the University of California at Berkeley as part of their own overall Health and Medical Sciences program, room was planned for a total of some twenty major content courses—six quarters, three in each year (the University of California curriculum is organized on the quarter system), and three courses in each of the six quarters or eighteen courses plus two more in the summer session between the two years, or twenty courses all told. Of these, eight would be in the basic biological sciences, and as much as possible they would be taken by our students (called by Berkeley the Mental Health Option Students) together with the medical students (the Medical Option) in their experimental program in regular medical education within that same overall Health and Medical Sciences program on the campus—which is, of course, another whole story. The eight courses decided upon for our students in the biological sciences, for the most part taken together with the medical students in the Medical Option, are: introductory anatomy, developmental physiology, a survey of the principles of biochemistry, and an introduction to general pathology, essentially in the first year, to be followed by neuroanatomy, introduction to neurobiology, the physiology of drug action, and psychopharmacology, essentially in the second year.

An exactly comparable number, eight courses, were planned in those same two preclinical years in psychological science, built on psychoanalytic psychology as the basic organizing framework for conceptualizing the phenomena of normal and abnormal mental functioning. These courses, designed to be far more comprehensive in scope than what is ordinarily encompassed of psychological science in the usual behavioral science offerings of departments of psychiatry to the medical students in the regular medical school teaching curriculum, comprised a three quarter sequence in the theory of the mind and of mental functioning, a two quarter sequence in growth and development through all the stages of the life cycle, and a three quarter sequence in the various forms of psychopathology. Actually, shortly after the start, a ninth psychological course, on psychological measurement and testing, was added to the curriculum.

In the third main area, that of social science, our own general state of lesser theoretical conception of the dimensions of social science knowledge critical to the mental health professional enterprise is reflected perhaps in a lesser array, of originally four, later boosted to five courses, in these first two preclinical years drawn from the domains of anthropology, sociology, and public health. These are readings in medical anthropology, the sociology of mental health, mental health epidemiology, sociocultural factors in health and illness, and psychosocial problems in a changing culture.

This all adds up to twenty, actually even a little more, core content courses to which the program planners added across the two years two other dimensions. The first is a sequence of integrating seminars in which the students of all the various options in the Health and Medical Sciences program (the Medical Option, our Mental Health Option, a Genetics Counseling Option, etc.) share classes in which clinical problems in the health sciences are presented that call for the integration of biological, psychological, and social science perspectives. In further keeping with trends in all modern medical education that call for some clinical exposure and demonstration of clinical relevance and application from the very start of the professional education and even in the once inviolate preclinical years, there is likewise a series of practicum experiences during those first two years which include: (1) There is observation and demonstration from prenatal clinic, labor and delivery room, and newborn nursery through the variety of educational, health, social welfare, and work settings in which individuals move over their entire life span on to senior citizens centers and nursing homes for the elderly and infirm. These are all correlated with the classroom sequence in growth and development patterned on the Eriksonian eight-stage conceptualization of the life cycle. (2) There is the concomitant acquisition during those two years of some basic interviewing concepts and skills, knowledge of the rudiments of physical examination and differential diagnosis (organic from functional). There is toward the end of the second year, participation in the initial intake process in the psychiatric clinic, assessment of psychopathology, and the formulation and recommendation of the proposed psychiatric treatment plan.

All of this is clearly an immensely packed first two preclinical years of mental health professional training, every bit as packed as the like period of medical school education, but with a different mixture designed to more specifically and more relevantly prepare the future mental health professional practitioner for the kind of career work upon which he or she will be embarking. It is certainly by the same token a different kind of (professional) schooling from the very differing ethos, work tempo, and work focus of the usual academic graduate education. Upon its successful conclusion—the first two preclinical year sequence—the student receives an interim master's degree in Health and Medical Sciences from Berkeley, and advances to our next three-year clinical phase leading to our new doctorate-level degree. If the planned program is indeed successful in this way, it should bring our student to the next phase, our three clinical years of training, differently, and we trust more appropriately, equipped for many of the specific requirements of that clinical training than the medical student who has gone on through the regular clinical years of medical school. Unless of course that medical student has undertaken an extensive mental health or behavioral science specialization track, which is available in at least some medical schools, in which case the student will more or less have individually tailored for himself or herself the basic components of what we have put together in the program I am presenting to you today.

The three clinical years in our setting take place under the auspices of the medical school at the University of California in San Francisco, and are based centrally at both the Langley Porter Institute, the psychiatric facility of our school's Department of Psychiatry, and at our major affiliated program at the Mt. Zion Hospital Department of Psychiatry. These three clinical years though closely related to, are not just coterminous with, the clinical training experience of our psychiatric residents in those same settings. First, they have already had very intensive teaching in many of the areas that are ordinarily covered in the didactic curriculum of most psychiatric residency training programs, growth and development, the theory of mental functioning, psychopathology, psychodiagnostics and psychiatric treatment planning. They have also had less intensive but nevertheless much more teaching than medical students in the related social and behavioral sciences as they illuminate the psychosocial dimensions of mental health and illness. They have clearly not had the same intensity, depth, and breadth of experience with the phenomena of somatic illness in all its guises nor the range of responsibility for people seriously ill with the often life-and-death decisions in which young physicians are immersed during their internship experiences. Apart from the seasoning of clinical judgment that comes from these accumulating experiences, they play an important part in the gradual acquisition over time of those physicianly qualities (a phrase I owe to Leo Stone) of clinical concern, compassion, commitment, and acceptance of responsibility that shape us as individuals who will fulfill the high moral and ethical requirements of the Hippocratic oath to which we have each subscribed on behalf of our suffering patients.

It is with all this in mind that we have shaped our three-year clinical training sequence somewhat differently from that of the psychiatric residents with some lesser didactic curriculum in the areas of stronger preparation of our Doctor of Mental Health students and a good deal greater emphasis in both the didactic and experiential realms on the interface with somatic medicine and the phenomena of serious somatic illness. An example of this is a sequence of observational preceptorships in the offices of such practicing primary care physicians, internists, pediatricians, neurologists, or obstetricians. This overall three-year clinical curriculum has not yet all jelled to the same degree even as the two-year preclinical sequence (itself subject to constant modification as we go along) since it is also newer. Our program has actually been operational since the fall of 1973 when we took in our first pilot class (of only six) and we now have four classes actually in the pipeline (the more recent two being classes of twelve), with our most advanced students now in their fourth year only and not due to graduate until the summer of 1978.

Basically, though, what we have created is an overall five-year postcollege curriculum, leading, after the first two preclinical years at Berkeley, to a master's degree in the Health and Medical Sciences program there, and then after the subsequent three clinical years within the Department of Psychiatry at the U.C. San Francisco School of Medicine, at either the Langley Porter Institute or at the Mt. Zion Hospital Department of Psychiatry, leading to the D.M.H., Doctorate of Mental Health, degree from the University of California. This we trust will be in adequate and proper fulfillment of the training goals set down in our initial program planning guidelines in 1971 and summarized in our basic program document, Proposal for a Doctoral Degree in Mental Health (San Francisco School of Medicine, Department of Psychiatry, 1975) as follows:

1. The program to be developed would be at the graduate level, starting with the completion of the bachelor's degree and ending with a doctoral degree.
2. It would be a minimum of four, and more likely would be five years in duration.
3. It would include both didactic and experiential elements. Didactic material would be emphasized during the first two years to prepare students for intensive clinical training in the latter years and would continue to a lesser extent in years three, four, and five. In addition,

practicum experiences, essential to the program, would begin in the
first year, but would become primary in the latter years. This design
is intended to avoid artificial separation in the curriculum.
4. The curriculum would span three major content areas—the biological sciences, the psychological sciences, and the social sciences.
5. Each of the three areas would include both theoretical and applied elements [p. 11].

Coming to this point, and bringing you, in following this narrative, to this point, is still not the end of our story, the effort to create
a new mental health professional able in the 1970s—and on into
the future—to deal with the problems of mental health and illness,
that is, with the varieties of patients in the mental health service
delivery system, competently, comprehensively, and autonomously.
There is still, after the successful completion of the entire professional training period, and the award of the doctoral degree in
recognition of that achievement, the issue of societal acceptance
and legal recognition via appropriate examination and licensure of
these graduates to practice what they have been trained to do.

This licensure issue is the one to which our organizational energies are now turning, now that the program development and the
working out of curriculum and degree approval has progressed as
far as it has. We have of course up to now had constant contacts
with both the State Department of Health, under whose auspices
we have been authorized to train through the provisions of AB1503,
California legislation of 1972 designed to promote innovative programs in health manpower training (and ours has been the first
mental health training program approved under this authority). We
have had contact as well, all along, with the various state legislators
especially concerned with health manpower legislation and licensure issues in the health sciences.

Our concept is again clear and simple; it is that of a limited
medical license. Unlike regular medical licensure, which empowers
the licensee to practice any of the branches of medicine or surgery,
psychiatry of course included, and which empowers that licensee to
utilize any of the recognized medical or surgical therapeutic procedures, including the administration of all approved drugs, the license we seek is one limited to mental health practice and to the
deployment within that of only those drugs relevant to mental health
practice, essentially the psychoactive agents. This is in principle not
different from the kind of limited drug license long accorded to

dentists who may use those drugs relevant to dental practice, anes-thetics, analgesics, and antibiotics, but of course are not allowed to use those drugs in the management, for example, of congestive heart failure, or all the other ailments that are *not* part of dental practice. And, of course, the examples of very current interest and legislative flux have to do with the recent licensure in some states of nurse practitioners to use certain common or routine drugs in the handling of the normal immunizations of childhood and the common infections and illnesses of primary pediatric practice, or the licensure in some states of optometrists to use diagnostic drugs in the assessment of disorders of eye refraction.

Clearly, this final step will be even more vital to our program (as vital as drug license is comparably for dental practice) if our graduating practitioners are truly to be able to carry out all the functions for which we are training them in relation to the mental health needs of the patients in the mental health service delivery system. These functions I have listed earlier, and in full circle, I can now list them again in the light of the detailing of the educational program and curriculum that we have devised and inaugurated and have been operating for four years now in an effort to train more relevantly for them than we have been doing up to now via our traditional mental health disciplinary training routes. The three main functions are, again: (1) psychotherapy, whether individual or family or group, whether short- or long-term, whether geared to immediate crisis resolution or long-term reconstruction; (2) the management and treatment of patients in hospitals, employing the whole inpatient setting for its protective, nurturant and controlling functions; and (3) the deployment of the psychoactive drugs.

Some of our graduates may of course want more advanced train-ing, full psychoanalytic training, beyond what is offered within our doctoral level mental health professional training program. In this regard, we want to consider them as on a par with graduating psychi-atric residents and eligible to apply for full psychoanalytic training on the same basis of individual suitability and readiness as any regu-lar medical candidate for analytic training. This will of course re-quire permission from the American Psychoanalytic Association and the process of obtaining that approval has already been set into motion through official inquiry both nationally, and locally in San Francisco. Thus far, we have obtained unanimous approval for this training eligibility from both the Education Committee and the

Board of Trustees of the San Francisco Psychoanalytic Society and Institute. The further steps are now pending.

At this point, our history is thus obviously very much still in process and still incomplete, and I bring it to you in part of course to share the story of the unfolding of what we who have been involved in it feel to be a major experiment in mental health education. It is an experiment which, if successful, may herald over time—perhaps a long time—a significant restructuring of the mental health professional arena, with major new accommodations amongst the current mental health professional disciplines as well as new accommodations, not just with psychiatry but also with medicine as a whole. My purpose has also been to enlist your own sympathetic involvement, not necessarily in joining into like experiment yourselves in your own institution, though of course we would welcome that, as we have already the five or six major universities that are now contemplating taking the same step that we have inaugurated. At least we want to enlist your own sympathetic involvement (however enthusiastically or skeptically you may view the development) in the process of giving this experiment its fair trial and in its objective and critical assessment over time as we compare our students and graduates and how they function with comparison cohorts of students and graduates in our concomitant ongoing training programs in all our traditional mental health practitioner disciplines—psychiatry, clinical psychology and psychiatric social work. Such evaluation we are doing and have built in from the very initial period of program planning and it will perhaps for the wider professional world be our most important single activity.

My accounting to you of all of this has by now of course been very long and I have avoided, as I stated I would, all the uncertainties and all the practical problems of how such an enterprise does get funded (and its permanent funding is not yet assured). I have not discussed how a new degree proposal can get accepted within the bureaucratic and hierarchic complexity of a major university structure. In an era of constricting resources and the sharpened competitive divisiveness created by real or potential impact upon other existing programs in the same or related mental health arenas (and even though the establishment of this degree program within the university structure has gone far indeed, the doctoral degree is still not yet fully assured). Nor have I discussed how licensure can be successfully achieved via a legislative process responsive to all sorts of public and special interest pressures, not all of them friendly to this new enterprise (and of course licensure is not yet assured). I have also avoided the fascinating story of our successive classes of students, the kinds of students that they are (so different and broader in mixture than the usual medical students from whom our psychiatric practitioners derive, who come overwhelmingly from within a much narrower spectrum of interests and college preparatory experiences). I have not recounted the nature of the teaching and learning experience with a pioneering body of students willing for the excitement of the vision to make their career commitments with an experimental five-year program that they knew from the beginning did not yet have its degree or its licensure or any adequate mechanisms for proper stipends or financial aid during the long and arduous training process.

All of that is itself another story, perhaps even a more human as well as more practical story. This today is more the story of the idea, of the original conceptualization of a particular vision of how the training needs in the field of mental health could be better, more appropriately, met than by the various pragmatic and mostly unplanned mechanisms that had evolved during the normal evolutionary processes of a growing field in a changing world, and how that vision has been subsequently reconceptualized by a group that undertook to transform the dream into a functioning reality in a manner best fitted to the altered particulars of its context in current place and time in the field. And as part of that, it might indeed in the long run prove to be a major and decisive contribution of psychoanalysis as both a psychology and a psychotherapy that it has played so central a role in this, we hope successful, effort to render through deliberate creation a new and more rational model of the mental health professional enterprise.

3.

Psychotherapy Research: One Paradigm

THE QUESTIONS WE WANTED ANSWERED

My paradigm—I know it best—is the Psychotherapy Research Project (PRP) of The Menninger Foundation created from within an informed and skilled clinical community, and dedicated to psychoanalytic psychotherapy as a vehicle for helping the emotionally ill. It is this clinical community that decided to try to learn more from and about its central professional activity, to seek more precise answers to two simple though far from single-minded questions: First, *what* changes take place in psychotherapy (the outcome question); second, *how* do those changes come about, through the interaction of what constellations of factors in the patient, in the treatment and therapist, and in the patient's ongoing life situation (the process question).

Within that strategic framework, the first decision was that this research would be a naturalistic study of psychotherapy carried out in its natural habit, unencumbered and uninfluenced by the fact of the research even by any knowledge on the part of the participants that the therapy was the subject of research study. In accord with the prevailing treatment programs of the institution, half the patients studied were in psychoanalysis, and half in other modes of psychoanalytic psychotherapy. Finally, a population of forty-two (21 in each group) was determined, a number limited by what could be managed within available project resources, given the comprehensiveness of the individual study undertaken with each case and the complexity of the design that evolved for the handling of the data generated. The criteria for our naturalistic study required that (1) each patient be treated by that modality deemed clinically most indicated (i.e., no random assignments); (2) that there be no traditional normal controls, control groups, waiting list groups, or other nonclinical research impositions, yet principles of control could not be abrogated but rather implemented in other than these standard ways; and (3) that the therapy under study be carried through its natural course without either therapist or patient influenced by or even being aware of the research study—hence, no intrusions upon the therapy by recording devices, tests, questionnaire tasks, and the like. The challenge then was to build the research study as comprehensively as possible around this "natural" psychotherapy, given all the barriers erected against all the usual kinds of access to research data and of experimental manipulation and control.

SELECTION OF PATIENTS

The patients were the usual patient population in intensive therapy at The Menninger Clinic. They had come or been sent to Topeka for treatment because their illness was severe enough not to be readily amenable to standard outpatient therapy in their home setting, but with exclusion of those so ill that intensive concomitant hospital treatment would be a major component of their total therapeutic management. In nosological terms, they comprised severe psychoneuroses, character neuroses, and impulse neuroses, addictions and sexual disorders, narcissistic and borderline characters; there were no open psychoses, organic brain disorders, or innately retarded. Half were men, half women, of the usual adult psychotherapy ages (20 to 50 years old). (Such a range excluded those whose age might have confounded the study: the young by growth and developmental processes, or the older by somatic illness and aging processes.) Their socioeconomic and demographic characteristics were those of patients who could come to such a treatment setting—white, upper and upper-middle class, intelligence quotient range from 140 down to 100. In research terms, this was a reasonably homogeneous, but far from representative population sample.

THE DIAGNOSTIC PROCESS AND PREDICTIONS

The research study was built around the usual clinical diagnostic process carried out with all patients coming to treatment at The Menninger Clinic. This process included an intensive psychiatric case study, a comprehensive projective psychological test battery, a social history obtained from a responsible relative, and the overall case formulation and treatment recommendations (planning and prognostication) derived from the clinical case conference that completed each diagnostic workup. These data, available in the clinical records, were the basis for the research team's Initial Study of each case. The formal research built upon this clinical study was just a methodical effort, as rigorous as theoretic and empirical knowledge allowed, to make systematically explicit what is ordinarily almost totally implicit in clinical discourse; that is, the explication of those variable factors within the patient, the therapist, and the treatment, and within the interacting life situation of the patient that together were felt to determine the probable treatment course and outcome.

Twenty-eight patient variables were conceptualized and grouped into eight major areas of psychic functioning. These variables were thought to be always operative, often only implicitly, in formulating an understanding of the patient, his life history, character structure, emotional illness, and the treatment plan and prospects. Except for sex, these were neither demographic variables, since the population was fairly homogeneous, nor diagnostic categories, since the patients had roughly comparable degrees of illness severity. Rather, they were personality variables—for the most part, complex clinical judgments about intrapsychic organizations. Examples included the nature of the core neurotic conflicts, the severity and nature of the symptoms, the patterning of the defenses, the anxiety and affect tolerance, the resiliency and strength of the ego, the nature of the motivation for change, the transference dispositions that would expectably unfold. Each was defined in terms of general theoretical understanding of psychodynamic theory and more specifically in terms of idiosyncratic usage within our clinical community. Based on study of the regular clinical material available in the case record, two researchers (the Initial Study team) made consensus assessments in writing of each patient chosen for research study, on each of the twenty-eight patient variables.

Similar consensus assessments were made in writing on each of seven situational variables. These were not related to the facts of life situation, job, marital status, family and friendship constellations, and the like, but were rather related to the impact; that is, the psychologic meaning of the life situation in terms of its degree of stressfulness, its conflict-triggering components specific to the core neurotic conflicts of that individual, its supports, its growth opportunities, and its mutability. Though treatment and therapist variables could not of course be assessed prior to the therapy, the Initial Study team could make detailed predictions about the expected course and outcome of the planned therapy, based on the detailed research assessment of this patient, in this life situation, starting out in the appropriate clinically indicated treatment course for him or her; that is, appropriate in terms of our current theoretical understandings and accumulated practical experience of each of the proffered psychoanalytically based psychotherapeutic modalities. These predictions were systematically explicit in regard to the course: the expectable unfolding of themes, issues, and transference positions; the consequences of various contingencies, likely life events or interactions, to the therapeutic course, and the like. Systematically explicit predictions also were made to the outcome: the reach and the limitations of changes in symptoms, manifest behavior patterns, and in impulse–defense configurations; structural alterations in the ego; acquisition of insights, and similar components.

The overall initial study in each case, both its assessments and predictions, was then completed with a logical (not psychological) analysis of the discursive clinical predictions, embedded as they were in clinical context and qualification, in the form of one-sentence specific predictive statements. These followed a tripartite logical model: *if* (under these conditions, given these events or contingencies), *then* (these consequences, events, changes), *because* (of these factors in the patient or his life situation, and these theoretical assumptions about how therapy induces change). There were approximately fifty such discrete if-because-then predictive statements per case, or about two thousand specific predictions to be tested in the forty-two cases. However, the same assumptions often underlay many predictions within a single case—or underlay predictions across many of the cases—the assumptions under test finally totaled about three hundred with an even smaller number seen as major or critical to our theory of therapeutic change.

Given the competence and skill of the clinical assessment of the variables, the tests of the predictions would ultimately be tests of those theoretic assumptions that taken together, constitute our functional theory of therapy. Obviously, with so many possible reasons why predictions could come out or go awry, apart from the adequacy and cogency of these theoretical assumptions, no single test or combination of tests could decisively confirm or refute a particular assumption under scrutiny. But if the majority of the predictions embodying a particular theoretical assumption were sustained, its plausibility would be strengthened, while if the majority of predictions embodying an assumption were not borne out, its plausibility would be diminished. Thus empirical knowledge of a systematically altered array of assumptions underlying therapeutic change could accrue as a result of the project, and help to form a more precisely defined (more empirically supported) theory of therapy.

To make this testing of predictions more precise and freer of retrospective bias or circular reasoning, the evidence necessary at the end to sustain or refute each prediction was set down in advance. This predetermined evidence statement—event, manifest behavior, or clinical judgment of an altered intrapsychic state—was then set into an evidence form, a statement of expected outcome for each prediction embedded among two or three plausible alternatives, with the expected correct outcomes (evidence) marked in advance by the Initial Study team. The initial study in each research case, then, comprised the assessments of relevant patient and situational variables, the clinical predictions of expected treatment course and outcome, the prediction form for the discrete predictive statements in accord with the if-then-because model, and the evidence form for the keyed predicted outcomes. A final step was the patient's placement at the start of therapy on a 100-point, clinically anchored, global rating scale that unified the judgments of seven subscales, the Health-Sickness-Rating-Scale (HSRS); and a statement of the HSRS change predicted for the termination of the therapy.

TREATMENT OF THE PATIENT

At this point, the research study of the case was suspended while the patient underwent the prescribed treatment course to its natural conclusion. Through a monitoring system in the clinic record room, where monthly progress notes are routinely filed on each Menninger Clinic patient, the research team was notified of a pending treatment termination of each of its flagged cases on which a research initial study had been done. The team then reactivated the research inquiry, and notified the therapist that this particular patient he or she had been treating (for whatever length of time—months or years) was a member of the PRP population. At that point, the therapist, and through the therapist, the patient, found out for the first time that they had been chosen for research inquiry. They were then asked to cooperate in the study of the terminating therapy. For this study, the Termination Study team (for purposes of noncontamination of the research, different from the Initial Study team) sought access to all routine clinical records on the case: these records ranged from daily process notes for more than a thousand hours of analysis to the minimum monthly progress notes required by clinic regulations. The team also sought a series of interviews with the patient, the therapist, the supervisor of the therapy if there had been one,[1] and others significant in the patient's life (e.g., close family members, clinic staff, employers). Finally, the projective psychological test battery that had been initially administered was repeated. In a very few instances, where the patient's cooperation could not be secured or where, because of the nature of the treatment or the nature of the termination, direct patient involvement seemed contraindicated, a truncated study was still done using only the clinical records and interviews with therapist and supervisor (but not involving the patient directly).

All of the clinical data thus gathered and studied upon treatment termination were then systematically ordered into the Termination Study. The study comprised the following: reassessment of the identical array of twenty-eight patient variables and seven situational variables in their now changed cross-sectional status after treatment; assessment of about thirty treatment and therapist variables; content areas of the treatment such as themes, transference paradigms, course, changes in specified attributes or dimensions; formal aspects of the treatment, such as basic techniques, types of

---

[1] In order to ensure minimal adequate levels of therapist competence, so that failures of predictions or of expectable events could not be ascribed to lack of skill and experience on the part of the therapist, all therapists whose cases were studied by the project were at least five years beyond their basic clinical training period. However, some of them were candidates in the psychoanalytic institute and their psychoanalytic cases were therefore supervised; and of the cases in psychotherapy, even some with quite senior therapists were in continuing supervision within the clinical structure of the institution.

subject matter including past versus present, reconstruction and memory, dream and fantasy, style and form, and the like; personal attributes and professional qualities of the therapist, and the climate of the therapist–patient interaction, with data delineated then concerning all predictive areas of therapeutic course and outcome; the completed evidence form including the actual results of the evidence for and against the specific predictions; new HSRS rating at termination; plus a new set of predictions, about ten per case for the events of the follow-up period with predicted status at follow-up time; and a new HSRS predicted for follow-up (changes and gains either consolidated or eroded). In each case, the termination study was completed upon treatment termination, but before the patient's return to his or her home community—most of the patients had come to Topeka for treatment from literally around the country.

FOLLOW-UP STUDY

Between the two and three years later,[2] the PRP patients were contacted for follow-up study as prearranged. Follow-up was not done by mail, questionnaires, or telephone, but by each patient's return with a significant family member to The Menninger Foundation at the project's expense for a week-long visit. A new cross-sectional assessment, including psychiatric interviewing, repeat of the projective psychological test battery administered now for the third time, and social history from the accompanying relative, was completed. The assessments aimed to duplicate the original workup so far as the altered circumstances allowed—that now the patient was not coming because of mental suffering from which he or she was seeking surcease, but rather as someone coming (out of varying motives) to help the quest for the accrual of knowledge about psychotherapy.

The clinical data thus gathered and studied were comparably systematically ordered as follows: another reassessment of the twenty-eight patient variables and seven situational variables as now seen cross-sectionally at follow-up; reassessment of the thirty treatment and therapist variables as reviewed in the light of the posttreatment events in the patient's life; another completion of the

[2] In keeping with the protocols in cancer treatment, the project originally had planned five-year follow-ups, but the exigencies of extramural funding (Foundations' Fund for Research in Psychiatry, the Ford Foundation, and NIMH) were such that, given the length of the treatments under study, up to eight years in some instances, optimal follow-up time intervals had to be partially compromised.

evidence form, in the light of the posttreatment events; as well as
the completion of the second evidence form for the predictions
specifically made at the time of termination study for the follow-up
period; and a last HSRS rating for the follow-up time. Though a few
patients would not cooperate fully in follow-up study (i.e., they
spoke on the phone but would not return to Topeka), and a few
were unavailable (i.e., they died in the interim, in each instance
from illness-related causes), between information gleaned from the
patient and from collateral sources such as treating physician, family
members, and friends, enough data were secured to fill out an adequate follow-up study in every instance. In that sense (thus differing
from many psychotherapy projects otherwise organized and with
different population bases) the PRP had a 100 percent follow-up
study rate.[3]

Thus, some forty-two documented case studies were recorded
over approximately a twelve-year span. Four years were needed to
accomplish the initial studies at the rate of about one per month,
ten per year, each representing about forty hours of work for each
of the two members of the Initial Study team. Therapeutic courses
were followed up to eight years in duration,[4] and each of these was
followed by a Termination Study. Two to three years of follow-up
time were required for each case. These records included all of
the imposed research forms, assessments of the relevant variables
(patient, therapist and treatment, and situational), across the three
points in time (initial, termination, and follow-up), along with the
logical if-then-because analysis of the individual prediction studies,
the keyed and then the outcome evidence forms, and the HSRS for
each point in time, as predicted in advance and then as actually adjudged.

Data Analysis

Three main avenues of data study and analysis were then followed.
The first was a case-by-case *clinical* study. All of the material on

---

[3] In fact, much more serious than patient attrition was the problem of researcher attrition, the problem of keeping reasonably intact a large fifteen-to-twenty-member multidisciplinary research group comprising individuals with varying research and career commitments
over the long ongoing life of the project, two decades all told, while interests and lives
necessarily changed. We succeeded well enough in this.

[4] Even after eight years, not all therapies were naturally terminated. However, the reasonable assumption was made that at that point the therapy had reached a stable plateau, and
could be assessed as a "cut-off termination" with the fact of the continuing therapeutic

each case (several hundred pages in each instance) was read and abstracted into one four-part document, the case study. The parts are (1) initial study: summary of the patient as he or she first presented, with presenting history, cross-sectional initial assessment, and predictions to therapeutic course and outcome; (2) termination study: summary of the treatment, the cross-sectional termination assessment, and prediction to follow-up course; (3) follow-up study: treatment and its consequences as seen retrospectively through the subsequent follow-up course, and the cross-sectional follow-up assessment; and (4) synthesis of the treatment course and outcome: an overall statement about what had been clinically learned in that case about the determinants of the course and outcome of the therapy. These individual case studies, averaging fifty to seventy pages each, are comprehensive descriptions of a treatment course and the patient changes that eventuated.[5]

The second main avenue of data study and analysis was the Prediction Study itself. The predictions, as already indicated, started as clinical predictions of the kind that usually mark clinical discourse, as implicit aspects of the clinical dialogue, implicit in every statement of diagnosis and prognosis, of treatment planning and therapeutic expectation embedded in clinical context, qualification, and often ambiguity. By the logical analysis of the tripartite if-then-because formal model the predictions were transformed into discrete explicit predictive statements (average 50 per case, about 2,000 in all), and then tested by specified predetermined evidence or outcome criteria, keyed in advance to the predicted outcomes, and presented for subsequent judgment according to actual outcomes within an array of plausible alternative predictions. It is important to remember that specific predictions were made in advance, with the evidence necessary to confirm or refute them at the end also specified in advance, and that at the end, outcome judges with no knowledge of what predictions had been made among the plausible

---

relationship itself part of the adjudged outcome status. There were five such cases; three of them did come to formal termination in the interval before follow-up study.

[5] These detailed protocols are stored both at The Menninger Foundation, Topeka, Kansas, and in my own files, 290 Beach Road, Belvedere, California 94920. They are the bases of my book, *Forty-Two Lives in Treatment* (1986), in which each of the forty-two is individually described in summary form, which is the final overall clinical accounting of the work of PRP, its findings, and its conclusions. The book includes follow-up data on as many of the original research population as could still be traced and reached, follow-up extending thus for some of them over the entire three-decade span of the project, 1954 to 1986. An abbreviated sample case study of a single patient, however, including the entire verbatim interpretive synthesis, had also been published earlier (Wallerstein, 1968).

alternative outcomes presented in the evidence form, had to judge which outcomes had actually taken place.

Such keying of the predicted "correct" answers on the multiple choice evidence form would thus provide an easy entry to the adequacy of the reasoning chain that went into each prediction, a chain explicit in the assumptions in the *because* clauses of the tripartite logical statement of each specific prediction. As already indicated, the assumptions (about 300 in all) grouped into a hierarchically organized logical network of increasing generality and causal accountability, constitute our currently held, but never before systematically or empirically scrutinized, theory of psychoanalytic therapy.

Out of the systematic confirmation or disconfirmation of groups of predictions linked to particular assumptions would come a strengthening or diminution of the credibility or plausibility of those assumptions, and hence an altered hierarchically organized tree and a better, more rigorous theory of therapy (i.e., better linked to empirical data based on actual outcomes of actual predictions). In this sense, the creation of this prediction study and the advance elaboration of the hierarchical organization of the assumptions that underlay the original predictions, together with alteration of that hierarchical organization in the light of the actual outcomes of those predictions, can be seen as in themselves a major advance in the theory of psychoanalytic therapy beyond its state, characterized by Rapaport just a decade earlier as consisting of only "rules of thumb" in contrast to what he felt was the comprehensiveness and articulation of psychoanalysis as a theory of personality and of psychopathology.

The full story of this Prediction Study from conception to completion is in two monographs, one on method and in prospect (Sargent, Horwitz, Wallerstein, and Appelbaum, 1968) and one on results and in retrospect (Horwitz, 1974). Another aspect of the prediction study now requires mention; that is, a circling back to the statement made earlier that though the usual control methods of the experimental paradigm could not be followed in this naturalistic study, control principles would nonetheless be built appropriately into the project design. Actually, four methods of control were evolved based more on the appropriate selection of clinical material than on its manipulation. The first method, intrapatient control (i.e., using the patient as his own control), is based on the individual prediction study. Through setting out the predictions, the necessary evidence, and the assumptive base all in advance, control is introduced into observation, and post hoc reconstruction and rationalization are avoided. The other control methods will be stated in the context of the next main avenue of data study and analysis, the quantifying techniques built upon the Fechnerian method of paired comparisons.

The third avenue, the semiquantitative way of data study and analysis, stemmed from the consideration that in addition to their qualitative clinical complexity and subtlety most of the patient, treatment and therapist, and life-situational variables also have a somewhat quantitative "more or less" dimension, and that it is a clinically commonplace and congenial operation to compare two patients, two treatments, or two life situations and say that this is greater than that, that this one has more tolerance for anxiety than the other patient, and so forth. We therefore could set up the task, albeit a laborious one, of comparing every patient with every other patient for each of the patient, treatment and therapist, and life-situational variables that lent themselves to such quantitative extrapolation (which was most of them) at each point in time (initial, termination, and follow-up) that the variable was assessed.

Twelve was selected as the manageable size of each batch of variables because that number seemed to be about as many different patients as could be kept in mind at one time for purposes of comparative judgment on any particular characteristic of the patient, the treatment, or the life situation. For each variable at each point in time, paired comparison of each patient against each other in a batch of twelve meant sixty-six comparative judgments ($12 \times 11/2$) —hence the laboriousness, since this would only be one batch of twelve out of the forty-two (and therefore would require multiple batches), which would all be then repeated for each of about thirty-five variables thus adjudged, and then repeated for all of them at each point in time. A further refinement: after judgment on the first batch of twelve for a variable, the next batch consisted of six from the prior batch alongside six new ones, until the last or seventh batch consisted of six from the immediately preceding batch and the six circled back from those in the first batch that had only been used once. Thus each variable of each patient was adjudged in two batches of twelve; the overlapping could lead to a comparative arraying of all the patients on each variable at each point in time from the most often chosen to the least often.

It is these resulting ordinal rankings of the various patient, treatment and therapist, and situational variables that lent themselves to interpatient comparison and contrast by permitting the selection of patients alike in respect to certain variables while dissimilar in respect to other variables. The rankings also lent themselves both to quantifying statistical handling via factor analytic techniques and to nonmetrical mathematical handling via the facet theory and multidimensional scalogram analysis (MSA) techniques of Guttman and Lingoes.[6]

To come back now to control methods, clearly the paired comparisons can be used for interpatient control, for if groups of patients can be selected who are alike in certain variables while dissimilar in others, then some variables can be controlled while the variability of others is investigated. This was the second control method utilized.

The third was a parallel and independent prediction study made on the basis of blind study of the initial psychological test protocols alone. This prediction study was then compared with the predictions derived from the total clinical case study. The fourth control method, sometimes encountered, was the so-called inadvertent control. This control occurred when patients, who because of finances, geography, or differing judgment on the part of the treating clinicians were treated by therapeutic approaches not deemed the therapy of choice by the research team. In such instances it was considered possible to ascertain whether changes that the researchers felt could only come about in the therapy of choice, nonetheless eventuated when other approaches were used. Obviously, this control method would again test the necessary conditions for change, that is, the underlying assumptions about the theory of therapy or about how change takes place.

The preceding pages must seem to describe an inordinately complex pyramiding of design and execution. In order to accomplish all its aspects, the project involved an interdisciplinary research team of about 15 members who worked over a period of a decade

---

[6] For a full description from conception to completion of these statistical and mathematical ways of data analysis built upon the semiquantitative paired comparisons, reference is made to two other monographs, again one on method and in prospect (Sargent, Coyne, Wallerstein, and Holtzman, 1967) and one on results and in retrospect (Kernberg et al., 1972). Important in the Sargent et al. exposition is the basis for the treatment of the ordinal rankings that emerged from the paired comparisons as having enough cardinal properties to be meaningfully handled by correlational methods (intercorrelations of the final scaled scores) and factorial studies (factor analyses of the intercorrelation matrix).

and a half in order to make some systematic simultaneous inroads into both the process and the outcome issues of change in psychotherapy. It is notable that the work was set into inquiry by the two seemingly simple initiating questions: What changes take place in psychotherapy and how do those changes come about? Clearly, there have been any number of other research paradigms developed for study in this arena, but each group of clinicians and of clinical researchers must have its own conceptions of its field of endeavor, its own commitments to the issues, and the questions in the field that both warrant and are amenable to systematic research inquiry, and its own proper sense for the construction of a research design that is at once true both to the requirements of objectivity in science and also true to the nature of the field and its phenomena, in this case, the clinically complex and subtle field of psychoanalytic therapy.

How well this project has succeeded in that task others can perhaps attest by studying its written record. The project's seventy or more publications[7] recount the initial conception and design; the delineation of the various sets of variables and the methods for the several lines of data analysis including the clinical case studies, the individual patient prediction studies, and the interpatient group statistical and mathematical studies; the varieties of operational problems encountered in implementing the study in accord with the chosen design; the alterations in clinical and theoretical thinking enforced by the emerging data; and finally, the various expositions of results in the several areas, already specifically referred to in the monographs that have come to publication or are still in process.[8] Additionally to be mentioned are two other books on overall results from the project. One book studies only the situational variables themselves over the three points in time, in order to highlight the interaction between the external and the internal in effecting intrapsychic change (Voth and Orth, 1973). Another book, published subsequent to this article, studies the comprehensive projective psychologic test battery protocols and their changes over the three points in time (Appelbaum, 1977).

[7] The entire project bibliography (from 1958 to 1986) consisting of over seventy publications, including seven books and monographs, and singly or multiply-authored by over fifteen investigators, can be obtained from Robert S. Wallerstein, M.D., 290 Beach Road, Belvedere, California 94920.

[8] Since this publication, I have published the book already referred to, *Forty-Two Lives in Treatment* (1986), the final clinical accounting of the work of PRP, its findings, and its conclusions.

CONCLUSIONS

Thus, a description of a psychotherapy research project in its purpose and scope, its method and design. What can one additionally say in briefest compass of its overall results? These have in large part already been established in detail. The prediction study (one of the three main avenues of data study and analysis) has presented in two monographs the specific fate of the two thousand or so individual discrete predictive statements and, more importantly, their implications then for the three hundred or so theoretical assumptions that underpinned the predictions, assumptions that, hierarchically and logically arranged, articulate into the fabric of the psychoanalytic theory of therapy. Similarly, the quantitative study (another of the three main avenues of data study and analysis) has in two monographs presented in detail the fate of the various specific hypotheses on the relationships among the seventy or so patient, treatment and therapist, and situational variables as tested via both our statistical factor analytic techniques and our nonmetrical mathematical facet theory and multidimensional scalogram analysis techniques. The predictions, the assumptions, the variables, and the correlations are many, detailed, and particular. Reference can only be made to the monographs mentioned.

What of the overall sweep, the broad clinical knowledge that has accrued to the field? This as stated is the subject matter of *Forty-two Lives in Treatment* (Wallerstein, 1986) built on the case-by-case clinical studies of the forty-two project cases. In largest overview and in preview, if there is one overriding generalization, it is that the achieved result with psychoanalysis, the most far-reaching reconstructive therapy, often enough falls somewhat short of its ambitious aims, although in different ways with different kinds of patients. In contrast, psychoanalytically based psychotherapies, with more modest goals in terms of basic change, often achieve results that exceed expectations. Out of this partial convergence the more exact delineations of the indications and a more precise prognosis across the array of different kinds of patients may emerge, for both psychoanalysis per se and for the other psychotherapeutic modalities derived from it.

This highly condensed overview of this project has, I trust, given clearly enough a sense of the nature of the enterprise, this particular psychotherapy research project, and what one can learn from it about psychotherapy, human helping, and human communication. I hope that at the same time it has also conveyed something of the sense of wonder and of absorbing excitement that is the emotional fuel that sustains such an enterprise.

4.

Assessment of Structural Change in Psychoanalytic Therapy and Research

Psychic structure and structural change are among the most central and, at the same time, most problematic concepts within psychoanalytic theory; they are also crucial to any effort at elaboration of the theory of psychoanalytic therapy, and at differentiation of the processes and outcomes of psychoanalytic therapies from psychotherapies conducted within other theoretical frameworks.

Rapaport's (1960) statements on structure have been widely regarded as both the most succinct and the most definitive. He stated, "Controls and defenses are conceptualized structures: *their rates of change are slow* in comparison with those of drive–energy accumulations and drive–discharge processes" (pp. 28–29; emphasis added). And, "In contrast to the drive processes, whose rate of change is fast and whose course is paroxysmal, the factors which conflict with them and co-determine behavior appeared to be invariant or at least of a slower rate of change. The observation of these *relatively abiding determiners of behavior and symptom* seems to have been the foundation on which the concept of structure was built" (p. 53; emphasis added). Sandler and Joffe (1969) carried this conception even further. They differentiated mental functioning into the experiential realm of the mind, that is, the realm of *experience* of the phenomenal content of wishes, impulses, memories, fantasies, sensations, percepts, and feelings, all that we can "know" and that can be either conscious or unconscious. They sharply contrasted this with the nonexperiential realm of forces and energies, of mechanisms and apparatuses (i.e., the network of explanatory constructs and principles we designate as the psychic apparatus). They then squarely declared that all "the more stable components of the nonexperiential realm can be considered to be *structures* in the sense in which they have been defined by Rapaport, i.e., as organizations which are permanent or have a relatively slow rate of change" (p. 82).

This kind of formulation of psychic structure is by no means as simple, coherent, or unproblematic as it may at first appear. Kernberg (1984a), for example, in a statement on psychoanalytic therapy research said, "structural intrapsychic change refers to a significant modification in the assumed, underlying, unconscious *intrapsychic conflicts* that determine the development of symptom formation" (pp. 251–252; emphasis added). Here the meaning of structure and structural change is linked to intrapsychic conflicts, that is, *mental contents* (not mechanisms or apparatuses); the definitional ground has been shifted into Sandler and Joffe's experiential or phenomenal realm. This usage of Kernberg's, which is reflected in his well-known conceptualizations of self and object representations and the affective valences that link them as central building blocks of intrapsychic structure, though the diametric opposite of Rapaport's and Sandler and Joffe's, seems to carry an equally congenial and plausible clinical and theoretical ring.

Within this wide disparity in the very definitional framework, additional unclarities in the conceptions of structure and structural change abound. What, for example, is the level of generality or specificity at which to formulate concepts of structure? Are structures to be as global and encompassing (and diffuse) as the tripartite id, ego, and superego? Or are they as particulate as specific enduring individual memory traces or unconscious fantasy formations? Or are they to be located at the intermediate level, pitched by Kernberg, of self and object representations and their affective bonding within larger entities of psychic instances? In relation to this congeries of issues, Schwartz (1981) summarizes:

> The issue is clarified by noting that people acquire specific contents (words, ideas, images, etc.) but also learn how to learn, i.e., learn

how to attend, concentrate, anticipate the future and organize experience. In this context, people also learn how not to learn, i.e., they learn to employ a set of defensive operations that restrict experience. . . . At issue is whether specific contents, general abstractions, global frames of reference (such as the distinction between reality and imagination) and generalized defensive and controlling structures can *all* be subsumed under the rubric of psychic structure. A good theory has a wide range of application. Nevertheless, a good theory also has limits. . . . Applying the term structure to cognitive skills, defensive operations *and* specific contents may be good theory or the use of the term structure in a loose or even metaphoric sense [p. 62; emphasis added].

Another major unclarity rests in the opposition posited by Rapaport between control mechanisms (for example, defenses) on the one hand, as structures because of their enduring nature (slow rate of change), and the instinctual drives, on the other hand, which can fluctuate sharply and rapidly in intensity of pressure, expression, and direction, and are therefore presumably not structures, that is, not structured. In the light of all the considerations concerning the hierarchical structuring of the unconscious instinctual pressures adduced by Schur (1966), is this really a tenable dichotomy? To make this question concrete, should we therefore *not* speak of structural change when manic behavior gives way to depressive behavior? Or is this supposed to depend on whether such a shift is only transitory or truly enduring? And how about when the long-time masochistic doormat behaves sadistically, either in a sporadic out-of-character eruption, or again in a seemingly more lasting "change of character"? Or, as a last such example, when the confirmed thief is suddenly—but lastingly—transformed into an honest man, as in the conversion experience of Jean Valjean with the bishop in Victor Hugo's *Les Misérables?*

Given this definitional and conceptual morass around the *meaning* and *usage* of structure, and therefore around structural change, it is no wonder that we have no established consensus as to what constitutes *evidence* for structural change (as presumably brought about in psychoanalytic therapy by interpretation leading to insight, followed by adequate working through) as distinct from "only" adaptive or behavioral or symptomatic change. The latter can presumably occur without insight, on other bases in dynamic psychotherapies, like supportive psychotherapies conceived within a psychoanalytic framework, or in other kinds of psychotherapies conceived out of a different theoretical base than psychoanalysis, or even in the absence of psychotherapy altogether.

These very same difficulties around the constructs of structure and structural change emerge also when they are approached within a clinical rather than a conceptual framework. I can illustrate this with a clinical example and data drawn from larger, long-term clinical material (Wallerstein, 1986). The example selected should at least be clinically persuasive about the observable data and the identifiable evidence that bear on issues of structure and structural change. The following account is from the verbatim interpretive synthesis of the original writeup of the treatment course and outcome of a patient called, in my (1986) book, the Adoptive Mother.

The patient had come to psychiatric evaluation presenting as her central problem her inability to be a proper mother, culminating in the return of an adopted child to the adoption agency after four months of mounting distress. Diagnostic study revealed the presenting distress to be a reflection of core neurotic conflicts (1) in the area of feminine sexuality, of her basic sexual identification, of activity-passivity, of her competitive rivalry with men and her need to dominate them; and (2) in the area of oral–dependent deprivations and frustrations. At the time of termination study and again at the time of follow-up study, there was general agreement by patient and analyst (and research investigators) that after three years of analysis, only partial resolution of intrapsychic conflict had occurred, although there was a very substantial and very satisfying alleviation of the originally presenting symptoms of recurrent anxiety, bitter depression, and acute life crisis.

The transference models that had been activated and seemingly worked through in this analysis were clearly evident. There was the initial position of the nurse (the patient was a nurse) objectively reporting to the physician about the symptoms of a third party—herself, the patient. This was a struggle over detachment versus involvement, the struggle to overcome her distrust that any good could come from emotional closeness. Alongside this were the abreactions of penitent to priest-confessor (the patient was a devout Catholic convert), the seeking of forgiveness for her own unlovableness via a more tolerant superego figure. Once these initial positions were worked through, the main core of the analytic work revolved around the two major transference images of the terrible father who mistreated mother, and the good, kind, understanding mother who sheltered and protected. As clearly documented in close study of the analytic work, the negative mother transference, though it was clearly evident in the analytic material (for example, a dream, in the termination phase, of the patient beating to a pulp her interfering mother who had interrupted the patient and her husband at intercourse) was never fully developed or analytically worked out. In fact, the analysis ended prematurely at precisely the point when this kind of material was pressing to the fore; that is, the transference neurosis had unfolded but was never adequately resolved.

The process notes from the termination phase of the analysis amply support this view. During the same period as the dream just referred to, there were fantasies of her mother indulging in the very same forbidden sexual behaviors that were interdicted to the patient; a memory of mother having told her about the degenerates (men), and what they do; the childhood fear of mother catching her masturbating (and the association to the analyst peering at her); fear of homosexual fantasies she would have had if she had had a woman analyst. Hatred was gingerly expressed toward mother and father as partners in crime. The patient also mentioned her strong discomfort on kissing her mother-in-law in greeting or at parting after a visit. In another dream of this period, the patient spilled her jewels, and these were restored to her by the analyst. In her associations she toyed with this as the symbol of the restoration of her femininity. She associated to the pregnancy and miscarriage she had had early in her marriage, but then veered away to a bossy reaction to the analyst's presence, taking up a critical, defensive, "masculine" position. All these conflicts were active in the material of the termination phase of this analysis without concomitant evidence of insightful mastery or new ego positions.

Nonetheless, the patient felt pressured to draw the analysis to a premature close before this material was ever worked through. Her own awareness of this was caught in the complaint about "orders from headquarters" (her husband) pressing her to terminate so that she and he could move to their new home in a distant city. She asked, "How can I go when I can't make peace with my own dead mother?" Despite this, she did leave, ascribing her decision to the increasing importunities of an ever more demanding husband or, at other times, admitting she could have stayed in treatment longer if she really wanted to, and that her husband would have been willing to delay his plans for her. At the point of leaving there was again a general agreement on the part of the patient, the

analyst, and the research investigators, that the analysis ended on
the same note of positive attachment and sustained good feeling
toward the analyst that had characterized the predominant transference mode throughout—gratitude to the fatherly analyst, who was
also the good mother who cared.

What accounted for this limited outcome in terms of structural
change with termination prior to the full analysis of the negative
mother imago, which was so centrally tied to her core conflicts and
their symptomatic expression? Research study revealed what seemed
to be a number of contributory influences within the treatment: (1)
The analyst was heavily influenced in the direction of a "defense
analysis" that focused more on interpretation of defense and resistance and less on specific content meaning of inner impulse or its
transference manifestations. Interpretive effort often seemed partial
and one-sided. (2) This interlocked with a particular learning problem that seemed to characterize this analysis. This was the analyst's
difficulty in showing the patient the transference meaning of phenomena, for example, of acting out, without seeming critical and
punitive. It seemed that for this analyst, acting out was characteristically to be directly suppressed—or ignored. He did not rely on the
patient's ability to come to understand its meaning in a way that
would be sufficient to control it. (3) In addition to this specific
learning problem, a particular countertransference issue seemed to
operate to limit the full effectiveness of the analyst's work. The
patient was a woman whom he would go to any lengths to help,
from whom he was willing to take a lot, and who perhaps made him
too anxious to really deal effectively with her bossy and competitive
ways. (4) A last problem specifically noted within the conduct of
the treatment lay in the analyst's tendency to tread lightly in analyzing the meaning of the patient's religious beliefs and feelings. In
part this may have been in defensive deference to the husband's
(and the patient's) anticipated fear that psychoanalysis would undermine—that is, take away—the patient's religious faith; in part it
may have been a reflection of a more general attitude of reluctance
to explore the meaning of religion in intrapsychic life. In any case,
it is clear that the meaning of religion and of her relationship to
God was never brought into deliberate analytic focus, despite its
obvious connection with the unexplored aspects of her relationship
to her mother. Rather, the disappointment with her religion with
which she began the analysis shifted to the same note of heightened
faith and good feeling that characterized every other aspect of the

ending state of the analysis. How much her renewed religious fervor represented the coin she paid to keep her husband's love; how much the relative sexual inhibition with which she ended the analysis represented the conviction that sexuality to be moral must be paid for by pregnancy, and that therefore if pregnancy were banned, so also must sexuality; and how much aggressive charge resided in the demandingness with which she continued to "storm heaven"—all these were relatively unexplored territory.

Thus, a variety of influences within the specific conduct of the analysis could be felt to contribute to the analytically limited outcome. That they by themselves did not necessarily account for this outcome or for its specific form, is attested by the other side of the coin—the limitations on the possible result of the analysis predicted at the time of pretreatment study from the diagnostic psychological test protocols, that is, from the side of the patient. It was observed that the nature and form of the acute decompensated state in which the patient had initially presented herself for treatment gave evidence of the disorganizing anxiety that could be potentially generated by the regressive experience of psychoanalysis. The patient's own awareness of this was reflected in her early panicky "fear of losing control." It was predicted that at a point of achievement of good symptom relief, and of substantial if not complete gains toward more adaptive reaction patterns, rather than face the danger of further regression, the patient would prefer to consolidate and "quit while she was ahead"—and she could do this by invoking reality pressures and supports from without, and by remobilizing her potential for counterphobic mastery from within. This is exactly what seems to have happened. Furthermore, it was specified that the area of incompleted work would be in relation to the negative mother transference and the patient's hostile identification with the malevolent, feared, and hateful preoedipal mother imago. Again, this is exactly what seems to have happened. In fact, the very life solution she came to at the end of the analysis, to have a grateful feeling to mother figures, to maintain her marriage with its problems glossed over, and to try again to adopt children even at the price of considerable inner turmoil, was in itself an expression of the unresolved identification with mother—she chose to be a martyr, like mother, burdened with children and with an unsatisfactory husband.

In terms of this major limitation drawn from the nature of the patient's personality structure and of her illness across the expectable outcome of the analysis, the termination was perhaps at the best possible point of improved functioning. This was so whether it was deliberately planned technically (for which there was no special evidence) or sensed intuitively and pushed for by the patient; abetted by the already stated problems within the therapist's handling of the treatment that likewise worked to keep it less than fully interpretive and to allow significant sectors of intrapsychic functioning to remain in repression and unanalyzed.

Two corollary predictions had been made initially, one having to do with the first phase of the treatment, the other with the prospects of postanalytic treatment. The first prediction was of the desirability in this case of an initial period of preparatory psychotherapy in order to help arrest the acute decompensation. Again, though this does not seem to have been done deliberately, it worked out that way. The patient spent the first two months (40 hours) sitting up rather than on the couch. She expressed herself as too anxious to directly accept the psychoanalytic structure.

The other prediction, which was based on the expectation that the analytic result would be incomplete, and that the patient would be left liable to recurrent anxiety, and perhaps even transitory symptom formation in the face of continued environmental triggering of her core conflicts, had to do with the form of future treatment. It was stipulated that this should not then be an effort to analyze further what had remained unanalyzed from the first treatment (for the same reasons), but that this should rather be a supportive–expressive psychotherapy aimed at helping her utilize the previous analytic accomplishments to stabilize herself in the face of new stresses.

In effect, this is also what happened. The patient did not seek further psychotherapy in an explicit way. She rationalized this on the basis of the higher treatment fee in her new community, which she could not afford. What she did instead was to call on a variety of helping hands—none specifically for psychotherapy. There was the priest who admonished her regarding her duties to her husband and to their future together—including the child he encouraged her to adopt; there was the family physician who prescribed medications to help her cope with the tensions and anxieties any such moves would generate; there was the understanding adoption agency social worker, sympathetic to her plight, to whom she could pour out her burden of grief, of worry, of discouragement. The patient thus combined the ingredients of her supportive–expressive psychotherapy, and insured that any more ambitious psychotherapeutic effort was precluded.

On this basis the patient was able to go ahead and adopt two children, albeit with considerable psychological strain. With the consolidation of the success of the first adoption, a girl, there was enough accrual of circular gratifications and enough increment to her self-esteem and her self-confidence, to enable her, three years later, to adopt a boy. Thus, with an analysis that was incomplete and with important transference components unanalyzed, the patient could nonetheless achieve her original treatment goal—to be able to be a proper wife and mother. Indicative of the nature of the incompletely analyzed transference fantasies which underpinned these significant treatment changes was the patient's voiced desire on the occasion of her research follow-up visit to see her ex-analyst and to show him her adopted daughter, the successful "fruit of his labors."

I have not here given any context, either in the life history of the patient prior to the analysis, or in the treatment history during the analysis, for these observations and inferences from the final interpretive synthesis that relate to the theme of structural change achieved—and not achieved. I trust that what has nonetheless emerged from this highly abstracted and summarized account is the kind of assessments of the process and outcome of analysis our research program engaged in in order to understand the changes in life functioning achieved (which to this patient added up to a very satisfactory therapeutic result, since she did after the termination of her analysis go on to successfully adopt two children in her new community, albeit with some recurrent difficulties). We tried to relate these changes in life functioning to the degree of internal (structural) change achieved; in this case, in the sense of thoroughgoing conflict resolutions, the psychoanalytic gain achieved was substantially less complete than the experienced psychotherapeutic gain.

How then does this clinical presentation relate to the discussion of the ambiguities and confusion about the terms structure and structural change considered from the conceptual standpoint, with which I began this essay? Clearly, the *clinically* adduced evidence for both the reach and the limitations of the changes achieved in terms of enduring resolutions of intrapsychic conflicts has been in the terms framed by Kernberg (1984a); that is, of underlying and unconscious mental representations or contents that have been rendered substantially or only partially conscious and in the process of working over have been, to whatever degree, modified into new dispositions or capacities. This is all clearly in the experiential realm demarcated by Sandler and Joffe (1969). How this in turn reflects enduring alterations (partial *or* thorough) in underlying *structures* that determine the new dispositions or capacities in abiding ways, that is, in the nonexperiential realm where Sandler and Joffe, and of course also Rapaport (1960) have placed the psychoanalytic conceptions of structure, and what those underlying structural changes (again, of whatever degree) are assumed to be, has not been directly addressed in this presentation thus far.

It is exactly at this conjunction, where the major *open questions,* clinically, conceptually, *and* in empirical research terms, around our *theory of (psychoanalytic) therapy,* reside. And it is this state of affairs, and these kinds of theoretical and clinical considerations, which I have elaborated to this point, that frame the conceptual problems for any empirical research approach into the nature of the processes and outcomes of psychoanalytic therapies that are linked to (dependent upon) the concepts of structure and structural change. If one is to be able to explore empirically, clinically, or researchwise, the proposition that the kinds of changes, as well as the presumed bases of the changes that come about or are brought about, differ in the expressive analytic therapies from those that occur in the supportive psychotherapies (albeit psychoanalytically informed and guided), or in other kinds of therapies carried out within other guiding theoretical frameworks, then we would need to have consensually agreed upon, as well as reliable indices of intrapsychic "structures" and also (certainly for research purposes) a consensually agreed-upon, as well as reliable, metric along which structural *change* could be reasonably and reliably assessed—for example, some scale anchored to clear and concise descriptions of scale points, preferably illustrated by clinical vignettes.

The first issue in approaching this problem from a formal research standpoint is the same question of definition. How will we choose to define structures in *empirically* meaningful ways, and how then will we be able to define structural change, by what criteria or hallmarks? This is, to begin with, a question of the status of the concept of structure. In contrast to the structures of the body (organs, tissues, cells, intracellular bodies, molecules, atoms, etc.) which are palpable or visible at various levels (at least down to the atomic and subatomic level), the structures of the mind—psychic structures—are only useful explanatory *constructs.* As such, psychic structures have no tangible substance, have no clear-cut inherent hierarchical differentiation of levels; they are theory-bound, and therefore change in conception, even within an overarching psycho-analytic theory, as that theory itself evolves and changes. That is, structure can be conceptualized within an ego-psychological frame-work in terms of impulse–defense configurations, within a Kleinian framework in terms of good and bad part objects (in the paranoid position) and ambivalently held whole objects (in the depressive position), within an object-relational framework in terms of self and object representations and the affective valences that bind them, and within a self-psychological framework in terms of a varying cohe-sive or vulnerable bipolar self. This, despite the fact that the over-arching theory within which all these constructs have meaning is declared to be (the same) psychoanalysis. By contrast, other theories of mental functioning, like behavioral theory, accord these struc-tural constructs no ontological or epistemological status at all.

A next research issue is that of determining the dimensions and the level at which the concepts of psychic structure and struc-tural change can be heuristically useful and empirically manipula-ble. For such purposes, Freud's original ego-psychological macrostructures of ego, id, and superego just will not do. E. Bibring (1937) elaborated in detail what kind of structural changes are to be looked for in the id, the superego, and the ego, as the outcomes of a successful psychoanalysis. From a research perspective, the problem with this is that these macroconcepts are just too global, too experience-distant, and too difficult (if not impossible) to make operational in ways that do not oversimplify and therefore distort their representations to the point where the psychoanalytic clinician will no longer accept them as the same thing, or accept research results that come from studying them as having any evident relation to the living clinical enterprise. On the other hand, we do not want to be down to the level of such microstructures as individual stable memory traces or abiding fantasies (built engrammatically into some substrate of neurobiological functioning). At this level of con-struct, structures are, for practical purposes, almost infinite in number.

We seek, then, some workable intermediate level, we hope, ex-perience-near, and with reasonable conceptual and explanatory links to empirical observables. The defense mechanisms of the ego (or alternatively, impulse–defense configurations) is one set of con-structs that naturally comes to mind at this juncture. They have a long and stable history in psychoanalytic thinking (A. Freud, 1936;

G. Bibring, Dwyer, Huntington, and Valenstein, 1961; Wallerstein, 1983b), and have been widely incorporated into everyday psychological thinking. Additionally, they have a ready relation to observables, that is, all the varieties of *defensive behaviors* from which we infer the operation of the postulated defense mechanisms (see Wallerstein, 1983b). And they can shift along dimensions of range and flexibility, of modulation and moderation in deployment, of perspective, tolerance, and objective appraisal, and of enhanced awareness and insight, all potential measures of structural change along constructed pathological–normal continua.

However, it is precisely at this point—at this so-called intermediate level—that the different theoretical perspectives in psychoanalysis (e.g., the ego psychological, the object relational, the self psychological, the Kleinian, the Bionian, the Lacanian) each have differing understandings of what we call intrapsychic structure, what its significant dimensions and units are, and how one is to assess change in structure. At this stage in the theoretical development of psychoanalysis, consensus on these concepts is simply not possible; in fact, this is probably the most salient dividing line among these alternative (and competitive) theoretical perspectives within analysis.

Rather than deciding on dimensions and units of intrapsychic structure and of structural change that reflect a particular theoretical position within psychoanalysis, our research group has sought to formulate assessable "psychological capacities" (character propensities) that adherents of all prevailing psychoanalytic theoretical perspectives will agree to be attributes that comprehensively describe personality functioning. There will necessarily be a shift if there is "underlying" change in intrapsychic structures, however those intrapsychic structures or that structural change are conceptualized. That is, sustained change in these "psychological capacities" should be consensually accepted as reflecting underlying structural change, which may then be formulated differently by adherents of different theoretical positions.

To this point, fifteen such "psychological capacities" have been elaborated by our group,[1] descriptive together of the array of personality attributes and dispositions that in sum describe an individual's character and characteristic modes of functioning. They are intended to be comprehensive and, as far as possible, nonoverlapping.

---

[1] Since this publication, subsequent reformulations have expanded this to a list of seventeen discrete "psychological capacities" some of them considerably reconceptualized.

TABLE 4.1
Scales of Psychological Capacities

1. Self-Esteem
   - Grandiosity
   - Self-Depreciation

2. Zest for Life
   - Overexcitement
   - Absence of Enthusiasm
   - Low Investment in Life Activities

3a. Sense of Self (as Agent) —————— Disruption of Sense of Agency
3b. Coherence of Self —————— Disruption of Coherent Self

4. Commitment to Reality
   - Overvalues Own Perceptions
   - Overwhelmed by Other Points of View

5. Empathy
   - Emotional Absorption
   - Emotional Blunting

6. Commitment to Standards and Values
   - Moralism
   - Selfishness
   - Delinquency

7. Commitment in Relationships
   - Compulsive Overinvolvement
   - Limited, Tenuous Involvement

8. Reciprocity
   - Exploitation of Others
   - Surrender of Self

9. Self-Disclosure
   - Indiscriminate Self-Disclosure
   - Avoidance of Self-Disclosure

10. Reliance on Self and Others
   - Rarely Able to Rely on Others
   - Rarely Able to Rely on Self
   - Unreliable

11. Trust
   - Extreme Suspiciousness
   - Extreme Gullibility
   - Untrustworthy

12. Affect Tolerance
   - Out of Control "Affect Storms"
   - Hypercontrol

13. Appropriate Self-Assertion
   - Aggressiveness, Bullying
   - Unwillingness to Accept Limitations
   - Inhibition. Timidity

TABLE 4.1 (continued)

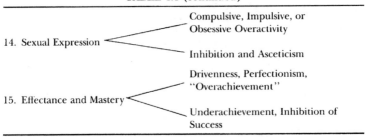

14. Sexual Expression
- Compulsive, Impulsive, or Obsessive Overactivity
- Inhibition and Asceticism

15. Effectance and Mastery
- Drivenness, Perfectionism, "Overachievement"
- Underachievement, Inhibition of Success

They are designed to be low-level (experience-near) theoretical constructs, readily and reliably inferred from observable behaviors (interview interactions, anamnestic material, i.e., behaviors in the widest sense of the word). In this they are in contrast to more abstract concepts, such as intrapsychic "structures" intended to represent the central elements of comprehensive personality theories. Not only are these underlying "structures" conceptualized differently within different psychoanalytic theoretical perspectives, but, as compared with our "psychological capacities," they are inevitably much more experience-distant and therefore (whatever their putative linkage to observables, like the conceptual relation between the constructs, defense mechanisms, and the observable, defensive behaviors), much harder to *define consensually* and *assess reliably* when put to operational test (as we found out in the course of considerable effort to do just this with even the classically agreed-upon and most clear-cut defense mechanisms).

The "psychological capacities" we have developed tentatively are listed in Table 4.1, with first approximation designations that are still unrefined. Each is named for the "normal point" of a bidirectional scale, signifying the two directions of deviation from the point of normal or optimal functioning, that of over- and that of underexpression. Since it is of the nature of human psychological functioning that deviations can be in the "hyper" and the "hypo" directions simultaneously (as in the usually rigidly controlled, affectively inhibited individual with periodic eruptions of explosive affect storms), the scales we are constructing are not stretched along a single dimension from "hyper" to "hypo" with an optimal midpoint, but are expressed with both deviating potentials strung out in a similar direction from the so-called "normal" or optimal ideal point. This makes explicit that any individual can be placed on both deviating arms away from the healthy point at the same time, and can progress toward health or "normality" consequent to analytic therapy along one or both of the scales leading to it. To begin with, we are creating a crude scale metric (anchored with illustrative clinical case vignettes) of just three nodal points away from the healthy i.e., mild, moderate, and severe maladaptive deviations.[2]

Study of our fifteen selected capacities will reveal that they are anchored in and derived from core elements of psychic functioning according to psychoanalytic theory; the deployment and management of the libidinal and aggressive drives; the control and modulation of impulse and affect; the relatedness to objects; the differentiation and integrity of the self functioning; the intactness and effective functioning of the ego ideal and of the superego; the quest for mastery and effective adaptation. It will remain an empirical question to determine how distinct and independent these capacities (dimensions of, or rather reflections of, psychic structure) are from one another as against being overlapping and intercorrelated, as well as how exhaustively they comprise the relevant universe necessary to a comprehensive understanding of the individual's adaptive and maladaptive functioning and change in functioning.

At this early point in our research program, our tasks ahead are still major in both the methodological and the substantive realms. The tasks of method that are ahead are large enough. They are to create and refine our fifteen mainly bidirectional scales, each scale pair having four points with one of the points (the normal or optimal) shared by each pair; to then anchor these scale points in clear and concise—and persuasive—illustrative clinical vignettes that will help make the scales both congenial in spirit with, and easily usable by, the research-interested clinician. We would then establish the reliability of the scale assessments and of the assessment of change along the scale consequent to psychoanalytic therapy across a wide spectrum of psychopathological formations and character types. Finally, and this is most crucial, we would demonstrate that our scales represent assessments reliably measuring changes in psychological capacities (and consequently in underlying

---

[2] As emphasized in this paragraph, at this point the scales are still tentative and the designations and definitional language still unrefined. Also, it is already clear that not all of them are best conceptualized as simply bidirectional with maladaptive deviations in just two opposed directions, of hyper- and hypofunctioning; with some of them there seem to be deviating direction that can be oppositely countered in two different ways, thus having a scale with three rather than simply two (symmetrically) deviating arms.

"structures") that are separate from and not identical with changes in just manifest behaviors or overt symptoms.[3]

Of course, beyond all these questions of method are our central questions of substance. Where symptom and behavior changes have occurred consequent to analytic therapy (psychoanalysis or psychoanalytically oriented psychotherapy), when does structural change, as rigorously defined and measured in the ways just indicated, also occur, and under what conditions? What conditions in the nature of the patient's personality functioning or psychopathology, and what conditions in the nature of the therapist's functioning or interventions? The crucial question here is whether such "real" structural changes (as demonstrated by changes in our assessed "psychological capacities") can or do come about concomitant with the symptomatic and behavioral changes, only in expressive analytic therapy, operating through the interpretive uncovering and insightful resolution of unconscious intrapsychic conflict. Or do they also come about as a consequence of (psychoanalytically informed and guided) supportive psychotherapeutic techniques geared not to the interpretation of resistance and defense, but to the bolstering of defenses and the restoring of the ego's damaged or faltering adaptive and coping capacities.

It is my provisional finding in the Psychotherapy Research Project of The Menninger Foundation (Wallerstein, 1986) that concomitant and proportionate structural change accompanied whatever degree of symptomatic and behavioral change was achieved in just about every instance in the more expressive and more purely psychoanalytic treatments. But equivalent structural change also accompanied the achieved symptomatic and behavioral changes in almost half the patients treated with a more ego-supportive and conflict-suppressive (and non-insight-aiming) therapeutic mode. It is our aim in the present research program to explore this issue more precisely through our carefully constructed, scaled, and tested

---

[3] Since the publication of this article, our research group has reformulated our psychological capacities into a list of seventeen discrete dimensions (Wallerstein, 1994); created 4-point scales for each of thirty-six subdimensions, each scale point anchored by one or more clinical vignettes; devised a semistructured research interview with probe questions for each dimension, designed to elicit specific information relevant to that dimension that had not emerged in the initial diagnostic interview(s); completed a "content validity" study of our scales (DeWitt, Hartley, Rosenberg, Zilberg, and Wallerstein, 1991); and completed two reliability studies of the scales, using a different outpatient population in each, with very satisfactory results. The reliability studies are now being prepared for publication. The reliability studies also contain ratings on a variety of standard self-report measures for use in helping establish scale validity.

instruments for the more reliable independent assessment of psychic structure and structural change, and also to study in closer detail the conditions under which structural change can eventuate in supportive treatments that are (at least in theory) not geared toward that end. Last, with adequate enough follow-up (and the 30-year follow-up period for many of the cohort of 42 followed through their entire long-term treatment careers and subsequent life careers in the Menninger project gives us a proper, albeit a rigorously ideal, model for emulation), we shall be able to discern the extent to which the instances of true structural change induced in non-insight-aiming supportive psychotherapies compare in stability, in durability, and in proof against future environmental vicissitude with the kinds of structural changes induced in the interpretive, uncovering, and insight-aiming expressive and purely psychoanalytic modes.

The original Psychotherapy Research Project of The Menninger Foundation was also preoccupied with the paired questions, what changes take place in intensive psychotherapies (the outcome question), and how those changes come about, through the interaction of what factors in the patient, in the therapy and the therapist, and in the evolving external life situation (the process question). One of its early articles was on "The Problem of the Assessment of Change in Psychotherapy" (Wallerstein, 1963). A methodologic problem then resided in the only limited success of the effort to come to grips with the issue of the meanings of psychic structure and structural change, to create measures for them independent of measures of changes in behaviors and symptoms, and to ensure that the assessments of structural change could be applied to the patient outcomes independent of the techniques (more expressive or more supportive) by which the discerned changes had come about. Our present research effort is designed to tackle that set of problems. Whatever success is achieved will in turn help clarify the psychoanalytic theoretical and clinical issues to which this essay has been addressed: What do we mean by structure and structural change (the theoretical question), and how are they evident in the material of the treatment process (the clinical question)?

5.

Outcomes of Psychoanalysis and Psychotherapy at Termination and at Follow-Up

INTRODUCTION

Any discussion of the efficacy (the outcomes) of psychoanalysis and of the linked psychoanalytic psychotherapies as treatment modalities, as discernible upon treatment termination or at follow-up, necessarily interlocks with a host of interrelated definitional, conceptual, methodological, and practical considerations that cover all the major theoretical and technical issues of the psychoanalytic therapies as treatment procedures. These include (1) the goals of these treatment modalities, both ideal and practical (realizable); (2) the issues of suitability or treatability as against analyzability which is not the same thing, though the two are often conflated; (3) the indications and contraindications for these treatments as these have evolved over time with increasing experience and expanding theoretical and technical knowledge, including here the issues of widening or narrowing scope for analytic treatment and of "heroic" indications for analysis; (4) the role of the initial diagnostic and evaluation procedures in proper (differential) treatment planning (as against the view that only a trial of analysis or trial of treatment can lead to proper formulation and prognostication); (5) the place then of prediction (including the question of predictability) in relation to issues of outcome, of expectable reach and limitation; (6) the theory of technique, how treatment works, by what procedures it achieves its goals, a statement, that is, of the relationship of means to ends; (7) the similarities and differences between psychoanalysis and the dynamic psychotherapies, as compared from the viewpoint of different therapeutic goals projected for patients with differing illness pictures set into differing character organizations, determining through these differences the appropriate specific technical approaches from within the available range of psychoanalytically based psychotherapies; (8) the criteria for "satisfactory" treatment termination; (9) the evaluation of results, a conceptual as well as technical issue, involving the issue of assessment of therapeutic benefit as against analytic completeness in terms of resolution of intrapsychic conflict and structural changes in the ego; (10) what theoretically constitutes the ideal state of mental health and the unavoidable impingement upon efforts at its empirical assessment by value judgments as well as by the vantage point and the partisan interests of the judge; (11) the place of follow-up assessment as a desirable, feasible, and appropriate activity (or not) in relation to psychoanalytic therapies, for research or clinical purposes; and (12) the place of the continuing accretion of experience and knowledge in relation to all these areas by the traditional case study method innovated by Freud, as against the desirability or necessity for more formal systematic clinical research into these issues, by methods, of course, that are responsive to the subtlety and the complexity of the subjectivistic clinical phenomena, while simultaneously remaining loyal to the canons of empirical science.

There is a considerable, and in some cases a vast literature, mostly clinical, but in some instances also research, in relation to each of these areas of inquiry. In order to maintain a delimited and manageable focus upon the central questions of this chapter, all of that will be excluded as specific foci in this presentation, except as any of it becomes momentarily germane to its argument. Rather, I wish to focus in explicit fashion just on the issue of outcomes in psychoanalysis (with reference, where relevant, to the psychoanalytic psychotherapies) as assessed primarily at treatment termination, but also, especially in recent years, with a growing focus on planned follow-up assessment as well. Also, the primary focus will be on formal and systematic research study rather than the far larger and much antecedent clinical and theoretical literature on these issues out of which, of course, have grown the questions to which the research studies have been addressed.[1]

EARLY STATISTICAL STUDIES—FIRST-GENERATION RESEARCH

As early as 1917, within the first decade of the introduction of psychoanalysis in America, Coriat reported on the therapeutic results achieved in ninety-three cases based upon his own "personal investigation and experience" (p. 209). Seventy-three percent were declared either recovered or much improved and these rates were nearly equal across all his diagnostic categories, though the more severe cases required greater lengths of treatment. As with all the early statistical studies to be noted here, the judgments of improvement were made by the treating clinician, according to (usually) unspecified criteria, and with no individual clinical detail or supporting evidence to enable the reader to either see the basis of the judgment or to arrive at an alternative or different conception.

In the 1930s, several comparable but larger-scale reports emerged from the collective experiences of the Psychoanalytic Clinic Treatment Centers of some of the pioneering psychoanalytic training institutes. Fenichel (1930) reported from the first decade of experience of the Berlin Institute, the first formally organized psychoanaltic training institute in the world. During that first decade, 1955 consultations were conducted and 721 patients were accepted for analysis. Sixty percent of the psychoneurotic cases were judged to have received substantial therapeutic benefits, but only 23 percent of those who were adjudged "psychotic."[2] However, essentially the same proportion was declared to be unchanged or worse in the two diagnostic categories, 22 and 24 percent respectively. Six years later, Jones (1936) reported on 738 applicants to

---

[1] This same focus frames a comprehensive, 45-page report (including tables and a nearly exhaustive bibliography) entitled "On the Efficacy of Psychoanalysis" (Bachrach, Galatzer-Levy, Skolnikoff, and Waldron, 1991) prepared by the Subcommittee on Outcome Research of the Committee on Scientific Activities of the American Psychoanalytic Association. Reference is made to that report for a more detailed and inclusive discussion of the issues covered in this chapter as well as for strategic and tactical recommendations for future research directions.

[2] Psychotic here is to be taken as ambulatory and in some sense functioning in the community though considered "psychotic" from the standpoint of the quality of the mental life.

the London Psychoanalytic Clinic of whom 74 were taken into psychoanalysis. Forty-seven percent of the neurotic cases were judged to have benefited substantially, with only 10 percent judged unimproved or worse. Of the fifteen psychotic cases, all but one were treatment failures. Alexander (1937) reported on 157 cases from the Chicago Psychoanalytic Clinic. Here 63 percent of the neurotic cases, 40 percent of the psychotic, and 77 percent of those designated psychosomatic were judged to have received substantial therapeutic benefit, with no more than 10 percent in any category judged unchanged or worse. Kessel and Hyman (1933), two internists who followed up 29 cases referred for psychoanalysis, again reported the neurotic cases to have benefited (all but two) and the psychotic ones unchanged or worse.

In a 1941 review article evaluating the results of psychoanalysis, Knight combined the findings of the Berlin, London, Chicago, and Kessel and Hyman studies and added one hundred cases treated at The Menninger Clinic between 1932 and 1941, where the overall results were judged to be completely comparable to the other studies in the observed outcomes with neurotic and psychotic cases. The overall composite tabulation thus comprised 952 cases, classified into neurotic, psychotic, psychosomatic, and "other" categories by whatever (unspecified) criteria governed the original judgments. The combined substantial therapeutic benefit rate was approximately 60 percent for the neurotic, close to 80 percent for the psychosomatic, and only 25 percent for the psychotic, with about 20 percent unchanged or worse among both the neurotic and the psychotic. Knight made particular reference to all the pitfalls of these simple statistical summaries, the absence of consensually agreed upon definitions and specified criteria, the crudity of nomenclature and case classification, and the failure to address issues of the experience and skill of the therapists in relation to cases of varying degrees of severity.

The most ambitious study of this first generation genre was the report of the Ad Hoc Committee on Central Fact Gathering Data of the American Psychoanalytic Association (Hamburg et al., 1967).[3] This committee was originally established in 1952, collected data

___
[3] Though the span from Coriat (1917) to this study (1967) is a half-century, I call them all "first generation" in terms of their degree of conceptual and methodological sophistication—the state of the art that they represent—rather than in temporal terms (though of course each "generation" was either initiated at a later point in time than its predecessor or spanned a later period of time).

over a five-year span, and produced a report to the membership (unpublished) in 1958. The data consisted of ten thousand initial responses to detailed questionnaires submitted by the three hundred and fifty then members and the four hundred and fifty then candidates in training in the American, plus a little over three thousand termination questionnaires submitted upon treatment completion. The criteria for both diagnosis and improvement were unspecified (as with all the previous studies) and numerous flaws in the original questionnaire construction led to many unintended confusions, ambiguities, and omissions in the responses which led to the original decision against scientific publication of the findings. In the early 1960s, however, a successor committee to the first was charged with reviewing the data in order to try to salvage what was still scientifically useful and publishable. The Hamburg committee ultimately produced an "experience survey" (American psychoanalysis, circa the 1950s) comprising three areas: (1) facts about the demographics and the sociology of analytic practice; (2) analysts' opinions on their patients' diagnoses; and (3) analysts' opinions on the therapeutic results achieved. Judgments were made about changes in symptoms, in the patients' feeling states, in their character structures, and in their total functioning. Not unexpectedly, the great majority were declared substantially improved.

In the following year, Feldman (1968) reported on the results of psychoanalysis in clinic case assignments based on the eleven-year history of the Clinic of the Southern California Psychoanalytic Institute. This consisted of one hundred and twenty analytic patients selected from nine hundred and sixty evaluations, and represented a total sample, consecutive and unselected. The patients seemed more comprehensively evaluated and studied than those in the earlier reports, having been chosen after four to five hours of group interview and committee discussion followed by a careful review of the detailed semiannual institute reports gathered, so long as they were still clinic patients and their analysts not yet graduated (some of the patients could be followed into private practice status after the institute graduation of the analysts). Efforts were made to specify improvement criteria in the poor, fair, good, and very good categories. Difficulties were experienced for the research due to lack of clear and agreed-upon criteria, concepts, and language for diagnostic assessment, analyzability, and analytic results. Improvement rates reported were again completely comparable with all the preceding studies, two thirds being in the good or very good categories.

Added all together, this sequence of first-generation outcome and efficacy studies of psychoanalysis, actually spanning a half-century from 1917 to 1968, were scientifically simplistic and failed to command the interest of the psychoanalytic clinical world. Most would rather agree with Glover in his ironic and dour assessment in the latter part of this period (1954), "like most psycho-therapists, the psycho-analyst is a reluctant and inexpert statistician. No accurate records or after-histories of psycho-analytical treatment exist: such rough figures as can be obtained do not suggest that psycho-analysis is notably more successful than other forms of therapy: and in any case none of the figures is corrected for spontaneous remission or resolution of symptoms" (p. 393). Later, he says: "In the case of adults . . . an after-history of at least 5 years is essential. Unfortunately it has to be admitted that satisfactory after-histories are seldom forthcoming: consequently our knowledge of the therapeutic range of psycho-analysis is vitiated by unchecked surmise which too often errs on the side of complacency" . . . the success of a child analysis cannot be satisfactorily checked until an after-history of 15 years has been secured . . ." (p. 398). It is polemics such as this that spurred what I call the second-generation studies, the efforts at more formal and systematic outcome research geared to overcome the glaring methodological simplicity that marked each of the studies described to this point.

FORMAL AND SYSTEMATIC OUTCOME STUDIES—SECOND-GENERATION RESEARCH

Introduction

The methodological flaws in the first-generation type statistical enumerations of psychoanalytic outcomes, which span the full half-century from 1917 to 1968, have already been indicated. In addition to the lack of consensually agreed criteria at almost every step—from initial diagnosis and assessments of analyzability to outcome judgments of therapeutic benefit and analytic result—and the use of these judgments by unspecified, and even unformulated, criteria, by the (necessarily biased) therapist, as the usually sole evidential primary database, there is also the methodologic difficulty that these studies have all been retrospective, with all the potential therein for bias, confounding, contamination of judgments, and post hoc ergo propter hoc reasoning and justification.

Efforts to address these issues, including the introduction of methods of prospective inquiry and even of fashioning predictions to be validated or refuted by subsequent assessment, began in earnest in the 1950s and 1960s. Three major projects based on studies of clinic cases from the Boston, Columbia, and New York psychoanalytic institutes stand out as the major representatives of this second-generation research approach. They will be discussed in that order.

Boston Psychoanalytic Institute Studies

In 1960, Knapp, Levin, McCarter, Wermer, and Zetzel reported on one hundred supervised psychoanalytic cases from the Boston Psychoanalytic Institute clinic, rated initially (prospectively) for suitability for analysis. Twenty-seven of these were followed up just a year later by questionnaires addressed to the treating analysts in order to ascertain how suitable the patient indeed had turned out to be—as discernible and judgable at this relatively early treatment point. To avoid the dangers of post hoc reasoning and reconstructive rationalization, the evaluation procedures (initial committee judgments on suitability and subsequent judgments of the treating analysts' questionnaire responses) were blind, and by different judges in almost all instances. Considering the variable quality of the initial clinic records, written by many different persons, which constituted the data on which prediction was based, there was fair but limited success in assessing suitability for analysis at the initial evaluation. However, two significant limitations of this study should be remarked. First, the testing of the predictions took place at only the one-year mark in treatment rather than more suitably upon the termination of the therapy. Clearly, much can change in this regard—in both directions—at later points in the analysis as everyone's clinical experience amply attests. Second, and this is an issue in all research on this model, the cases selected by psychoanalytic institute clinic committees for student analyses are already carefully screened with obviously unsuitable cases already rejected. The range of variability in the accepted cases is thus considerably narrowed, making differential prediction within that group therefore inherently less reliable.

Sashin, Eldred, and van Amerongen (1975), inspired by this

work, subsequently studied 183 cases treated at the same clinic between 1959 and 1966 on which final data were collected on 130 cases (72%) after an average of 675 treatment hours and at a point averaging six years after treatment termination. The authors referred to this as a "quantitative, systematic study" of the "patient factor predictability of outcome" (p. 345). Predictor variables were assessed by a 103-item evaluation rating questionnaire and via six major outcome criteria first elaborated in the article by Knight (1941): restriction of life functioning by symptoms, subjective discomfort, work productivity, sexual adjustment, interpersonal relationships, availability of insight, each fashioned into 5-point rating scales. Many predictor items were not rated by the judges (left unanswered too frequently, or showed insufficient variation, or showed poor reliability), and, of the forty-six items finally retained, only ten had any usefulness or predictive value at all in relation to assessed outcomes and that with only modest (albeit statistically significant) correlations. These few relationships, which might have appeared on the basis of chance alone, were studied to determine if they could be meaningfully understood in clinical terms but the groupings "made little clinical sense" (Bachrach et al., 1991, quoting Sashin et al., 1975, p. 894). In overall conclusion of these Boston Institute studies there was only fair prediction to judgments of analyzability as assessed at the one-year mark in treatment, and no effective prediction to treatment outcomes from the patients' characteristics as judged at initial evaluation. Nor was any effort made to distinguish therapeutic benefit from the successful navigation of an analytic process over the treatment course. Further Boston Psychoanalytic Institute studies by Kantrowitz and her coworkers will be described further on as representative of the third-generation psychoanalytic outcome research studies.

Columbia Psychoanalytic Center Studies

The Columbia Psychoanalytic Center project, contemporaneous with the Boston studies, was written up in final accounting in a sequence of publications in 1985 (Weber, Bachrach, and Solomon, 1985a,b; Weber, Solomon, and Bachrach, 1985), reporting in sequence the characteristics of the patients, the outcome study from sample 1 (1348 patients treated between 1945 and 1962), the outcome study (by somewhat altered and improved criteria) from sample 2 (237 patients treated between 1962 and 1971), and finally a clinical and methodological review with recommendations for future directions. These were geared to be prospective studies of large numbers of patients, with data collected from multiple perspectives over time (initially and upon treatment completion), with opportunities to compare and contrast findings in psychoanalysis (about 40% of the total sample) with psychoanalytic psychotherapy (the other 60%), all treated by the same body of therapists. The authors stated that all previous studies had been limited in at least one of the following ways: small sample size, inadequate range of information about outcomes, not based on terminated cases, or restricted to retrospective data. And no other had permitted comparison between large numbers of terminated analyses and psychotherapies, conducted by the same analysts, in which all pertinent information had not been retrospectively assessed. Also, criteria for therapeutic benefit were established distinct from separate criteria for analyzability (the judgment about the success of development of an analytic process). Criteria of therapeutic benefit comprised (1) the circumstances of treatment termination; (2) clinical judgments of overall improvement; and (3) change scores on various indices of improvement. Criteria of an evolved analytic process comprised judgments about (1) patterns of handling psychological data; (2) more flexible use of ego resources; and (3) transference manifestations during treatment.

A most striking finding from this project was that uniformly and across every category of patient the therapeutic benefit measures always substantially exceeded what were called the analyzability measures (presumably, measures of an evolved analytic process). For example, only 40 percent of those who completed analyses with good therapeutic benefit were characterized as having been "analyzed" by the project criteria. (The elucidation of the meaning of this startling kind of finding turned out to be a major focus of the findings and conclusions of the Psychotherapy Research Project of The Menninger Foundation [Wallerstein, 1986, 1988b] to be described below). An equally striking finding is that the outcome of these treatments, both in terms of therapeutic benefit and analyzability, was only marginally predictable from the perspective of the initial evaluation, whether employing the direct predictions by the clinic's Admissions Service Chief, or the various scales of the presumed predictor variables. This was of course fully in keeping with previous known studies, for example, the Boston Institute studies cited, and of course were linked to the fact that these various analytic clinic populations were all carefully screened cases where those presumed to be overtly unsuitable had already been eliminated. As the authors cautiously state (Weber, Bachrach et al., 1985a), "the prudent conclusion from these findings is *not* that therapeutic benefit or analysability are *per se* unpredictable, but that once a case has been carefully selected as suitable for analysis by a candidate, its eventual fate remains relatively indeterminate" (p. 135).

Another significant finding of interest was that "retrospective assessments of patient qualities by the treating analyst show a more substantial relationship to outcome than assessments made at the beginning of treatment" (Weber, Bachrach et al., 1985a, p. 136). This could clearly be based on either the greater accuracy of retrospective judgments at termination or on their greater contamination or on some undetermined admixture of both. More expected were the findings that those selected for psychoanalysis were assessed initially as functioning at higher levels than those selected for psychotherapy. Those in psychoanalysis achieved greater therapeutic benefit than those in psychotherapy, especially when the analyses continued longer, beyond the candidates' graduations and into their private practices. This positive correlation between therapeutic benefit and treatment length did not hold for the psychotherapies in the same way which caused the authors to "suggest that treatment length and therapeutic benefit are related for psychoanalysis, but perhaps not necessarily for other psychotherapies where progression does not pivot upon a natural process requiring years to evolve" (Weber, Bachrach et al., 1985a, p. 136–137). This is, of course, a conclusion to which many might take exception.

In overall conclusion, the authors stated that their sample (sample 1) was three times larger than any previously published, that it was the first to have a psychotherapy comparison group, and one of the first (along with the New York Institute study to be described next) to make the conceptual distinction between analyzability and therapeutic benefit. They did state as a major limitation, "We do not feel that the circumstances of this investigation provide more than the most rudimentary exploration of the contribution of the analyst's qualities to the treatment process" (p. 138)—and this omission of course can be a major contributor to the poor level of predictability of treatment outcomes. They say in this regard that "Not only may it be that a fundamental assessment of analytic potentials may only be possible in the course of analysis . . . but there are also matters of changing life circumstances and the *analyst–analysand match* to be considered" (p. 138; emphasis added).

Sample 2 was a smaller sample gathered a decade later with some refinements in methods of data collection and some differences in observational vantage points, but in almost every particular all the findings of sample 1 were replicated. These confirmations were all reinforced from a data source that had not been tapped in sample 1, namely patient accounts elicited from patient questionnaire responses before and after treatment. Again, cited as of particular interest was that "the evidence so far suggests that less than half the cases taken into analysis by candidates develop an analytic process and that the figure is not substantially higher for more experienced analysts" (Weber, Bachrach et al., 1985b, p. 261) and here they cite from the New York Institute studies (to be described next).

Overall, they conclude from both samples—over a more than twenty-year span—that:

> Our findings in both studies and those of Erle (1979) and Erle & Goldberg (1984) [the New York Institute investigators] show that a substantially greater proportion of analysands derive therapeutic benefit than develop an analytic process, and that the development of an analytic process is associated with the highest levels of therapeutic benefit. Yet, what we do not yet know precisely is the nature and quality of therapeutic benefit associated with the development of an analytic process and without its development [p. 261].

This last question of course, as already mentioned, was the central focus of the Psychotherapy Research Project of The Menninger Foundation, being carried out over this same time span, to be described further on (under third-generation research studies).

The final article by these authors in their series of four (Bachrach, Weber, and Solomon, 1985) was devoted to a review of clinical and methodological considerations. They stressed the advantages of their project over other comparable studies: (1) that the N was very large; (2) that it was a prospective study with prearranged schedules and hypotheses and predictive evaluations done before outcomes were known; (3) that they used many (clinically meaningful) scales; (4) that aside from evaluations by patients and therapists, they used independent judges; and (5) that psychoanalysis and psychotherapy were comparatively assessed. Nonetheless, they acknowledged that theirs was essentially an opinion poll; "What we did was to have analysts assess cases in their customary ways and to have them express their judgments on quantitative dimensions . . ." (p. 381); that is, trying to make the opinions reliable and comparable through the use of standardized quantitative rating scales. This method, however, also made their work clinically relevant: "It is precisely because our methodology pivoted upon a clinical survey of psychoanalysts about their own cases and the cases of candidates, and was consistently framed according to standard clinical precepts, that we believe our findings bear correspondence to the findings of psychoanalytic research proper," that is, the findings from the traditional psychoanalytic case study method.

The most important substantive conclusion from the project had to do with the relationship of therapeutic benefit achieved to the development of a properly psychoanalytic process:

> The observation is that some patients treated by psychoanalysis develop an analytic process and achieve therapeutic benefit, while others achieve therapeutic benefit while not apparently developing an analytic process. By analytic process we refer essentially to a collaborative endeavor between analyst and analysand in which increasingly intense and cyclic analysis of resistance and transference in free association evolves into the development of a transference neurosis and transference phenomena, and where continued analysis leads towards enhanced awareness and mastery of intrapsychic conflict which we conceptualize as structural change. . . . By therapeutic benefit we refer to the non-specific amelioration of symptoms and the general improvement in the mental economy of patients [p. 382].

However, the linked and almost equally important finding was that the predictability of these developments "remains relatively indeterminate *among carefully selected cases*" (p. 381), or stated alternatively "that most suitably selected patients treated by psychoanalysis achieved substantial gains; though the level of these gains is no more than marginally predictable from the perspective of initial evaluation" (p. 386).

New York Psychoanalytic Institute Studies

The New York Psychoanalytic Institute studies (Erle, 1979; Erle and Goldberg, 1979, 1984) were similarly constituted, though with more of a focus on the study of treatments carried out by more experienced analysts. They began (Erle and Goldberg, 1979) with a comprehensive and sophisticated treatment of the conceptual and methodological issues involved in proper outcome research (together with an excellent review of the literature on these issues), which they subsequently summarized as follows:

> In a review and discussion of the problems in the assessment of analyzability . . . we noted: (a) a lack of consistency in the definition of terms; (b) difficulty developing and validating criteria for patient selection; (c) the assumption that prediction of analyzability is, or might be, reliably made at the outset of treatment; (d) failure to differentiate between analyzability and therapeutic benefit; (e) the need for a prospective study which would assess all phases of an analysis: selection, prediction, analytic process, and outcome [Erle and Goldberg, 1984, p. 715].

Their actual studies were two in number. The first (Erle, 1979) consisted of a sample of forty supervised analytic cases selected from eight hundred and seventy applicants to the Treatment Center of the New York Psychoanalytic Institute over a two-and-a-half-year span in the late 1960s. The results were completely comparable to those of the Boston and Columbia centers. Twenty-five of the patients terminated satisfactorily (i.e., by mutual consent), but only eleven of these were considered complete; twenty-four of the patients were judged to have benefited substantially, but only seventeen were judged to have been involved in a proper psychoanalytic process. Those who stayed in treatment for longer periods were judged to be more suitable and had better outcomes, though three of the nine who were in treatment more than six years were declared to have benefited substantially in an intensive psychotherapeutic sense, but were judged to be not analyzed or analyzable. A sample of forty-two private patients from seven analyst colleagues of the author who were started in the same calendar period and assessed in the same manner as the Treatment Center patients showed substantially comparable results. The second study (Erle and Goldberg, 1984) extended the work to a sample of one hundred and sixty private patients gathered over a subsequent five-year time span from sixteen cooperating experienced analysts. The treating analysts' evaluations ranged from those "made for analysis" to those taken into analysis on the basis of "heroic" indications (p. 722). The

outcomes from these experienced analysts were completely comparable to results of their own (and those of others) earlier studies of
clinic patients treated by candidates.

Pfeffer Studies (New York) and San Francisco and Chicago Replications

Over a parallel time span to these relatively large sample outcome
studies of psychoanalytic clinic patient populations (as well as some
comparison private patient groups) assessed by pre- and/or posttreatment rating scales and grouped statistically, Pfeffer at the same
New York Treatment Center initiated a wholly other kind of outcome and follow-up study of terminated psychoanalyses by intensive
individual case studies of a research-procured population (Pfeffer,
1959, 1961, 1963). His first report was of nine patients who had
completed analyses under the auspices of the New York Treatment
Center and who agreed to a series of follow-up interviews by a "follow-up analyst" who had not conducted the treatment. The interviews were open-ended, once a week, and were considered
"analytic" in the sense that they were "structured around the issue
of results, but remain[ed] unstructured within this framework in
that the patient . . . [took] the lead in introducing and elaborating
various themes relating to results" (1959, p. 420). They ranged from
two to seven in number before the participants agreed upon a natural close. The chief finding, and in all instances, consisted of the
rapid reactivation of characteristic analytic transferences, including
even acute and transitory symptom flareups, as if in relation to the
original treating analyst, with then rapid subsidence, at times aided
by pertinent interpretations, and in a manner that indicated the
new ways of neurotic conflict management achieved in the analysis,
and of course, "Those aspects of the transference neurosis that are
unanalyzed remain organized as transference residues which are
available for neurotic reactions in certain life situations" (p. 437).

In the last of this sequence of three reports (1963), Pfeffer
essayed a further description as well as a metapsychological explanation of these "follow-up study transference phenomena" (p. 230).
"The recurrence in the follow-up study of the major preanalytic
symptomatology in the context of a revived transference neurosis
as well as the quick subsidence of symptoms appear to support the
idea that conflicts underlying symptoms are not actually shattered

or obliterated by analysis but rather are only better mastered with new and more adequate solutions" (p. 234). The neurotic conflicts thus "lose their poignancy" (p. 237).

The metapsychological explanation is that

> in the regression of the analytic process the person of the analyst initially becomes the present-day representative of the oedipal father of the past. Then with the resolution of the transference the analyst becomes, in addition, the father in relation to whom the oedipus complex is resolved. In the course of the analysis, the person of the analyst becomes, and after the analysis remains, it is here suggested, a permanent intrapsychic image intimately connected with both the regressively experienced conflicts and the resolution of these conflicts in the progression achieved [p. 238].

Two other research groups, one in San Francisco (Oremland, Blacker, and Norman, 1975; Norman, Blacker, Oremland, and Barrett, 1976), and one in Chicago (Schlessinger and Robbins, 1974, 1975, 1983) replicated the Pfeffer studies, with some slight alterations in method, and confirmed what has come to be called "the Pfeffer phenomenon." In the San Francisco studies, the subjects were chosen from among individuals who, it was agreed, were very successfully analyzed and yet "specific areas of incompleteness were discovered when 'successful' cases were called back for restudy" (Oremland et al., 1975, p. 820). And in their further study they concluded that "the transference neurosis is not obliterated during analysis. Rather, the patient experiences, understands, and senses varying degrees of control over it—i.e., it becomes a structure that comes under the control of the unconscious ego" (Norman et al., 1976, p. 491). And to bring these two statements together, the "infantile neurosis had not disappeared. What had changed was the degree to which it affected his everyday life" (Norman et al., 1976, p. 492). The Chicago studies, with a more developmental focus, more specified and focused change criteria, and a larger sample likewise confirmed the Pfeffer findings. In overall summary in their book:

> Psychic conflicts were not eliminated in the analytic process. The clinical material of the follow-ups demonstrated a repetitive pattern of conflicts. Accretions of insight were evident but the more significant outcome of the analysis appeared to be the development of a preconsciously active self-analytic function, in identification with the

analyzing function of the analyst, as a learned mode of coping with conflicts. . . . The resources gained in the analytic process persisted, and their vitality was evident in response to renewed stress [Schlessinger and Robbins, 1983, p. 9].

This focus on the development of the self-analytic function (at least to some degree) as a proper and expectable outcome in successful analyses has been highlighted as well by M. Kramer (1959) and G. Ticho (1967). The overall finding from all three groups that even in analyses considered highly successful, neurotic conflicts are not obliterated or shattered, as was once felt, but are tamed, muted, lose their poignancy, is echoed in the well-known analytic quip that we all still recognize our good friends after their analyses.

Overview

Characteristic of these second-generation studies, whether the group-aggregated broad statistical accountings, the Boston (Knapp et al., 1960; Sashin et al., 1975), the Columbia (Weber, Bachrach, and Solomon, 1985a,b; Weber, Solomon, and Bachrach, 1985; Bachrach, Weber, and Solomon, 1985), and the New York (Erle, 1979; Erle and Goldberg, 1979, 1984), or individually focused, in-depth research studies, Pfeffer in New York (1959, 1961, 1963), San Francisco (Oremland et al., 1975; Norman et al., 1976), and Chicago (Schlessinger and Robbins, 1974, 1975, 1983), was the failure to conceptually or practically separate out outcome results discerned at treatment termination from the issue of the stability or not of these results as revealed at some established follow-up point subsequent to the termination with all the different possibilities, for consolidation and further enhancement of treatment gains, for the simple maintenance of treatment achievements, or for actual regression back toward the pretreatment state.

Conceptually this was a failure to accord specific theoretical status to what Rangell (1966) has called the "postanalytic phase" (pp. 718–725). A variety of possible courses characterize this phase. Some analyses are finished with no returns by the former patient. In other cases the door is clearly left open for any returns that might be indicated. For example, "It is frequently the case that a patient with an optimum ending will call again, even years later, for a specific and localized need to which he is immediately accessible. The path between the analyst and the patient's unconscious can remain surprisingly open, so that a 'deep interpretation' may be made almost at once [in a single interview] with convincing receptivity and effective results" (p. 719). And if this is not possible, if there is too rigid an avoidance of further contact, it is more likely that there has been a flaw and a major incompleteness in the termination. And in still other cases the analytic relationship can be succeeded by a social or interprofessional relationship of greater or lesser constancy and intensity. Again, this can be rendered problematic in two opposite directions.

> At one extreme there is an undue retention of "the analytic attitude" when it is not only no longer indicated, but is actually inhibitory and harmful. . . . At the other extreme, however, in an effort to avoid or undo such an outcome, there is sometimes a gratification or stimulation of the patient by a premature and excessive social intimacy which is reacted to as a threatened seduction. . . . In contrast to both of these, the desired goal should be a transition to a normal interchange in which the analyst can be seen and reacted to as a normal figure and no longer as an object for continued transference displacement [p. 722].

Actually, in the third-generation studies to be now described, where the distinction between results at the termination study point and at a subsequent prearranged follow-up study point (anywhere from two to five years later), becomes a clearly demarcated research focus—among the advances over the second-generation studies—many more form variants of posttermination therapist–patient contact or interaction are delineated.

COMBINED PROCESS AND OUTCOME STUDIES: THIRD-GENERATION RESEARCH

Introduction

What I am calling the third-generation studies of the results of psychoanalysis have been actually contemporaneous in time with the (conceptually) second-generation studies that have just been described. These are systematic and formal psychoanalytic therapy research projects which have essayed to both assess psychoanalytic outcomes across a significant array of cases and to study the processes through which these outcomes have been reached via the intensive longitudinal individual study of each of the cases. In this they have combined the methodological approaches of the group-aggregated studies (the Boston, the Columbia, and the New York Erle and Goldberg) with the individually focused studies (the New York Pfeffer, the San Francisco and the Chicago). Like the best of these second-generation studies, they have constructed careful definitions of terms, have constructed rating scales, and have tried to operationalize their criteria at each assessment point. They have been prospectively constructed studies starting with initial pretreatment assessment of the patients. Unlike the second-generation studies, they have carefully separated outcomes at termination from functioning at a specified subsequent follow-up point with an effort to account for further changes, in either direction, that took place during this "postanalytic phase." Bachrach et al. (1991) in their comprehensive survey of research on the efficacy of psychoanalysis singled out the newer Boston Psychoanalytic Society and Institute studies (Kantrowitz, 1986; Kantrowitz, Paolitto, Sashin, Solomon, and Katz, 1986; Kantrowitz, Katz, Paolitto, Sashin, and Solomon, 1987a,b; Kantrowitz, Katz, and Greenman et al., 1989; Kantrowitz, Katz, and Paolitto, 1990a,b,c,) and the Psychotherapy Research Project of The Menninger Foundation (Wallerstein, 1986, 1988b) as the only ones that met their array of specifications (Bachrach et al., 1991, p. 905).

Newer Boston Psychoanalytic Institute Studies

The Boston studies were undertaken in the 1970s and came to publication in the following decade. Twenty-two supervised psychoanalytic cases at the Boston Psychoanalytic Institute clinic were selected for prospective study, with the initial assessment based on a psychological projective test battery with measures then constructed of variables salient to therapeutic change, alterations: (1) of affect availability, tolerance, complexity, and modulation; (2) of level and quality of object relations; (3) of adequacy of reality testing; and (4) of the nature and level of motivation for change. Seven-point rating scales were constructed for each variable. The analyses were all conducted at a frequency of four or five times weekly, and lasted from two-and-a-half to nine years. Approximately a year after termination the initial projective test battery was repeated and both the patient and the treating analyst were interviewed.

A series of three papers (Kantrowitz, Paolitto et al., 1986; Kantrowitz, Katz et al., 1987a,b) describe these results. Nine of the twenty-two (41%) were felt to have had a successful analytic result, five (23%) had a modified (limited) analytic result, and eight (36%) were felt to be unanalyzed. Nonetheless, the greater number achieved therapeutic benefits along each of the change and outcome dimensions, affect management, level and quality of object relationships, and adequacy of reality testing. Along each dimension the therapeutic benefit achieved exceeded the analytic result in terms of the degree of successfully completed analytic work. Of course, "the better the analytic result, the greater the improvement in the capacity to modulate affect [for example]" (Kantrowitz, Paolitto et al., 1986, p. 546). But also "The improvement [in level and quality of object relations] occurred even though approximately one-third of these patients were in treatment which their analysts perceived as having failed to even partially resolve the transference neurosis" (Kastrowitz, Katz et al., 1987a, p. 35). And overall, "In support of the Menninger findings [still to be discussed], the Boston study found that change in affect management (availability and tolerance), as measured in projective test data is associated with at least partial resolution of the transference neurosis; such change can and does occur, however, without a transference neurosis being established or resolved" (Kantrowitz, Paolitto et al., 1986, p. 551). That is, a consistent and important finding was that therapeutic benefit was achieved by the majority of the patients and regularly in excess of what could be accounted for by the evocation and the interpretive resolution of the transference neurosis. This will be further elaborated in the discussion of the Menninger project; there a major focus was on the effort to explicate the mechanisms of change on bases other than interpretive resolution of intrapsychic conflict.

Though most patients in the Kantrowitz et al. studies derived significant therapeutic benefit from their analytic experience, successful outcome could not be predicted from any of the predictor variables. This led these investigators to speculate "that a particularly important omission [from the predictor variables] might have been consideration of the effect of the [therapist–patient] match in shaping the two-person psychoanalytic interaction" (Kantrowitz, Katz et al., 1989, p. 899). By "match" they meant "an interactional concept; it refers to a spectrum of compatibility and incompatibility of the patient and analyst which is relevant to the analytic work. . . . The interaction may facilitate or impede the engagement in, and the resolution of, the analyst process" (p. 894). And "match . . . covers a broader field of phenomena in which countertransference is included as one of many types of match. . . . Match . . . can also refer to observable styles, attitudes, and personal characteristics . . ." (p. 895); these are not necessarily rooted in conflict. And though, "This mesh of the analyst's personal qualities with those of the patient has rarely been a special focus of attention . . . most analysts when making referrals do consider it; few assume that equally well-trained analysts are completely interchangeable" (Kantrowitz, 1986, p. 273).

This same team then went back for follow-up interviews with this same patient cohort in 1987, now five to ten years after the treatment terminations, this time including the retrospective assessment of the goodness of the analyst–patient match as one of the variables helping determine the patient outcomes (Kantrowitz, Katz, and Paolitto, 1990a,b,c). Nineteen of the twenty-two could be located and eighteen agreed to the two-hour semistructured interview and open-ended treatment review (audiotaped and later transcribed). There were then four available data sets, the pre- and posttreatment projective tests, the interviews with the analysts at the termination point, the interviews with the patients at the same point, and the 1987 follow-up interviews with the patients. A variety of change measures were used; global improvement ratings, affect tolerance and management, level and quality of object relations, adequacy of reality testing, work satisfaction and accomplishment, and overall self-esteem. Overall results at the follow-up point comprised three consolidated and further improved, four stable, six deteriorated somewhat but restored with additional treatment, four deteriorated and remained so despite additional treatment, and one returned to the original analyst and was still in treatment and therefore not counted (Kantrowitz, Katz, and Paolitto, 1990a).

The most striking finding, however, was that again the stability of achieved gains in the follow-up period could not be predicted from the assessments at termination. That is:

> The stability of psychological change five to ten years after termination of psychoanalysis could not be predicted by the analysts' assessment of the development and at least partial resolution of the transference neurosis during the analysis [p. 484].

[Or put alternately] psychological changes were no more stable over time for the group of patients assessed as having achieved a successful analytic outcome concomitant with considerable therapeutic benefit than for the other group of patients assessed as having achieved therapeutic benefit alone [p. 493].

When the focus was on the assessment of the development of the self-analytic function, presumably both a goal of treatment and a criterion for termination ("We define self-analysis as the capacity to observe and reflect upon one's own behaviors, feelings, or fantasy life in a manner that leads to understanding the meaning of that phenomenon in a new light" [Kantrowitz, Katz, and Paolitto, 1990b, pp. 639–640]), again, though thirteen of the eighteen described a variety of self-analytic processes, there was no direct relationship between the attainment of the self-analytic function and the maintenance of the therapeutic gains. "The present study suggests . . . that some patients are able to acquire what we have traditionally considered an important analytic result, the development of a self-analytic function, without working through the transference neurosis, if we accept their analysts' assessments" (p. 652).

And lastly, with the focus on the assessment of analyst–patient match (Kantrowitz, Katz, and Paolitto, 1990c), the authors did feel that with twelve of the seventeen, the kind of match (impeding or facilitating) did play a role in the outcome achieved. They gave examples of what they considered facilitating matches with good ultimate outcomes, impeding matches with poor outcomes, and more complex situations where the kind of match seemed at first to facilitate the unfolding of the analytic process, but later in the treatment seemed to have an influence in preventing the completion of the analytic work.

Menninger Foundation Studies

The other so-called third-generation psychoanalytic therapy research study to be described here is the Psychotherapy Research Project of The Menninger Foundation (PRP), the most comprehensive and ambitious such research program ever carried out (Wallerstein, Robbins, Sargent, and Luborsky, 1956; Wallerstein, 1986, 1988b). The intent of PRP was to follow the treatment careers, and insofar as possible, the subsequent life careers, of a cohort of patients (ultimately 42 in number), half in psychoanalysis, and half in other psychoanalytic psychotherapies—and each in the treatment deemed *clinically* indicated for him or her—from the period of their initial pretreatment, two-week-long comprehensive psychiatric evaluation, over the whole natural span of their treatments, however many years this might take, and then into planned follow-up inquiries, formally for at least several years after their treatment terminations and their (usual) return to their home communities, and with as much of an open-ended follow-up thereafter as circumstance might make possible and as the span of interested observation might last. Actually, the whole cohort of patients entered into their treatment over the span of the midfifties (contemporaneous with and even preceding the bulk of second-generation studies); their periods of treatment ranged from as short as a half-year in the case of unanticipated treatment disruptions, up to a full dozen years; 100 percent of the sample was reached for formal follow-up information at the designated two- to three-year mark; and over a third of the patients could be followed for periods ranging from twelve to twenty-four years beyond their treatment terminations, four of them actually still in ongoing treatment, and some of the total observation spans up to thirty years, until the time of writing of the book, *Forty-Two Lives in Treatment* (Wallerstein, 1986), with its final clinical accounting from this project written over the year 1981 to 1982.

The aim of PRP was to learn as much as possible about what changes actually take place in psychoanalysis and other psychoanalytically based psychotherapies (the outcome question), and how those changes come about or are brought about, through the interactions over time of what variables in the patient, in the therapy and the therapist, and in the evolving life situation that together codetermine those changes (the process question). How the project created and carried out a research program geared to try to answer those questions maximally has been described in detail over the thirty-year span of this research enterprise in some seven published books and monographs and about seventy articles. None of that will (or could) be repeated here.[4] At this point, it should just be iterated that three overall treatment groups were set up—psychoanalysis, expressive psychotherapy, and supportive psychotherapy—in terms of the then consensus in the psychoanalytic therapy literature on

---

[4] For a complete bibliography of PRP publications, write to Robert S. Wallerstein, M.D., 290 Beach Road, Belvedere, California 94920.

defining characteristics of these (discrete) therapeutic modes, together with differential indications derived from the dynamic formulations of the nature of the patients' lives, developmental history,
character structure, and presenting illness picture.

The project expectations within this framework were twofold,
on the one hand, the relatively modest one of giving a firmer empirical evidential base to this received conceptual wisdom and, on the
other hand, the more ambitious one of discerning and specifying
in more detail both the particular reach and limitation of the therapeutic outcome for each kind of patient appropriately treated within
each of the proffered therapeutic approaches. There was an especial
interest in the more empirical elaboration of the psychological
change mechanisms operative within both the uncovering (expressive) and the "ego-strengthening" (supportive) therapeutic modes.
Given this overall intent, what can be said about the actual therapeutic processes and outcomes as assessed some thirty years after the
project start after the fullest possible study of the patient cohort
across their treatments and their lives over this time span.

Forty-Two Lives in Treatment represents the full statement of the
findings and conclusions (Wallerstein, 1986). For overall capsule
summarization of the main highlights here, I can best report
through a lengthy quotation from the concluding part of a summarizing paper (Wallerstein, 1988b).[5]

> I will bring our overall conclusions together as a series of sequential
> propositions regarding the appropriateness, the efficacy, the reach
> and the limitations of psychoanalysis (varyingly "classical" and modi-
> fied) and of psychoanalytic psychotherapy or psychotherapies (vary-
> ingly expressive and supportive)—always of course with the caveat,
> as this was discerned within this segment of the overall patient popu-
> lation . . . those (usually sicker) individuals who have been brought
> to or have sought their intensive analytically guided treatment within
> a psychoanalytic sanatorium setting.

---

[5] A note is in order in regard to the relationship between the outcomes, to be described
at this point, achieved in psychoanalyses and psychoanalytic psychotherapies as discerned in
PRP, and the outcomes described in the literature, achieved in nonanalytic psychotherapies
and in drug treatments of mental and emotional disorders. The results (outcomes) are not
strictly comparable for a variety of reasons. A most critical reason has to do with the difference
in outcome criteria. In the drug treatment of depression or the behavior modification treatment of phobias, for example, the outcome criterion employed is the amelioration of the
specific target symptom. In psychoanalytic therapies, whether psychoanalysis proper or the
range of psychoanalytic psychotherapies, the outcome criterion has to do with overall change
in personality functioning in all relevant areas, with specific symptom abatement part of and
subordinate to the overall change in behaviors, attitudes, and propensities, that is, character
and personality change.

1. The first proposition has to do with the distinctions so regularly made in the psychodynamic literature between "structural change" (gratuitously called "real" change), presumably based on the interpretive resolution of unconscious intrapsychic conflicts, and "behavioral change" or change in "manifest behavior patterns" that are (invidiously considered) "just altered techniques of adjustment" and presumably are all that can come out of the other, nonexpressive, noninterpretive, non-insight-aiming change mechanisms, i.e., the varieties of supportive psychotherapeutic techniques and implementations that I have presented in this paper. Intrinsic to this way of dichotomizing between kinds of change has always been the easy assumption that only structural change or real change as brought about through conflict resolution marked by appropriately achieved insight can have some guarantee of inherent stability, durability, and capacity to weather at least ordinary future environmental vicissitudes. It goes without saying that the commonplace value distinction automatically follows: that change brought about by expressive-analytic means is invariably "better," and this is, of course, the basis for the widely believed clinical operating maxim, "Be as expressive as you can be, and as supportive as you have to be." It is clear from the experiences documented from our PRP study that I question strongly the continued usefulness of this effort to link so tightly the *kind* of change achieved (real change, better change) with the intervention modes, expressive or supportive, by which it is brought about. If we accept the observations made from the study of our PRP cases that the changes reached in our more supportive therapies and via intrinsically supportive modes seemed often enough to be just as much structural change, to be just as stable and enduring, just as able to help the patient cope with life's subsequent happenstances, as the changes reached in our most expressive-analytic cases, then we must accept that the one way (the interpretive-uncovering way) does not have such an exclusive corner on inducing true structural change.

2. The second proposition has to do with the conventional proportionality argument, that therapeutic change will be at least proportional to the degree of achieved conflict resolution. Put this way, this proposition is almost unexceptionable, since it is clear that there can be significantly more change than there is true intrapsychic conflict resolution, on all the varying (supportive) bases through which change can be brought about, as well as properly proportionate change where the change is all or "purely" on the basis of conflict resolution with accompanying insight—if such an ideal type ever actually exists in practice—but it would be hard to imagine real conflict resolution (and accompanying insight) without at least proportional concomitant change in behaviors, dispositions, attitudes,

symptoms, etc. However, in the closely related arena of the proportionality of therapeutic change to the degree of attained insight (as distinct from conflict resolution), I have already indicated in passing that we had three instances within our PRP population of achieved "insight" seemingly in excess of induced change. This, of course, is a common enough problem and a frequent enough complaint, both within and about psychoanalytic treatment, and has been the subject of considerable discussion in the psychoanalytic literature. In our own three instances such concepts as undigested intellectual insights or of insights within an ego-weakened or psychotic transference state were invoked. What is meant here, of course, is insights that for varying reasons are not consequent to true conflict resolution and do not reflect it.

3. The third proposition, often linked to the proportionality argument, but in the light of our findings much more debatable and clearly separated from it, has to do with the necessity argument that effective conflict resolution is a necessary condition for at least certain kinds of change. It is certainly clear that an overall finding from our project—and almost an overriding one—has been the repeated demonstration that a substantial range of changes, in symptoms, in character traits, in personality functioning, and in life-style rooted in lifelong and repressed intrapsychic conflicts, have been brought about via the more supportive psychotherapeutic modes and techniques, cutting across the gamut of declared supportive *and* expressive (even analytic) therapies, and that in terms of the usual criteria—stability, durability, and capacity to withstand external or internal disruptive pressures—these changes can be (in many instances) quite indistinguishable from the changes brought about by typically expressive-analytic (interpretive, insight-producing) means.

4. A counterpart to the proposition based on the tendency to overestimate the necessity of the expressive (analytic) treatment mode and of its operation via conflict resolution in order to effect therapeutically desired change has been the other proposition, based on the happy finding that the supportive psychotherapeutic approaches, mechanisms, and techniques so often achieved far more than were expected of them—in fact often enough reached the kinds and degrees of change expected to depend on more expressive and insightful conflict resolutions—and did so in ways that represented indistinguishably "structural" changes, in terms of the usual indicators of that state. In fact, proportionately, each within its own category, the designated psychotherapy cases did as well as the designated psychoanalytic ones. More to the point, the (good) results in the one modality were not overall less stable or less enduring or less proof against subsequent environmental vicissitude than in the other. And

more important still, within the psychotherapy group (of 20), the changes predicted, though more often predicated on the more expressive mechanisms and techniques, in fact were more often actually achieved—often the same changes—on the basis of the more supportive mechanisms and techniques.

And even more within the psychoanalysis group (22), in almost every case there were modifications, parameters, etc., some analytically resolved but mostly not, and all of them in the direction of more supportive modes and aspects, so that even by our liberal PRP criteria, there were only 10 (not quite half) of the psychoanalytic cases who were in overall retrospect viewed as having been in essentially unaltered analyses, 6 who were in substantially modified (in supportive directions) analyses, and 6 who were considered really converted to varyingly supportive–expressive psychotherapies. By the usual stricter criteria of customary outpatient psychoanalytic and psychotherapy practice, just about every single one of our PRP psychoanalytic cases would be considered substantially altered in varyingly supportive directions. Put into overall perspective, more of the patients (psychotherapeutic and psychoanalytic alike) changed on the basis of designedly supportive interventions and mechanisms than had been expected or predicted beforehand, on the basis of either our clinical experience or our theoretical positions.

5. Considering these PRP treatment courses from the point of view of psychoanalysis as a treatment modality, just as more was accomplished than expected, and more stably, and more enduringly with psychotherapy, especially in its more supportive modes, so psychoanalysis, as the quintessentially expressive therapeutic mode, was more limited—at least with these patients—than had been anticipated or predicted. This has been, of course, a function of a variety of factors. In part it has reflected the whole ethos of the psychoanalytic sanatorium and the psychoanalytic treatment opportunities that it is intended to make possible. The dominant theme here has been the concept that the psychoanalytically guided sanatorium, with its possibilities for protection, care, and life management of the (temporarily) behaviorally disorganized and incompetent individual, could make possible the intensive psychoanalytic treatment of patients who could not be helped to resolve their deep-seated personality difficulties satisfactorily enough with any other or lesser treatment approach than psychoanalysis, but who also could not tolerate the rigors of the regressive psychoanalytic treatment process within the usual outpatient private practice setting.

This, of course, is what has led to the concept of psychoanalysis on the basis of so-called heroic indications, which by the nature of the kinds of patients brought to The Menninger Foundation, necessarily

OUTCOMES

143

comprised such a substantial segment of our PRP psychoanalytic population. In our PRP experience, however, the central tenets of this proposition were found wanting; these particular patients characteristically did very poorly with the psychoanalytic treatment method, however it was modified by parameters, and however buttressed with concomitant hospitalization, and they in fact comprised the great bulk of the failed psychoanalytic treatment cases. On the other hand, there were certainly enough instances of very good outcomes among the very ill and disordered in supportive–expressive psychotherapies that we can feel that the whole broad spectrum of "sicker" patients who are being talked about here can indeed do much better in an appropriately arranged and modulated supportive–expressive psychotherapy, if the ingredients are put together skillfully and imaginatively enough, and if one can ensure truly sufficient concomitant life management. That last stipulation, concerning the need for adequate life management, is of course one of the central keys to the success of the treatment recommendations being proposed here, and, by that token, reaffirms a proper role either for the psychoanalytic sanatorium or for some less controlled life regimen made more possible by modern-day, psychoactive drug management. The big difference is in the departure from the effort at psychoanalysis per se (even modified psychoanalysis) as the treatment of choice for these "sicker" patients in that setting. On this basis, I have spoken of the failing of the so-called heroic indications for *psychoanalysis* and am instead inviting a repositioning of the pendulum in its swings over time around this issue, more in the direction of "narrowing indications" for (proper) psychoanalysis along the lines marked out by Anna Freud.

6. The predictions made for prospective therapeutic courses and outcomes tended to be for more substantial change and for more permanent change (i.e., more "structural change") where the treatment plan and implementation were to be more expressive-analytic, and where these changes were expected to be more based on thoroughgoing intrapsychic conflict resolution through processes of interpretation, insight, and working through. And pari passu, and again in terms of the conventional psychodynamic wisdom, the more supportive the treatment was intended to be (had to be), the more limited and inherently unstable the anticipated changes were predicted to be. What our research study has revealed in great detail is that all of this was (again, overall) consistently tempered and altered in the actual implementation in the treatment courses. The psychoanalyses, as a whole, as well as the expressive psychotherapies as a whole, were systematically modified in the direction of introducing more supportive components in widely varying ways, and by and large

accomplished more limited outcomes than promised (hoped), and, as indicated, with a varying but often substantial amount of that accomplished by noninterpretive, i.e., supportive, means. The psychotherapies, on the other hand, often accomplished a fair amount more, and in several of the more spectacular cases a great deal more, than initially expected and promised, and again, however the admixture of intervention techniques was originally projected, with much of the change on the basis of more supportive modes than originally specified [Wallerstein, 1988b, pp. 144–149].

Which brings us to the question, What did all this labor in PRP add up to in relation to the issue of results and efficacy in psychoanalysis and in psychoanalytic psychotherapy? Again, I can quote from that same 1988b paper just quoted at length.

It can be most broadly generalized as follows: (1) The treatment results, with patients selected either as suitable for trials at psychoanalysis, or as appropriate for varying mixes of expressive–supportive psychotherapeutic approaches, tended—with this population sample—to converge, rather than diverge, in outcome. (2) Across the whole spectrum of treatment courses in the forty-two patients, ranging from the most analytic-expressive, through the inextricably blended, onto the most single-mindedly supportive, in almost every instance—the psychoanalyses included—the treatment carried more supportive elements than originally intended, and these supportive elements accounted for substantially more of the changes achieved than had been originally anticipated. (3) The nature of supportive therapy, or better the supportive aspects of all psychotherapy, as conceptualized within a psychoanalytic theoretical framework, and as deployed by psychoanalytically knowledgeable therapists, bears far more respectful specification in all its form variants than has usually been accorded it in the psychodynamic literature. And (4) from the study of the kinds of changes reached by this cohort of patients, partly on an uncovering insight-aiming basis, and partly on the basis of the opposed covering-up varieties of supportive techniques, the changes themselves—divorced from how they were brought about—often seemed quite indistinguishable from each other, in terms of being so-called real or structural changes in personality functioning.

In the light of the conceptual and predictive framework within which the Psychotherapy Research Project of The Menninger Foundation was planned and implemented three decades earlier, there is of course considerable real surprise in the overall project findings:

that these distinctive therapeutic modalities of psychoanalysis, expressive psychotherapy, supportive psychotherapy, and so on, hardly exist in anywhere near ideal or pure form in the real world of actual practice. Real treatments in actual practice are inextricably intermingled blends of more or less expressive–interpretive and more-or-less supportive–stabilizing elements. Almost all treatments (including even presumably pure psychoanalyses) carry many more supportive components than are usually credited to them. The overall outcomes achieved by those treatments that are more "analytic" as against those that are more "supportive" are less apart than our usual expectations for those differing modalities would portend. The kinds of changes achieved in treatments from the two ends of this spectrum are less different in nature and in permanence than again is usually expected, and indeed can often not be easily distinguished. None of this is where, three decades ago, we expected to be today. From another perspective, in terms of the corridor comments made by practitioners in informal interchanges about the conditions and nature of professional practice, which reflect what they regularly find that they do in actual practice as against how technique is conceptualized for formal presentation in professional meetings, our PRP research conclusions are far less surprising [Wallerstein, 1988b, pp. 149–150].

PRESENT STATUS AND FUTURE DIRECTIONS

Convergence of Empirical Process and Outcome Studies

Two major directions dominate contemporary investigation of psychoanalytic treatment processes and outcomes, circa 1990; the first is an effort at convergence of empirical psychoanalytic process studies with the outcome studies described in the accounting of the several generations of outcome research, and the second is a more clinical concern with the values, both clinical and research, that would accrue from the more systematic building of routine follow-up inquiry into regular clinical psychoanalytic practice.

The first current direction is exemplified in the contents of *Psychoanalytic Process Research Strategies*, edited by Dahl, Kaechele, and Thomae (1988). From the 1960s to the 1980s a variety of psychoanalytic researchers, almost all in the United States and the former Federal Republic of Germany, studied microscopic moment-by-moment psychoanalytic interactional processes, in single hours or in small segments of hours, using audiotaped and transcribed psychoanalytic treatment hours. Many of the most significant of these are represented by chapters in Dahl et al. Each group developed its own concepts of the basic units of the psychoanalytic situation and psychoanalytic process, its own instruments to measure these, and utilized these in relation to its own available database, though there was some sharing of sample hours from a particular psychoanalytic patient (Mrs. C) across a number of these groups. The book by Dahl et al. represents an effort to contrast and compare findings from these disparate studies in a search for principles of convergence. In the Introduction by Dahl, the hope is expressed that this convergence will be found in the principle enunciated in the initial chapter by Strupp, Schacht, and Henry (1988, pp. 1–14) "that the description and representation, theoretically *and* operationally, of a *patient's conflicts,* of the *patient's treatment,* and of the *assessment of the outcome,* must be congruent, which is to say, must be represented in comparable, if not identical terms" (p. ix). This proposed fundamental integrative principle is called the principle of problem-treatment-outcome congruence (PTO; p. 7).

An effort was made to put this principle to systematic empirical test. Wallerstein organized, under the auspices of the American Psychoanalytic Association, a Collaborative Multi-Site Program of Psychoanalytic Therapy Research, bringing together a total of sixteen ongoing psychoanalytic therapy research groups, studying psychoanalytic treatment processes and/or outcomes, including among them all the United States groups represented in the book edited by Dahl et al. Also included were outcome study groups from the third-generation outcome studies (the group of Kantrowitz et al. in Boston, and Wallerstein's current successor group to the Menninger studies in San Francisco). This was in a design within which all of the groups could use their own concepts and instruments upon a common agreed-upon database from available audiotaped and transcribed psychoanalytic hours from already completed psychoanalytic treatments as well as upon such hours from new psychoanalytic cases, so that appropriate before and after studies (as well as planned follow-ups) could be prospectively built in. The comparing and contrasting of findings by all of these process and outcome study groups will enable us finally to determine the degrees of convergence of the concepts and instruments elaborated to this point by the different groups, and also to determine the degree and the nature of the imbrication of process and outcome studies, the degrees to which the principle of PTO congruence holds.

This is one direction that what I call fourth-generation studies is taking, and one which, if successful, promises to integrate not only the various psychoanalytic process studies carried out more or less independently over the past two decades, but also to integrate process studies with outcome studies, in a more complete fulfillment of an aim articulated as early as 1958 by PRP (Wallerstein and Robbins, 1958). We said then, "We believe that in theory process and outcome are necessarily interlocked and that the hypotheses that will yield the answers sought can only come from . . . study paying equal attention to both components. Any study of outcome, even if it only counts a percentage of cases 'improved' must establish some criteria for 'improvement,' and these in turn derive from some conceptualization of the nature of the course of illness and the process of change, whether or not this is explicitly formulated. Similarly, any study of process, in delineating patterns of change among variables, makes at varying points in time cross-sectional assessments which, if compared with one another, provide measures of treatment outcome" (p. 118)—a forerunner of the much later articulated principle of PTO congruence.

Enhanced Clinical Concern with Outcome as Assessed at Follow-Up

The second direction of outcome and efficacy studies stemmed from more directly clinical considerations. This effort was spearheaded by a panel discussion chaired by Joseph Schachter at the December 1987 meeting of the American Psychoanalytic Association, under the title "Evaluation of Outcome of Psychoanalytic Treatment," followed by the question, "Should follow-up by the analyst be part of the posttermination phase of analytic treatment?" (Panel, 1989). Schachter in his opening presentation on that panel posed the issue of the value of regular and systematic follow-up for a different—and more valid—perspective on psychoanalytic outcomes. He referred to a questionnaire on this subject, which he had distributed to analysts in five institutes to which he had secured a 52 percent return. It was clear from these questionnaire results that conventional practice characteristically employed a double standard in regard to follow-up contact. It was not expected with our patients, and when it occurred was usually regarded as an expression of unfinished business or something untoward in the prior treatment or treatment termination. But for ourselves, we take for granted the expectation of post-termination contact with our own training analysts.

Luborsky on this panel talked, from a review of his research studies, of the positive effects of follow-up contact in maintaining treatment gains, especially useful for patients with some deficiency in the capacity for internalization of a secure representation of the analyst. He also said that it provided a useful opportunity to assess the need for further therapy, but that also, negatively, it could hinder the completion of the work of termination and separation. Martin, from a clinical context, gave an experience survey which indicated that two-thirds of successfully terminated analytic patients nonetheless contacted their former analyst at some time within the first three years after termination (mostly by letter or phone). And as Johan noted "Martin pointed out that since we now accept the idea of adult developmental tasks, the door should be more than open for the analysand to return if and when he encounters new developmental tasks which bring him once again into unconscious conflict" (Panel, 1989, p. 817). Schlessinger, speaking from his research studies, pursued this same developmental theme, stating that every analysis is necessarily incomplete, that the posttermination phase is a period of consolidation of internalizations that constitute the developing self-analytic function and that this process is consistently facilitated by planned follow-up interviews.

Wallerstein on the same panel (Wallerstein, 1989b) began with the historical statement:

Psychoanalysis has never developed a tradition of systematic followup study to evaluate outcome and to improve technique and theory for a variety of reasons, partly theoretical, stemming from the conception of an unfolding transference neurosis and its analytical resolution as the precondition for cure [and that planned postanalytic contact between analyst and analysand would play into the perpetuation of transference fantasies and would represent a collusion reflecting some unanalyzed transference–countertransference residues], and partly historical, having to do with the happenstance of its development as a private practice-based discipline and training outside of the academic setting [where followup on treatment would more logically and naturally be built into the clinical operation] [p. 921].

Then drawing on the PRP experience, he focused specifically on the consideration of the impact of follow-up *qua* follow-up on the issues of treatment termination and resolution and on the nature of the posttreatment period from three perspectives, (1) the range of conscious reactions to, and degrees of cooperation with, the planned follow-up studies with these research patients; (2) the reverberating meanings of the follow-up experience including the potential for attenuating or delaying the psychological treatment closure, or oppositely, facilitating the treatment resolution; and (3) an experience survey of the varieties of continuing contacts with the treating analyst during the follow-up period, including returns to treatment. In overall conclusion it was stated, "I feel that we can be reasonably reassured that the impact of *planned* follow-up study on the termination and outcome of psychoanalytic therapies, while not always inconsequential, does not seem to be detrimental and can, in fact, prove helpful and providential to the patient's and the therapist's therapeutic purposes" (p. 939), and "that both our individual patients and our field as a science will profit thereby" (p. 940), by systematic, planned follow-up built into our regular clinical as well as research activities. On the same panel, several speakers from the floor offered cautionary statements: Calder that gains could still be at a price (in transference and countertransference acting out), and Firestein that the evidence was still unclear as to which way is best to consolidate treatment gains, follow-up or no follow-up.

Schachter pursued a number of studies in follow-up to this panel on follow-up (1990a,b). By questionnaire distributed to those who attended the panel, he learned from the returns that the audience's attitude toward follow-up had indeed shifted in the direction of more of them stating that they now either hoped to hear from the patient or that they would like the patient to return to see them at some specified period after treatment termination (1990a). Then by reexamining Wallerstein's data from *Forty-Two Lives in Treatment,* he stated his belief that Wallerstein's claim that in six of the forty-two cases, the follow-up seemed in some way to attenuate or delay processes that would otherwise have led to earlier psychological closure of the treatment course, was not supported by Wallerstein's detailed data (1990b).

OUTCOMES OF PSYCHOANALYSIS AND PSYCHOTHERAPY AT TERMINATION AND AT FOLLOW-UP

The most recent chapter in this story was a successor panel discussion, "Stability of Gain Achieved During Analytic Treatment from a Follow-up Perspective," also chaired by Schachter, at the December 1990 meeting of the American Psychoanalytic Association (Panel, 1993). For this panel, representatives of the two third-generation outcome studies, Kantrowitz and Wallerstein, were invited to give presentations in which each presented clinical data from two research-studied psychoanalytic cases—one in which treatment gains were consolidated, and even enhanced, during the posttermination follow-up period, and one in which there was regression toward the pretreatment status—in order to attempt to elucidate the determinants of an individual's course after treatment (i.e., why the individual tends toward consolidation or regression). Bachrach and Rangell were the invited discussants.

Wallerstein (1992), in his write-up for this panel, compared two treatment courses, two women with quite similar illness pictures (difficulties in being a mother, and unresolved hostile identifications with malevolent preoedipal mother imagoes), who had come to comparably seemingly satisfactory therapeutic results at treatment termination but who diverged sharply in their postanalytic courses. One was able to consolidate and extend her treatment gains, and this seemed related to the supportive family context, as well as to the availability and utilization of surrounding professional help, her family physician, the social worker in an adoption agency, and her parish priest. The other patient, who suffered a symptom regression and ultimately returned for reanalysis with the original analyst, ended her analysis alone and lonely, shouldering the responsibility for two children, both in therapy, and then entered an unhappy second marriage in which the ambivalent dependent relationship with the mother was reenacted, very different from the more secure dependency she had experienced with her first husband, who had died. In the report of the whole panel, Martin (Panel, 1993) summarized the two contrasting cases presented by Wallerstein, as well as the two presented by Kantrowitz, and then distilled from the formal discussions by Bachrach and Rangell the overall feeling that the factors shaping these differing posttreatment courses were indeed very complex, often ambiguous, and, at this stage of our development, still largely to be elucidated. It is indeed a very wide-open research arena.

It is clear overall that currently psychoanalytic therapy research, which has already yielded significant knowledge about the nature of treatment outcomes and efficacy as discerned at the termination and follow-up points through the first three generations of studies starting from 1917 and up to the present, is now poised at a new level and with the possibility for truly accelerating breakthroughs, both methodologically and substantively, as this current fourth generation of studies is carried out through its planned natural cycle.

Part II

Psychoanalysis as a Science and as a Profession

My professional lifetime involvement in psychoanalytic therapy research has carried with it a concomitant interest in the status of psychoanalysis as a science, whether we have warrant to consider it a science, and if so, what kind of science? This is necessarily a central question because research in the sense of systematic inquiry leading to incremental knowledge advance—in which successive hypotheses are put forth, and methods are devised to confirm or refute them—is a distinguishing hallmark of what constitutes a science, and what separates a scientific discipline from other avenues of intelligence. I have on two occasions organized my evolving views on the ever-present philosophy of science issues concerning psychoanalysis as science and they are the first two of the six articles in this section.

The first occasion was a plenary session address at the Fifth Regional Conference sponsored by the Chicago Psychoanalytic Society in March 1974, and this address was subsequently published as part of a collection of psychoanalytic essays in memory of George S. Klein. In that article, chapter 6, "Psychoanalysis as a Science: Its Present Status and Its Future Tasks," I discussed the kind of science I felt psychoanalysis to be, which then could give appropriate warrant to the entire formal and systematic psychoanalytic research enterprise. I also offered my views on how to reconcile or to encompass the two diverging directions in which I saw the considerations of psychoanalysis as science to be heading. On the one hand, there was the subjectively idiosyncratic hermeneutic or "hermeneutic science" enterprise, with its focus on recreating an agreed-upon story of a unique individual development, and with its general theory, or its variant metapsychologies, jettisoned completely. On the other hand, there was an objectively generalized system of rules or laws defining and explaining the functioning and malfunctioning of the human mind, with a retained, albeit altered and updated, general theory, that would be more consonant with developments in cognate disciplines concerned with human behavior and mental functioning. This is what I was calling "The Great Metapsychology Debate" that preoccupied the concerned literature during the 1970s.

My own take on this issue (in company with some other theorists) was that the uniqueness of psychoanalysis as a systematic theory of the human mind resided in its living simultaneously within both orientations, that of a generalizing science of the mind and that of a uniquely individual history and context. This necessarily poses a threefold task: (1) the elaboration in psychoanalytic clinical work of a distinctive life history through the ascription of meanings and the unfolding of coherence in the mental productions of the individual seeking help; (2) the concomitant delineation of the generalized lawfulness regulating how the human mind works across all individuals; and (3) the elaboration of the linkages, or canons of correspondence, between the phenomena in the two realms, both the historically determined and evolved individual configurations, and also the conceptualized explanatory operations that generalize across all mental life—clearly a very ambitious agenda still in an early developmental stage.

The second article, chapter 7, with the same title but a different subtitle, "Psychoanalysis as a Science: A Response to the New Challenges," was given as the Freud Anniversary Lecture at the New York Psychoanalytic Institute in April 1985, a decade after the prior article (chapter 6). By then, the preoccupations of this field of inquiry had altered. The concerns now were on the viability or credibility of psychoanalysis as any kind of science, rather than on what kind of science it could be considered to be. There were those who carried the new revisionism in theory even further than in the debates a decade earlier. This same side of theoretical revisionism was divided, however, into two opposed camps, each a more extreme extension of the sides of what I had called the great metapsychology

debate in the prior decade. On the one hand were those in favor
of putting psychoanalysis on a full-fledged natural science basis by
scrapping the existing metapsychologies in their entirety, in favor
of an information theory and cybernetic model of mental life, with
the mind functioning in a manner analogous to high-speed computers, all declared to be more consonant with our rapidly expanding
neurophysiological knowledge base. And on the other hand were
those who would carry psychoanalysis into a totally hermeneutic
direction, a solely humanistic, interpretive discipline, giving up all
pretense to any kind of scientific status at all, that is, to any search
for the testing of its propositions via any kind of canons of science.

After offering my views on the limitations and what I felt to be
the ultimate barrenness of each of these opposed approaches, I
turned to the other side of the new debate, the declaration that was
conspicuously advanced by the philosopher Adolf Grünbaum that
psychoanalysis was indeed in the natural science mold within which
Freud—never wholeheartedly, however—had cast it, but that as a
proposed natural science it was fundamentally flawed in seeking to
establish its probative value in the psychoanalytic situation where
Freud had asserted that it could be found, and that indeed no other
locus of inquiry was necessary. The balance of my article was a
rebuttal of Grünbaum's propositions and a reclaiming of a viable,
albeit developmentally still early scientific status for psychoanalysis,
with the continuing ongoing opportunities for the growth of an
empirical psychoanalytic research enterprise, via both the case study
method innovated by Freud, and also via formal and systematic research that is consonant both with the subtlety and complexity of
the subjectivistic phenomena under scrutiny, and yet loyal to the
reality principle as embodied in the canons of science.

The next four chapters in this section deal with the issues of
psychoanalysis as a profession. The first of these, chapter 8, "Psychoanalysis and Academic Psychiatry—Bridges," was a review of the
relationship (in America) of psychoanalysis and psychiatry as that
relationship had evolved over close to half a century. At first it had
been a close union, embraced enthusiastically in the 1940s and
1950s as mutually sustaining and rewarding, and there were even
calls at the time for an amalgamation of the two. But there were
subsequent increasingly problematic years, starting from the 1960s
with the spreading diversification of psychiatric interest and practice. This was accompanied by the increasingly strident calls for the
"remedicalization" of psychiatry, and the concomitant increasing

relegation of psychoanalytic theory, and the derived psychoanalytic psychotherapy, to a more peripheral role within the overall psychiatric scheme of things, even in some settings, to its virtual extrusion from psychiatry.

Chapter 8 represented both a cry of alarm over this major change in the relationship between psychoanalysis and psychiatry, and a plea and proposal to restore, and even to try to enhance, the role of psychoanalysis within academic psychiatry, and even more broadly in the university at large. I felt that this was essential to avert a prospective major alienation between the two disciplines, which I asserted would be to the detriment of both. As a reflection of the rapidly shifting climate concerning this increasingly embattled relationship between psychoanalysis and academic psychiatry, I published another paper (1983c), not included in this volume, only three years later than chapter 8, indicating a significant modification of the hopes, and proposed remedies, expressed in chapter 8. The occasion was fortuitous; I had been invited to prepare an address for the Fortieth Anniversary Celebration of the Topeka Institute for Psychoanalysis, from which I had graduated in 1958, to be held in Topeka, Kansas, in October 1982. In that talk, I first reviewed in detail the main arguments in chapter 8 on the increasingly distant and problematic nature of the relationship between psychoanalysis and psychiatry (especially academic psychiatry). I noted that the Topeka Institute was embedded as a full-time institution within The Menninger Foundation, itself a full-time psychiatric group practice dedicated to the mental health care of individuals suffering the whole range of mental and emotional disorders. Thus, the Institute had a unique opportunity amongst psychoanalytic institutes around the world—and an opportunity defaulted on by the academic medical and university world—to establish the kind of full-time professional training and scientific education that alone could give adequate assurance of the fullest continuing development of psychoanalysis as a science, of psychoanalytic research, and of the interacting enhancement of psychoanalysis and all the cognate disciplines of human behavior. These concerns and their proper remediation continue today to be both pressing and unresolved.

The next two papers in this sequence deal with visions for our futures, chapter 9, "The Future of Psychoanalysis," written with Edward Weinshel, and chapter 10, "The Future of Psychotherapy," the former written as part of an invitational series, published over a two-year span by *The Psychoanalytic Quarterly*. In addressing this issue, Weinshel and I divided our domain of inquiry into five sections, and offered our prognostications and advice under each of these headings, though not with the same space necessarily devoted to each. The five were: (1) psychoanalysis as a science; (2) psychoanalysis as a discipline; (3) training for psychoanalysis; (4) research in psychoanalysis; and (5) psychoanalysis as a profession. Though we varied in our expressed hopefulness concerning the central issues and the predicted future trends in each of these arenas, the overall message was, I feel upbeat, and properly so.

This was in some contrast to the companion article, chapter 10, "The Future of Psychotherapy" within psychiatry, which I wrote as a fervent plea for the preservation of an endangered species. This article was written as an invited plenary address to the California Psychiatric Association Conference in Berkeley in October 1990, under the conference title, "Creating an Integrated Psychiatry —Challenge of the '90s." There were two invited plenary addresses, mine and another on "The Future of Psychopharmacology." The latter was ebulliently optimistic; mine was a sober and tempered comparison of what psychotherapy training and practice had been for the psychiatrists of my generation with our residency training in the immediate post-World War II decade, with what it had become (deteriorated to) at the time of my address, some four decades later. I tried to put into the best light that I could what the future of psychodynamic (or psychoanalytic) psychotherapy could be in the now vastly altered climate in the mental health professions, as compared with what could now be seen as the halcyon days in which I had been trained and embarked on my own psychotherapeutic–psychoanalytic career. I also indicated that similar antipsychotherapy trends were likewise at work in each of the mental health professional disciplines, though with a different historical dynamic in each (and to a lesser extent in the others). At this point, a decade after that talk, the situation of psychotherapy training within psychiatry is in the same unaltered and parlous state, and my plea for remediation would be unaltered.

Chapter 11, "The Identity of Psychoanalysis: The Question of Lay Analysis," was written after the final resolution of the long-standing controversy over the question of nonmedical, or lay, analysis that had marked American and worldwide psychoanalysis, which I dated to a beginning in events as far back as 1910. The controversy had come to resolution with the settlement of a lawsuit over this issue in 1988, three-quarters of a century later. I conceptualized this long struggle as centrally over the identity of psychoanaly*sis*—in contrast to the identity of the psychoanaly*st*—a struggle in which I played a major role over the decades of my involvement in organized psychoanalysis, including being president of one of the defendant organizations in the lawsuit, the International Psychoanalytical Association, during almost the entire three-and-a-half-year span of the litigation. That controversy is the subject of an entire book that I have written, *Lay Analysis: Life Inside the Controversy* (Wallerstein, 1998). Chapter 11 is a statement of the main themes of that book, written in response to an invitation to deliver the keynote address at the winter meeting of the American Academy of Psychoanalysis in Santa Barbara, California, in December 1994.

I agreed to make that keynote speech if I could choose as my topic the history of the question of lay analysis, in order to address thereby the one major psychoanalytic organization in the United States that still insisted on psychoanalysis as a psychiatric subspecialty, with its training and practice to be denied to nonphysicians, or lay analysts. This topic was agreed to by the Program Committee and the leadership of the Academy, with the explicit understanding that my talk would be a plea for a reconsideration of the Academy's long-held position, a reconsideration in the light of the historical developmental dynamic in American psychoanalysis that I would present. The talk was indeed well received by both the leadership of the Academy and, I gathered, by the audience as well, but the official journal of the Academy declined to publish it on the grounds that it was irrelevant to the affairs of the Academy, since the history that it recounted was that of the American Psychoanalytic Association in relation to the International. The talk was therefore published elsewhere, not in the accustomed place for these keynote addresses within the official journal. Though many consider this long-standing issue old history now, the continuing stance of the Academy indicates that it is still far from being fully resolved, and the reverberating impact of the degree of resolution achieved upon the issue of the identity of psychoanalysis is far from being fully appreciated by the larger psychoanalytic world today.

6.

Psychoanalysis as a Science: Its Present Status and Its Future Tasks

In the field of psychoanalysis, few theoretical issues are more constantly and passionately argued—among both adherents from within and observers and critics, friendly and otherwise, from without—than the status of our discipline as a science. Its position is widely defended in debate, often against powerful arrays of outside scientists and philosophers of science, skeptics, as in the distinguished company, pro and con, gathered under the chairmanship of Sidney Hook for the New York University Institute of Philosophy in 1958, whose proceedings were published under the title *Psychoanalysis: Scientific Method and Philosophy* (Hook, 1959). But psychoanalysis is also called upon to defend itself against the less strident but equally concerned questions from within, which are given expression under the alternative notion that our discipline and our technique are, after all, yet more art than science, and taking strength from the individual artistic mastery achieved. And yet, at the same time, even among the most convinced and most knowledgeable proponents of psychoanalysis as a science, both its theory and its method *as science* seem continuously to require justification, because of our admittedly peculiar subjectivistic data, and our essentially private methods for gathering and validating that data, the latter ostensibly needed in the service of creating and fitting the observational and investigative method that is uniquely appropriate to the particular nature of the phenomena that constitute that science—in our case, we add, that peculiar science.

It would take us too far afield from our purpose here for me to essay any comprehensive historical review of these many arguments. The historian John Burnham (1967), in his far-ranging monograph on, among other things, the history of psychoanalysis as science, summarized these questions about the scientific status of psychoanalysis under the following headings: (1) its theoretical formulations, with their terms too loosely defined for the theories couched in them to be verifiable by usual scientific means; (2) the nature of the evidence used in psychoanalytic expositions, based as it is on the *private* data of the consulting room, with insufficient opportunity for fair counterevidence or alternative evidence; (3) the linked question of the dubious scientific credentials of evidence often drawn from such nonscientific fields as folklore, mythology, even the arts; (4) the interpretations of the evidence, with alternative interpretations often equally possible and plausible, and without adequate safeguards against the suggestion of the evidence through the interpretation; and (5) the undue reliance on analogical and metaphoric thinking, often with built-in creeping reifications. These selfsame questions have also been addressed in numerous presentations by research-minded analytic practitioners, with varying emphasis on the balance between assertion and doubt, between statement of secured or claimed status, and with concerned questions about the complex and difficult conceptual, technical, semantic, and even epistemological issues at stake. I want only to call attention, for example, to contributions focused on this particular area by Lustman (1963), Brenner (1968), Harrison (1970), and Ritvo (1971).

I myself have also been long identified with these concerns. It is within the comforting belief that we are indubitably a science—albeit one that has not been as scientific in its investigative and research endeavors as it might be, or as the evolving technology of scientific method would permit (by which I mean, of course, scientific method appropriate to the observational field of the science at issue)—that I have myself (together with my research collaborator, Harold Sampson [Wallerstein and Sampson, 1971]) made a long and detailed exposition of the array of issues involved. This exposition ranged from conceptual to methodological issues that beset research into our central interest and activity, the process of psycho-analytic therapy, and that have kept this research from being as firmly scientific as I think it can be.

Our arguments there were concerned, that is, to make better science out of the research study of our activities as a science. These arguments took their impetus from a guiding conviction that the traditional case-study method innovated by Freud, though it has provided a truly extraordinary range of insights into the structure of the mind, the organization of mental illness, and the forces that are at work and that make for change in the treatment situation, is not by itself sufficient to the present and future scientific needs of our field. We argued, therefore, for the need to formalize (i.e., to go beyond) the clinical case-study method as the *central* research instrument and research access to the therapeutic process in analy-sis. We were concerned with the need for more formal systematic research on the psychoanalytic process, while being at the same time properly mindful of the many problems and issues thereby raised in devising and executing such research in a manner at once meaningful and responsive to the subtlety and complexity of the phenomena and while still scientific in the best sense of that term (of loyalty to the reality principle, as it is embodied in appropriate canons of scientific inference).

At the same time, we expressed ourselves as fully cognizant of the extraordinary reach of the classical case-study method and of its still enduring power to effect the advancement of scientific knowledge in our field. The whole corpus of psychoanalysis, the closest in existence to a general psychology, comprehending the phenomena of both normal and abnormal personality develop-ment, attests brilliantly to the explanatory power of the theory de-rived from the data of the consulting room. And we know that, by contrast, whatever spectacular growth the more formal research method and research inquiry have undergone recently, they have to this point exerted but very slight influence on either theory or practice in our field.

One of the, to me, less significant issues—and controver-sies—concerning our field as science is the question of the appro-priate mix of these two avenues of continuing approach to new knowledge within and about psychoanalysis. A good many fear that the classical method of psychoanalysis has been reaching a point of rapidly diminishing productivity, and there is considerable talk about the sterility of much of the literature in our field (Kubie,

1966), and the dearth of new ideas (Bak, 1970) and creative activity (Kohut, 1970) within classical analysis. Kohut (1970), in describing the inquiry of the Ad Hoc Committee on Scientific Activities of the American Psychoanalytic Association into the concern that "all was not well with present-day scientific research in the field of psycho-analysis, in particular . . . a lack of original contributions, i.e., of genuine accretions to our knowledge" (p. 462), voiced the double suspicion "that (a) there is a dearth of new psychoanalytic insights in the *central* areas of psychoanalytic knowledge, and (b) present-day original contributions and the research enthusiasm of analysts tend to be devoted to the application of psychoanalytic knowledge to peripheral areas" (p. 463; emphasis added).

Kurt Eissler (1969), in his provocative paper "Irreverent Re-marks about the Present and the Future of Psychoanalysis," has developed this viewpoint furthest with his thesis that perhaps Freud, the founding genius of psychoanalysis, had exhausted in his own lifetime its major probabilities for fundamental new discovery, at least via its classical method. Eissler stated his view very directly:

> It is breathtaking to review what Freud extracted during the course of four decades, from the free associations of eight subjects who each lay on a couch for 50 minutes per day. The input–output quotient was here truly enormous. This question, however, remains: Did Freud extract from his patients' associations all the knowledge that is to be gained from the psychoanalytic situation? With one qualification, to be dealt with presently, I would say that the answer is yes [p. 465].

Or, to quote again, "the psychoanalytic situation has already given forth everything it contains. It is depleted with regard to re-search possibilities, at least as far as the possibility of new paradigms is concerned" (p. 469). "With [Freud's] death, psychoanalysis en-tered the phase of 'normal science'; it has stayed in it since then"—here Eissler is using the words *paradigm* and *normal science* in the sense made familiar to us in the work of Thomas Kuhn (1962, p. 465).

It would be a digression here to list the qualifications (actually more than one) with which Eissler sought to balance somewhat the views that he very deliberately stated so sweepingly, or to defend, as Gitelson (1964) did so cogently, the social and the scientific impor-tance for any science of its phase of "normal science" as problem-solving activity par excellence, representing in endeavors and ac-complishments the productive incremental labors of the whole orga-nized scientific community. For the purpose of exposition, I want rather to focus on Eissler's overall conclusion (representing, as I think it does, the viewpoint of many) that "all that can be learned by way of the couch Freud had already learned—at least, in terms of the paradigms that this knowledge called for. Research will now move away more and more from the treatment room to other scientific loci" (p. 468).

I know how invidious it can be to point to any single contribution at the implied risk of slighting others of comparable merit. I will leave aside all contributions that rest, in part at least, on data other than that generated in the psychoanalytic consulting room, such as Mahler's (1968) major expansion of our developmental theory and our knowledge of developmental process. I do want to note, from within the confines of the classical psychoanalytic method alone, the culmination of Kohut's investigations of the structure and the treatment of the narcissistic personality disorder in his book, *The Analysis of the Self* (1971), which has impressed so many as a landmark addition (albeit surrounded still by lively controversy) to our knowledge of the psychopathology and the psychoanalytic therapy of this important category of stubbornly refractory patients. I cite Kohut in part because he makes my point of the continuing vigor of the so-called traditional psychoanalytic enterprise, in response not only to the rather widespread view expressed in the quoted article by Eissler, but also to its echoing to some extent even by Kohut (1970) himself in the survey from the work of the Committee on Scientific Activities of the American Psychoanalytic Association.

My overall point is that we are a science which has internally two main investigative methodologies. (These exist, aside from its growth at its interfaces, at its interactions with adjacent or applied areas, and with the kinds of data generated by the particular phenomena and methods of those areas. These others are, for example, the data of cognitive and affective developmental process from direct child observation, the psychophysiological correlative data in the realm of psychosomatics, or the implications for our dream theory of the experimental psychological data of the dream laboratory.) There is the classical method, which, since Freud, has remained its chief wellspring, and the recently developing, more formalized and systematized, specifically psychoanalytic research on and about psychoanalysis as a process for the exploration of the human mind in depth (e.g., Gill, Simon, Fink, Endicott, and Paul [1968]; Wallerstein [1968]).

I do not propose at this point to discuss the methods and the related conceptual and practical issues involved in formalizing, or going beyond, the traditional case study as our chief research instrument. I hope it is clear, however, that I do not refer to experimental manipulation of the psychoanalytic process in any way. Paul Meehl (1973) is the most recent to remind us, as Lustman (1963), Brenner (1968), and Harrison (1970) did before him, that "An enterprise can be empirical (in the sense of taking publicly observable data as its epistemic base) *without* being experimental (in the sense of laboratory manipulation of the variables)" (p. 106). He adduces such respectable sciences as astronomy, geography, ecology, paleontology, and human genetics as obvious examples. What I refer to as formalizing and "going beyond" is the process of obtaining the data of the consulting room (of course with due safeguards for the privacy and the confidentiality of the patients involved) and studying those data in ways that are both clinically and scientifically relevant. This process requires systematized attention to such issues as: (1) the need to make the basic phenomena or primary data of psychoanalysis available to shared study, whether by use of systematically kept process notes or verbatim recordings, with all the problems of each; (2) the importance of reducing, ordering, and summarizing the data with attention to their relation to our inferences about them, and to what Seitz (1966) has called the "consensus problem" in psychoanalytic research—the issue of handling differences in inference or judgment among clinical experts; (3) the problem of the circumvention of circularity of clinical judgment, the handling of the danger of smuggling in confirmations of our predictive judgments through our interpretations of the subsequent data; (4) the problem of generalizing from very few cases; and (5) the problem of devising scientific controls where control groups in the usual senses are for the most part not appropriate and often not ethical.

All of these issues are surveyed at length in my paper with Sampson, "Issues in Research in the Psychoanalytic Process" (1971), which I have already referred to. But what I do want to state and emphasize here is that the *disciplined* use of the case-study method itself, though without the same overt conceptual paraphernalia of explicit "controls, dependent and independent variables, hypotheses, and predictions," is not just our traditional science and road to science as bequeathed to us by Freud, but a necessary vital and continuing part of our current and ongoing scientific march.

I do not refer here to the more extreme position, advanced by some (Ramzy, 1962, 1963), that every clinical analysis is after all not only a search but in its essence also a research, that "every psychoanalyst who merely follows the method he was taught to follow will discover that he has been doing research, just as Monsieur Jourdain, of Molière's *Le Bourgeois Gentilhomme,* suddenly discovered that he had been speaking prose for forty years without knowing it" (1963, p. 74). I *do* refer, rather, to the *scientific* understanding and therefore the scientific use of the "peculiar" (i.e., different from that of other sciences) nature of our data and the self-conscious exposure of our shared assumptions about how one acquires knowledge of the phenomena within our clinical field and the intellectual reach and limitation of those assumptions.

It may be useful in this context to remind ourselves explicitly of these usually unremarked assumptions. Erikson (1958), in a little-noticed article, spelled out most precisely the nature and the role of what he called "*disciplined* subjectivity" in the handling of clinical evidence and clinical inference. Waelder (1962) delineated this concept further in defending the role of "introspection or empathy" in this regard, arguing that though introspection and empathy are not infallible ways to know, they are certainly not negligible and give our science, *qua* science, at least one *advantage* over physics. This knowing process takes place by what Home (1966) has called "cognitive identification," in which the "meaning is known to us through an *act of identification* and not through an act of sense perception [in the usual sense] . . ." (p. 47). Kris (1947) has averred that the interpretation of meaning (understood in this context) works not by "producing" recall, but rather by completing an incomplete memory, thereby implying that validation within analysis consists of the judgment of goodness of fit. That is, "the situation existing previous to the interpretation, the one which 'suggested' the interpretation, must be described as one of incomplete recall (and therefore, as in some measure similar to the situation in which the memory trace was laid down)" (p. 246). It was Schmidl (1955) who developed this concept of validation within the system most fully, arguing for the fit of the specific Gestalt of what is interpreted with the Gestalt of the interpretation, in which not only are inferences made from a general empirical rule to a specific case but, additionally, certain elements of the specific life experience of the patient come to be connected with each other (a homely analogue being the unerring fit of the two halves of the torn laundry ticket).

At the same time, persuasive as we analysts find this chain of reasoning from "disciplined subjectivity" through to "goodness of interpretive fit" as respectable and appropriate science, it is precisely at this point that friendly philosophical critics like Meehl (1973) pose methodological caveats or at least methodological limits to what we can claim as substantiated (and agreed upon) scientific status. On just this issue of the evidential value of the verbal productions in psychoanalytic hours (how we decide we know what it is that has transpired), Meehl reminds us that the pendulum can swing between two opposed methodological errors:

> One mistake is to demand that there should be a straightforwardly computable numerical probability attached to each substantive idiographic hypothesis, of the sort which we can usually compute with regard to the option of rejecting a statistical hypothesis. . . .
>
> [But] the opposite error is the failure to realize that Freud's "jig-saw puzzle" analogy does not really fit the psychoanalytic hour, because it is simply not true (as he admits elsewhere) that all of the pieces fit together, or that the criteria of "fitting" are tight enough to make it analogous even to a clear-cut criminal trial. Two points, opposite in emphasis, but compatible: Anyone who has experienced analysis, practiced it, or listened to taped sessions, if he is halfway fair-minded, will agree that (1) there are sessions in which the material "fits together" so beautifully that one is sure almost any skeptic would be convinced, and (2) there are sessions in which the "fit" is very loose and underdetermined (fewer equations than unknowns, so to speak), this latter kind of session (unfortunately) predominating [p. 108].

Again, Meehl reminds us, with his statements of methodological qualifications, that whichever way we turn on each of our two major avenues of access to new clinical or theoretical discovery in the central core of our psychoanalytical enterprise, it is hedged by problems and difficulties—as is all new accretion of knowledge in science. That psychoanalysis has, however, earned the sophisticated attention of hard-headed philosophical positivists from without is external confirmation, if such be needed, that we are indeed to be considered a scientific enterprise, one in the state of "normal science" (again in Kuhn's sense) so staunchly described by Gitelson (1964) as that mixture of problem-solving activities within the prevailing paradigm or scientific worldview carried on by a scientific community at one with itself as a social movement. This is what Harrison (1970), in the title of his article, called "*Our* Science."

This kaleidoscopic and I hope not overly condensed overview of the present status of psychoanalysis as science is, I would trust, reasonably familiar terrain, on which we can have a reasonable degree of consensus, albeit with the varying emphases that reflect our individual scientific predilections for study and research. Given this assessment of our present position, let me now outline, if not our ordained future course as a science, for none can claim predictive prescience in such undertakings, at least what I see as some of our crucial scientific tasks ahead. Here we are confronted by highly personal choices. A goodly number of analysts, including several of the authors of articles I have already cited (Brenner, 1968; Eissler, 1969; Bak, 1970; Harrison, 1970; Kohut, 1970, 1973; Ritvo, 1971), have spoken and written with differing, individual voices in this arena, some with the word *future* central to their title. But I would like for my essay in this realm to take a step backward in our conceptual developmental progression, if not in time, and take my point of departure from a phrase I used to describe the basis of our very justification as a scientific enterprise—the phrase "if such be needed." For I think my best entry into what I see as the essential conceptual tasks facing our science in its coming development and extension lies in my starting with the consideration of the position advanced by the philosopher and analytic scholar Home, who, in 1966, questioned fundamentally many of the assertions made here by myself (and by the others whose views I have here collated) about the nature of the propositions of our field as constituting science.

Home's argument is embedded in what he calls the distinction between two fundamentally different ways of studying man: the scientific enterprise built in each of its various branches on the accumulation of lawful regularities and generalizations across the instances of the natural phenomena studied, and the humanistic enterprise built on the intensive unraveling of the historically bound, the uniquely creative, and the idiosyncratic. Within the framework of this distinction he asks, " 'What is psychoanalysis about?' 'What essentially characterizes its subject matter?' 'What sort of theories can validly be constructed about it?' " (p. 42). He feels that we analysts have difficulties in being clear or in being in clear agreement about such fundamentals, not because we speak different languages—Freudian, Kleinian, etc., minor differences for the purpose of his argument—but because of "lack of clarity about the *kind of thing* we are discussing and therefore about the *kind of logical*

framework in terms of which it can be understood and discussed"
(p. 43; emphasis added).

To Home, the answer *is* clear. Freud's fundamental discovery,
his basic insight, was that the neurotic symptom has *meaning*. But
this discovery carried unexpected and usually unnoticed logical consequences. According to Home:

> In discovering that the symptom had meaning and basing his treat-
> ment on this hypothesis, Freud took the psycho-analytic study of neu-
> rosis *out of the world of science* into the world of the humanities,
> because a meaning is not the product of causes but the creation of
> a subject. This is a major difference; for the logic and method of the
> humanities is radically different from that of science, though no less
> respectable and rational, and of course much longer established
> [p. 43].

This, however, was not the perception of Freud, the natural-
scientist product of the physicalistic school of Helmholtz. As Home
puts it: "it is not surprising that, in the excitement of so great a
discovery and one that opened up such vast new territories, Freud
should have overlooked the logical implications for theory of the
step he had taken" (p. 43). And so Freud proceeded to attempt a
science of psychoanalysis built on the operation of a succession of
models of the psychic apparatus, from the original neurological model
of the "Project for a Scientific Psychology" (1895), through the
reflex-arc or "picket-fence" model of chapter 7 of *The Interpretation
of Dreams* (1900), through to the full-blown tripartite structural
model of *The Ego and the Id* (1923) and *Inhibitions, Symptoms and
Anxiety* (1926a).

But here is the crux of what Home feels to be the confusing
intermingling, within the one conceptual arena of psychoanalysis,
of the premises, the phenomena, and the logical structure of the
fundamentally differing humanistic and scientific modes of thought,
leading often to statements in our discourse that Home feels do not
"in a strict sense, mean anything" (p. 42)—and he gives examples
of such statements.

What is this fundamental logical distinction that Home would
have us focus upon?[1] It is basically the difference between the humanistic act of interpretation and the scientific act of explanation.

---

[1] This issue of the extent to which psychoanalysis is a scientific enterprise versus a humanistic enterprise is *not* the same question as the extent to which psychoanalysis as a science (if
we take the side of the argument, to be developed further in this presentation, that it *is*
science) is biologically rooted—though the questions are felt by some to be related. For a

For a science basically asks "how" questions and receives answers in terms of mechanisms and causes; but a humanistic study asks "why" questions and receives answers in terms of reasons, that is, motives. And it is this last which Home avers is the only proper business of psychoanalysis—to discern individual meanings. This it does through specific acts of "cognitive understanding" or "cognitive identification." "In this mode of cognition [through identification], which is that used by the analyst in analysis, the observation of facts [i.e., the phenomena, the verbal and nonverbal behaviors of the consulting room] subserves the purpose of establishing an identification from which an interpretation can be made. The interpretation is a new kind of fact whose factuality depends on the accuracy with which the evidence has been interpreted and on the completeness of the evidence. Unlike a scientific fact, it cannot be demonstrated . . ." (p. 44).

A corollary to all this is the assertion that the mind, though a noun, is clearly not a thing, and every nounlike, thinglike attribute with which we endow it is nothing else than the play of metaphor. Caught up in this wholesale metaphoric bag, then, is of course not only our instinct theory, but also our whole theory of the mind in terms of the model id, ego, and superego, our conceptualized explanatory world of mental structures and functions and mechanisms and processes: the level, that is, of defense mechanism, of repression, and of the return of the repressed. In short, we have here all of metapsychological theory, and much, if not most, if not all, of the level of clinical theory as well (as set forth in the layerings described by Rapaport [1960] and Waelder [1962]). All this must be abjured in order to purify psychoanalysis and rid it of its currently built-in, irreconcilable contradiction that "on the one hand in clinical practice, and especially through the technique of free association, it assumes a spontaneous subject; on the other it reifies the concept of mind and elaborates a scientific type theory in terms of causes" (Home, 1966, p. 47). Indeed, this basic contradiction leads to a compounding of the confusion because the metapsychological words like *instinct* and *energy* and *tension* inevitably get used in relation to clinical experience and acquire a second clinically defined

comprehensive perspective on the natural-science bent and biological framework within which such a seminal thinker as Hartmann viewed and placed psychoanalysis, see Schafer's (1970) article "An Overview of Heinz Hartmann's Contributions to Psychoanalysis."

meaning that overlaps the first. Parenthetically, whether we are willing or unwilling to support Home's argument, we are all unhappily reminded of the many confusions between the clinical and metapsychological levels of theorizing that do beset our literature in just the ways that Home suggests.

What is the total thrust of this exposition of Home's position? That "psycho-analysis, growing up amidst the triumphant application of scientific method, understandably adopted the method for itself without considering whether it was logically appropriate. It has landed itself [thereby] in a morass of reified concepts; for scientific method demands the kind of facts which it can use" (p. 49). Let us not misunderstand Home to mean thereby that if psychoanalysis is not science, it is therefore any the less, for, as a final quotation from this provocative paper, "My aim has been to make the point that science is not just an improved version of humanistic thinking; it is a different kind of thinking with a limited field of reference, with different basic axioms and a different logical form" (p. 45).

I have quoted at such length from Home's paper, not just to explore the implications of the argument over the nature of psychoanalysis as science pushed to the extreme (I should say to the antiextreme, or rather opposite extreme), but also to state this argumental *direction* as the congenial, conceptual haven for a growing movement among psychoanalytic thinkers. It is a movement away from the decades of development of modern-day ego psychology in its aspiration toward a general psychology, and toward a comprehensive and comprehensible description and explanation of the function and structure of the human mind in health and in disease, a development that reached its apogee in the works of Hartmann and his collaborators and of Rapaport. For example, and far less extremist in its position, is the growing disenchantment among some of our most influential theoreticians, and among some of those who have been most directly influenced by Hartmann and Rapaport, with the often overgrown and overelaborated, clinically remote and experience-distant structure of our metapsychology. Differing from that of Home, this is an argument usually advanced not against psychoanalysis as science, but ostensibly on its behalf as a science, that is, making the effort to divest itself of *aspects* of, or even of all of its metapsychology, which is declared to be more a metaphysics than a (scientific) psychology.

In this regard, most has been written and argued over energy theory and the economic point of view, which Lustman (1969), who has been one of its staunchest defenders, says "has certainly been the single most attacked formulation in the literature" (p. 95).[2] I do not want to digress here into a discussion of these various viewpoints on energy theory and the closely related instinct theory

---

[2] The arguments pro and con are familiar and do not require repetition in this context. On the one side is the call by Rosenblatt and Thickstun (1970), who speak for a host of others (Kubie, Rubinstein, Holt, Gardner, Klein, etc.) in calling for the abandonment of psychic-energy theory as being hopelessly incongruent with any of the conceptualizations or usages of energy concepts in the realms of natural science, and as being additionally hopelessly unable, in terms of the tension-reduction model, really to deal with the phenomena it must be designed to explain, for example, the existence of pleasurable tensions. These authors call for the replacement of energy-theoretical models by information-processing models built in accord with previously learned affective expectations which then act as inducers, facilitators, or inhibitors of subsequent behaviors. They try to show how this alternate (putatively more scientific) theory is better theory, and better science, because it is more *translatable* into terms congruent with modern neurophysiological thinking (though not necessarily so translated yet); and how also the other metapsychological points of view, such as the structural, the dynamic, can survive intact enough when the energy-dependent aspects and interactions are dropped out. The argument they advance as to how the *dynamic* point of view, dependent as it is on the interplay of psychic forces, can be altered and still survive enough to maintain its essential structure and usefulness within the overall theory of the mental apparatus after energy theory is dropped out, is not, however, an altogether convincing one.

The opposite argument, equally familiar, is that made, for example, by Lustman (Panel 1969): that Freud was less influenced (or at least less misled) by the prevailing physicalistic theories of science of his day than is nowadays assumed in many quarters, and was rather more occupied with building the theory required to cope with the clinical problems that derived directly from his empirical observations. In this framework, the body of concepts called the economic point of view (psychic energy, cathexis theory, the pleasure–pain principle, etc.) was developed because of certain characteristics which Freud noted (and which still hold good) in symptoms, dreams, parapraxes, jokes, and in the course of psychoanalytic therapy. That is, Freud developed the concepts—and Lustman believes them to be still signally useful—to deal with (instinctual) phenomena characterized by increase, diminution, displacement, and discharge. More recently, Kohut (1971, 1972), that chief articulator of introspection and empathy as our central clinical tools, has at the same time compellingly articulated metapsychological theory in toto, including instinct and libido theory, as central to his theoretical explanatory system for the understanding and the treatment of narcissistic personality disorder. In his paper on narcissistic rage (1972), he defends this effort as follows: "As my final task I shall now attempt to explain narcissistic rage in metapsychological terms—even though I know that metapsychology has fallen into disrepute and is considered by some to be hardly more than a sterile thought exercise" (pp. 394–395). And he goes on to deploy such concepts as exhibitionistic libido, flow and discharge, psychoeconomic unbalance, and ego-regulatory capacities.

And to round out this array of arguments pro and con, I want only to call attention to Applegarth's (1971) scholarly review of the issues and her mediate position abandoning the complex psychoanalytic conceptualizations of different types of instinctual energies in favor of a conception of sexual and aggressive drives that differ not in their kinds of energies but in their pattern of mediating structures. She says: "The most extreme criticism of the energy theory takes the form of suggesting that all energic explanations be abandoned. It would seem to be difficult, however, to account for variations in intensities and for the very existence of conflict if we did not assume forces to be at work in the mental apparatus. . . . It is when we come to the idea of different qualities in energy, i.e., neutralization, fusion, binding, separate sexual and aggressive energies, that we are plunged into difficulties . . . these apparently qualitative differences in the energy can all be explained by differences in the controlling structures, so that the energy behaves differently, not because it is changed in itself but because it is differently directed" (p. 441).

which, as I have indicated, are both defended and attacked within psychoanalysis under the banner of differing views of what constitutes the essence of our science and of the theory appropriate to it. Rather, I want to call attention to a recent article by Schafer (1972) entitled "Internalization: Process or Fantasy?" which carries the assault on metapsychology, and by extension on the totality of the theory of the structure of the mind and its functioning, to a point that I feel approximates Home's assertion of psychoanalysis as fundamentally (and perhaps only) an individual and artistic enterprise. In this most thoroughgoing and radical critique of all metapsychological or structural or spatial constructions in our theorizing, Schafer begins with the concept of internalization as representing some kind of "insidedness"; and by asking "Inside of What?" through successive approximations, he logically dissects the concept to where the meaning is declared to be only fantasy and metaphor, and therefore misleading if it is proposed or used as part of science. In this progression, not only do such constructs as psychic energy and drive theory, force and instinct, disappear, but literally so does all of metapsychological (i.e., general psychological) conceptualizing via such terms as *structure, space, locus, superficial and deep, psychoanalysis as a depth psychology, levels and layers, underlying factors and causes, hierarchic organizations* (as of impulse and defense), *mental process or mechanism, regulatory structures, functions and relationships*. All this is eschewed as metaphor that states a fantasy (i.e., internalization is a "bloodless statement of an incorporation fantasy"; p. 412), but when posing as science it carries all the dangers of pseudoexplanation, of reification, of concreteness of thought, of making nouns out of adjectives and adverbs, and mistaking fantasies for things (processes). What we have left, according to Schafer, are but classes of mental events, and if we translate past what he calls the "simple (though not naïve) descriptions" (p. 435) into, for example, the language of internalization and of introject, "have we understood or conveyed anything more? If anything we are working with less" (p. 435).

Here, Schafer presses the argument perhaps even further than Home, for the latter at least has declared the essential act of psychoanalysis to be the act of interpretation, which he has called an ascription of meaning in terms of motivation. Schafer questions even the use of motivation words in the psychoanalytic process as also carrying the dangers of pseudoscience. Of this, he says:

Further considerations . . . would require formulating fundamental doubts concerning the logical necessity and legitimacy of using *motivation words* to explain behavior. This is so because the term "motive," for example, refers to a mover of action that is prior to it in time and "interior" to it as an inner or behind-the-scenes entity that is personlike in its comprehension and activity [p. 431fn.].

In so stating it, has Schafer brought psychoanalysis close to losing its distinctive character, moving it almost to an identity with the existentialist psychology that, translated into an approach to psychotherapy, regards the goal of therapy as but the assessment of experience in its moment-to-moment quality and texture, rather than, as traditionally in psychoanalysis, seeing the mind's experience as the backdrop for wishes and intentions, conscious or unconscious, in short the world of avowed or hidden meanings as motivations?[3]

In elaborating this thinking among psychoanalytic theoreticians in both hemispheres, I am not making the point that their views are on all fours with one another. Home speaks for the view that psychoanalysis is but an individual humanistic enterprise, accounting for the individual as creator of his own destiny in accord with the established and honored rhythm of the humanities. The many American authors (of whom Schafer is but the most radical exemplar) who would perform various degrees of major surgery upon the corpus of our metapsychology, and who, I think, thereby give up our efforts and our claims to a general psychology of the operations of the human mind in health and in illness, do so not in the name of the humanities but out of their particular conception of the nature of psychoanalysis as a science. They follow Bertrand Russell's definition of psychology as the science of those occurrences which by their very nature can only be observed by one person. As this kind of science, then, it too has its own proper (scientific) questions and its own rules of evidence and inference that guide judgments about the adequacy and propriety of the answers.

Whatever the scope of difference between these two views, what they do have very much in common is the sharp delimitation of the

---

[3] Since writing this paper, I have had the opportunity of studying Schafer's series of articles (1973a,b, 1975), in which he seeks to develop the fabric of an *action language* that will encompass and adequately describe the clinical phenomena of psychoanalysis, and stand in place of the whole of *psychodynamic* language, which is declared to be an anachronistic hindrance to our status and development as both a discipline and a science. The argument made in this series of articles, however, is very comprehensively represented in Schafer's earlier work, from which I have drawn in my presentation.

proper domain of psychoanalysis as a human enterprise. They say in effect that psychoanalysis has essayed far too much. It has attempted to be both an explanation of the mind of man, how it works, as well as an interpretation of the history of an individual man, why he believes as he does. In this it has been far more ambitious in one sense than physics. For physics attempts only to explain the behavior of particles in the mass, the huge agglomerated mass. It looks at any single particle as but the random variation within the lawful regularity that very precisely describes the behavior of the totality of the particles that constitute the mass. Psychoanalysis has historically caught itself up in trying both to describe the mind of man as a creature of nature across the mass (to answer what Home calls the "how" questions) and to understand the mind of each individual man under its scrutiny in its historically motivated determination (the "why" questions).

That the two endeavors have proceeded pari passu, and in ways that conceptually are not always distinguished one from another, has been a source of great complexity and unending confusion for us. It has led to what George Klein (1973), looking at this same dilemma, has called "two traditions of psychoanalysis," again two different kinds of science. Of these he says:

> [T]he important differences between the two traditions of psychoanalysis is not the energy-discharge model of the one—the so-called "metapsychology"—which is absent in the other. The more profound point of distinction is that they derive from two different philosophies of inquiry and explanation. Each leads to different conceptions of what psychoanalysis is all about, of where efforts at discovery should be directed, how psychoanalytic knowledge should be systematically organized, on what problems and in what settings we should do research, what objectives of explanation should be served in doing research. The tragedy is that the two orientations have often been confounded, creating theoretical and empirical havoc [p. 10].

Klein's answer, and here he is at one with Home and with Schafer, is to declare the one area totally out of bounds for our science, as but an impossible burden and confusion to the other. It is this trend that is the crux of the present major conceptual confrontation within our literature about our status as a science. I trust that it is clear at this point that, though I have used the exposition of this trend as a questioning base and a taking-off point, it is with the intention to propose a different, and opposite, path toward the resolution of these dilemmas—one that to me poses the coming conceptual task and therefore the future arena of activity for psychoanalysis as a science.

This problem was grappled with, in just these terms, in a panel discussion at a meeting of the American Psychoanalytic Association on "Models of the Psychic Apparatus" (Panel, 1971). On that panel, Modell took his point of departure in the same distinction between the two aspects, the two traditions, of psychoanalytic endeavor. He called it the two "contexts." In the one context, Freud, trying in his successive theoretical formulations and model building to demonstrate general "laws" of psychic functioning, analogous to the established "laws" of the physical sciences, placed man as a part of nature and subject to the same regularities that influence all other natural phenomena. But Freud also established another context of man as molded by civilization and not merely as a product of nature. And the products of culture do not have the same high generalizability (universality) as do the phenomena of nature. Here we are in the world of man's created environment: the psychosocial process and the idiosyncratically unique perspective that psychoanalysis as the unfolding of the history of a life shares with history in the collective, the assignment of meaning by the placing of observation into its given individual historical context.

Modell affirmed psychoanalysis to be that unique science that lives in *both* orientations—that of natural science and that of individual history—and simultaneously studies phenomena within both contexts. On that same panel, Brenner underscored that the historical approach is also, or can be, a scientific endeavor, subject to its own proper rules of evidence and of inference, despite the fact that historians of the past were often simply storytellers or perhaps patriotic deceivers, basically not yet trained in any scientific methods. What Modell and Brenner do here, of course, is to maintain the tension of keeping psychoanalysis in both its contexts, both its universes of discourse (unlike Home and Schafer and the many others who, in the service of conceptual clarification or perhaps of heuristic simplification, force it, or at least declare it, to be tenant in only one). But they do so, and here I believe their step is insufficient, without pointing to the kinds of canons of correspondence or of relationship that would make the double tenancy into a coherent theoretical (scientific) enterprise.

Such an effort toward seeking relationships within an overarching conceptual framework has been begun by Sandler and Joffe (1969) in their statement "Towards a Basic Psychoanalytic Model," in which they make a basic distinction between the experiential and the nonexperiential realms of the mind. The experiential comprises what we call the contents of the mind: "The realm of subjective experience refers to the experience of the phenomenal content of wishes, impulses, memories, fantasies, sensations, percepts, feelings and the like . . . experiential content of any sort, including feelings, *can be either conscious or unconscious*" (p. 82). This is the realm of the phenomena of mind that Schafer and Home declare to be the whole of the proper business of psychoanalysis, the realm of the "why" questions, where answers come in terms of meaning, or, in the language of George Klein (1973), of "intentionality" or "directional tendency." As stated, it is a world of both conscious and unconscious *experiences,* and the established work of psychoanalysis is to bring more fully into the ken of the individual whatever experiences he has, for whatever defensive or adaptive reasons, disavowed. I would only add at this point what I will state more fully further along: that it is a world that has its own proper rules of evidence and inference and is therefore part of our domain as science.

In sharp contrast to this experiential realm is what Sandler and Joffe call the nonexperiential realm:

> This is the realm of forces and energies, of mechanisms and apparatuses, of organized structures, both biological and psychological, of sense organs and means of discharge. The non-experiential realm is intrinsically unknowable, except insofar as it can become known through the creation or occurrence of a phenomenal event in the realm of subjective experience. From this point of view *the whole of the mental apparatus* is in the non-experiential realm, capable of becoming known to us (only to a limited extent) via subjective experiences of one sort or another [p. 82].

This is the realm, then, not of the *phenomena* of the mind, but of the explanatory constructions that order and establish sequences of regularity and interdependency among those kinds of phenomena. Such constructions represent the efforts of Freud and the ego psychologists who came after him to develop a comprehensive scientific theory of the mind, or, as it is usually called, a structure of the psychic apparatus. How can we, then, establish the relevance and the usefulness of this body of conceptualization in the face of those who declare it to be a mass of both unnecessary and confounding doctrine that forces psychoanalysis to ask the wrong kinds of questions. "How" questions seek answers in terms of "causes" and lead to the elaboration of a theoretical explanatory superstructure (as in the metapsychological points of view) that seems to involve theoretical models—for example, energy models—which few find wholly satisfactory and many find to be confusing metaphysics rather than science at all?

Sandler and Joffe build their pressuposition of the interrelatedness of the two realms into the very language of the distinction between the experiential and the nonexperiential realms of the mind. They put this relationship thus:

> There is an intimate relation between the experiential and the non-experiential realms. . . . Apart from the maturational influences, the mental apparatus develops only through conscious or unconscious awareness of changes in experiential content and related attempts to control that content. Thus the elements in the nonexperiential realm are employed, mobilized and changed—all outside the realm of experience—although changes in the non-experiential realm are mediated by experience and their employment or modification provides, in turn, new experiential data [p. 82].

As an example, they use *fantasying* as an organized mental functioning that falls wholly within the nonexperiential realm, and they contrast this with *fantasies*, "The image and feelings which are the products of fantasying [which] fall within the realm of experience (conscious or unconscious)" (p. 83). This distinction (and relation) between fantasying (in the nonexperiential realm) and a fantasy (in the experiential) is incidentally very akin to that made by Seymour Kety, the biochemical researcher in psychiatry, in his oft-quoted statement that "there can someday be a biochemistry of memory but never of memories." It is from this same position that I want to specify more fully my own perspective on the present and future tasks of psychoanalysis as science. For my paradigm instance, I would like to take the issue of defensive functioning because of its comparative simplicity, its centrality to all psychoanalytic conceptualizing, and its solid anchoring in the relatively experience-near level of clinical theory that is an essential element of theorizing, even among those who are most radical in eschewing the metapsychological superstructure of the psychic apparatus as superfluous and pseudoscientific.

I will begin by following Gill, who in his monograph on topography and systems in psychoanalytic theory (1963), draws the distinction between defense mechanisms (clearly in the nonexperiential realm) and defenses (equally clearly—to me—in the experiential realm). For a defense mechanism is nothing but a construct that denotes a way of functioning of the mind. It is a construct invoked to explain how behaviors, affects, and ideas serve to inhibit, avert, delay, or otherwise modulate unwanted impulse discharge. Defenses, on the other hand, are the actual *behaviors, affects,* and *ideas* that serve defensive purposes. Their functioning as defenses is explained *in terms of* the operation of the defense mechanisms—and it is the clarification of what we mean here by *in terms of* that is the locus of inquiry into what I call the explicit establishment of the canons of correspondence or relationship between these two realms of discourse, the experiential and the nonexperiential. For example, an exaggerated sympathy can be a defense against an impulse to cruelty. The postulated operative mental mechanism by which this is explained is called reaction formation. Defenses can range from discrete attributes or aspects explicable by reference to the simple operation of a single defense mechanism (as in the example just cited) to complex behavioral and characterological constellations that are likewise specific, recurrent, and serve defensive purposes, like clowning, whistling in the dark, or sour-grapes attitudes. These more complex configurations are variously called *defensive operations, patterns,* or *maneuvers.* They are made up of various combinations and sequences of behaviors, affects, and ideas, the operations of which are explicable by reference to a variety of the classicaly described defense mechanisms, admixed with other ego activities.

Using this model of defensive functioning (i.e., this distinction between defense and defense mechanism), our psychoanalytic scientific task as I conceptualize it is, then, threefold. One aspect is the systematic *clinical* examination, within the psychoanalytic situation (and through study, with whatever degree of research formalization, of the data generated in that situation) of the phenomena that we know as *defenses.* This is the systematic exploration of the experiential realm, the world of mental contents or events. In this instance, it comprises the study of the behaviors, affects, and ideas that, whether simply or complexly, hierarchically serve as defenses, that are usually unconscious in their defensive working and defensive purpose, though they are capable of being rendered conscious by psychoanalytic work. It is the realm of the "why" question that seeks answers in terms of ascriptions of meanings unique to the unfolding of the history of a single individual. It is this realm that Home and other like-minded thinkers I have quoted consider to be the whole of the proper business of psychoanalysis. But, to me, this exploration of the experiential realm constitutes only part of the domain of psychoanalysis, and likewise only part of the *science* of psychoanalysis. Here I refer to the rules of clinical evidence and interpretive fit that mark the methodology of the classical method of clinical case study and also to the rules of the more systematized formal research organization of the clinical data yielded by the consulting room. When successfully accomplished, study in this realm yields a comprehensive mapping of the defensive behaviors of the individual under study, in all their configural meanings, over time, and in relation to the shifting press of circumstances from within and without.

The second, companion task is the concomitant study and elaboration of the constructed organizations that we know as *defense mechanisms*. This is the conceptual substrate that expresses the regularity and the expectability that we discern as the integrity and identity of a recognizable and identifiable defense organization (and overall character organization) in the individual, as well as the generalizability and universality across individuals that leads to the lawfulness of the world of nature as studied by science. This, then, is the systematic development of the nonexperiential realm partaking of commonalities of process, mechanism, and structure. It is not a realm of experience; it therefore cannot be conscious, since, to quote Gill (1963), "logically speaking, one can become conscious only of a content which is the *outcome* of the working of the mind, not of the working itself." It is the realm of "how" questions, of the alignment of causes, forces, that determine processes and mechanisms that apply to the understanding of the operation of the psychic apparatus, the minds of all men, individually and in the mass. It is the world that Home and the others have ruled out as an improper and misconceived universe of discourse and of exploration for psychoanalysis—but to me it is the essence of what gives psychoanalysis its claim to be a *general* psychology of the mind in its normal as well as its disordered functioning (and this is quite apart from the question of how much of our metapsychological structure as currently developed we wish to subscribe to, alter, or replace).

And then there is the third scientific task, already alluded to in this presentation: the study of the linkages and the regularities in the juxtaposition between the "how" questions and the "why" questions, between the explanatory constructions of the nonexperiential realm (the conceptualized operation of the defense mechanisms) and the observed and inferred phenomena of the experiential realm (the historically determined and evolved configuration of defensive behaviors unique to that individual). In the example chosen, that of defense mechanisms and defenses, the correspondences subsumed by the phrase *in terms of*—that is, the idiosyncratic patterning and deployment of defensive behaviors accounted for *in terms of* the operation of particular combinations and permutations of the generally available armamentarium of possible defense mechanisms in human character—seem generally self-evident, simple, and nonproblematic. This is so because the example is drawn from the most directly clinical (experience-near) level of mental functioning. As the examples relate to constructions and observations further from immediate experience, the task becomes correspondingly more difficult. But it is in the establishment of such canons of correspondence at all levels of construction and of inference, however remote from direct experiencing, that I see the scientifically necessary burden of making psychoanalysis truly a science which is both a general psychology, a study of the general and lawful functioning of the human mind in health and disease, and also an idiosyncratic genetic unfolding of the succession of meanings and reasons, overt and covert, that the individual at study lives by and imposes upon his being in the world.

Having said all this, I need to add several caveats. First, it must be understood that I agree wholeheartedly with the concern of Home, Schafer, Klein, and others, as to the mischief and havoc that can arise from the haphazard intermingling and confounding of the two realms of discourse, the confusions that can arise between "how" questions answered in terms of mechanism (how does reaction formation work and where does it draw its strength?) and "why" questions answered in terms of reasons (why is there such an exaggerated cloying sympathy in this individual and what is its history?). But I differ from the authors just mentioned in considering both questions to be separately necessary (why this behavior at this time, and how, or through what operations, is it brought about?); both are separately necessary to a full psychological, that is, psychoanalytic explanation, as Freud was the first to tell us. For proper explanation, the two realms must be kept conceptually separate, yet at the same time they must be seen in their interrelatedness—and this last, of course, is the task of specification that psychoanalysis as science has hardly begun to face and systematically undertake.

Closely related to this is the point that much of the frequent confounding of the two realms results from the fact that, to a large extent, they share an undifferentiated language whose context does not always make clear—perhaps the author himself is unclear—the realm of reference of the particular usage. A familiar example is the usage of the phrase *pleasure-unpleasure* to signify either hypothesized libidinal tension discharge and arousal states (clearly in the "how" realm), or, often in the same paragraph, experiences of shifting affects (clearly in the "why" realm). Such semantic confusion through shared languages renders the task of maintaining proper conceptual separation between the realms of the "how" and the "why" even more difficult.

The final related caveat has to do with the kind of science that the psychoanalytic endeavor creates for us. What I want to make clear, if I have not already done so, is that the general psychological theory, the metapsychology, if you will, that I am talking about is truly appropriate to the particular nature of our subjectivistic data and the introspective and empathic methods by which we derive those data—relying, then, in our explanatory network on such necessary psychological constructions as, for example, those of overdetermination and multiple function. Thus I am not talking about a science modeled on physics or any other of the natural sciences, or any derivations via physicalistic physiology, that of Helmholtz or otherwise. I trust I am as ready as others to modify even discard aspects of our general theory, for example, the tension-reduction energy model, whose place may derive more from roots in scientific analogy than from an appropriate explanatory fit to our particular data. I am referring, that is, to what has here been called throughout, "our" science or our peculiar science.[4]

---

[4] Central, of course, to this statement of position is the conceptualization I have of the nature or meaning of *metapsychology*. To me, metapsychology is *not*, as it is to some, equivalent to a biological or neurobiological explanatory framework imposed upon the data and the phenomena of psychology. The degree of neurologizing of psychology that may be placed within the corpus of metapsychology, for example, via aspects of energy theory, can be removed from it (Applegarth, 1971; Rosenblatt and Thickstun, 1970), without harm to the essence of metapsychology. Rather, to me metapsychology is a *kind of generalizing*, of constructing general psychological explanatory systems via a variety of vantage points, simultaneously and systematically, the various metapsychological points of view—out of the conviction that only through the simultaneous and systematic deployment of these various perspectives can behavior be fully comprehended in its overdetermination and its multiple functions.

Let me now pick up from the example I have been using of the relation between defenses or defensive behaviors and defense mechanisms. The task of properly guiding observation and inference in the experiential realm and explanatory construction in the nonexperiential realm, and of establishing appropriate and adequate rules of correspondence between them, clearly becomes progressively more difficult the more remote from immediate experience is the level of organization and of conceptualization being dealt with. For example, in the sense used here, the concepts of self and of identity as psychic organizations coherent in space and continuous over time, yet subject always to growth and change, are more complex and more remote from the direct, immediately comprehended data of experience than the concepts dealt with from the more directly clinically anchored level of repression and defense and return of the repressed. Concomitantly, the corresponding experiential organization that these concepts of self and of identity relate to, the self (and the object) representations and the positive and negative identity formations, is also more inferential and at a greater remove from their observational base in what is directly experienced and comprehended—and with this there is a greater spread of conceptual distance and explicating to be bridged between the explanatory constructs and the experiential representations they are invoked to give coherence to. The problem, then, of establishing the proper rules of correspondence, the placement of the correct (more complex) "hows" in juxtaposition to the correct (more inferential) "whys" and the minimization of slippage, confounding, and confusion in so doing increases almost geometrically in complexity.

To jump still further from the direct data of experience, when we talk not of self and identity and their corresponding experiential representations but of the level of ego organization (or id or superego organization), we are again at an even greater conceptual distance from the constructs that make up the ego as a system of regulatory devices, structures, thresholds, and discharge channels and the experience-based inferences that comprise the ego as a class of aims or directional configurations of behavior and experience (Klein, 1973, p. 12).

But to chart this arena systematically with a logical theory of the mind, *how* it works, appropriate to and coordinate with a logical ordering of the observed and inferred data of individual history and experience, *why* it does what it does—these are the coming tasks as I see them, and therefore the future of psychoanalysis as a science. To me, it is the complexity and the special peculiarity of psychoanalysis as a science that it pursues its inquiry simultaneously in each of the two realms, the general and the individual, the how and the why, and in so doing forges concurrently the logic of their interrelationships. This set of tasks is the same whatever the substantive areas on which the psychoanalytic investigative searchlight is focused, whether in the areas of applied psychoanalytic study (literature, art, history, group process, and collective behavior, etc.), correlative psychoanalytic study (psychosomatics, child development, etc.), or within the core of psychoanalytic endeavor—the psychoanalytic situation. It is for this reason that I have made no effort in this presentation on the status of psychoanalysis as science to survey the present state of scientific activity in each of these substantive arenas.

I want to add, moreover, that the proper resolution of these scientific tasks for psychoanalysis will rest, and here I circle back to the beginning point of this presentation, on the fullest development and the simultaneous pursuit of each of the avenues of continuing approach to new knowledge and new conceptualizing within and about analysis—on both the classical method of the clinical case study and the more formalized and systematized research study built upon the basic data of the psychoanalytic process. Here, as elsewhere in analysis, we have the issue of two attitudes, two scientific predilections and scientific stances, each of which, in the integrity of its own pursuit, will serve as a needed corrective to the potential deficiencies of the other. While in the one approach we see a possible excess of concern with scientific rigor and publicly replicable data at the potential expense of psychological perceptivity and clinical feel, in the other approach there is danger of a possible excess of concern with subtle perceptivity and insight via empathic identifications at the potential expense of exactitude and confirmability. But it is my hope that between the two, an appropriate admixture will be found—not necessarily in any single investigator or practitioner—an admixture that I trust, with the growth over this present generation of a more formalized and systematized research endeavor in its proper relation to the whole body of psychoanalytic activity, will be found within and across the field as a whole. With this development, we can predict a healthy and vigorous future for psychoanalysis as a science in the pursuit of the difficult scientific tasks that I have tried to visualize.

7.

Psychoanalysis as a Science: A Response to the New Challenges

Psychoanalysis, in its essence, can be viewed as the psychological exploration of the riddle of the human mind in its ordered and disordered functioning. Its paradigmatic myth, the fable of Oedipus, contains within it the famous riddle of the Sphinx unraveled by Oedipus as the metaphoric tale of our life span. Oedipus himself went on to struggle toward painful insights into the riddles of our deepest and often darkest human passions. My intent in this paper is to focus back on what I consider to be the riddle of the nature of psychoanalysis itself: its claim to be a science of psychological explanation of these riddles of our existence, a claim that has been under constant challenge since the very inception of our discipline. This is a topic that the reader may recognize as an abiding interest of mine over the whole span of my psychoanalytic career, and it is a topic that I consider of great importance, as well as of current renewed timeliness.

In a paper on psychoanalysis as science almost a decade ago (chapter 6), I began with the statement that few theoretical issues are more constantly and passionately argued—among both adherents from within and observers and critics, friendly and otherwise, from without—than the status of our discipline as a science. Its position has had to be widely defended against a powerful array of philosopher-of-science critics, such as Ernest Nagel and Sidney Hook, who argued, for example, in the now famous New York University Institute of Philosophy Symposium, held as far back as 1958 (Hook, 1959), that the whole of psychoanalytic theory did not satisfy the most basic requirements of true science. These critics adduced evidence, compelling to them, in support of this viewpoint. This line of attack has been most powerfully stated in the writings of Karl Popper (1963), who dismissively declared psychoanalysis to be only a pseudoscience or a mythology, since its theoretical structure seemed to him elastic enough to explain any human activity or consequence as a confirmation of its postulates; therefore, it did not allow for the possibility of falsification, that is, of true testing, of its theoretical tenets.

Equally passionate criticisms have been made of our scientific credentials from within our ranks. The central scientific dilemma from an *empirical* perspective was very cogently posed in the 1966 paper by Philip Seitz on "The Consensus Problem in Psychoanalytic Research," or differently put, what to do when the experts disagree. This issue is clearly crucial to any situation involving interpretations based on inferences about complex internal states; it does not operate importantly in the realm of simple reliability tasks performed upon sensory observational data. But though psychoanalysis is centrally dependent upon such interpretations, as Rapaport (1960) stated, "There is [as yet] no established canon [in psychoanalysis] for the interpretation of clinical observations" (p. 113). And Glover (1952), in his role as a polemicist on the shortcomings of psychoanalytic research, even earlier had declared that there is "no effective control of conclusions based on interpretation, [and this fact] is the Achilles heel of psycho-analytical research" (p. 405).

That skilled psychoanalytic clinicians can construct differing but often equally compelling formulations of psychoanalytic case material, and that no ready method has been worked out to establish the truth claims of alternative formulations, has indeed helped propel the growing popularity of the hermeneutic movement in psychoanalysis. And yet these problems of consensus and of the lack of canons for interpretation are not the main problems in our claim to scientific status. Once we accord scientific credibility to our discipline on theoretical grounds, these empirical research issues *can* be conceptually approached and dealt with, although we have had only varying degrees of practical success to date. Many of the conceptual approaches to these empirical research questions were spelled out in a long paper I wrote in 1971 with a research collaborator, Harold Sampson, "Issues in Research in the Psychoanalytic Process."

The more central concern within our ranks about our scientific status has been on other than empirical grounds. It is rather the widely ranging, vigorous, and increasingly polarized controversy over the essential nature of our theory and our discipline. This intense debate has been sparked by the growing dissatisfaction among psychoanalytic theoreticians over the past two decades with the entire metapsychological edifice that had been brought to its position of almost unquestioned hegemony, at least within American psychoanalysis, in the ego psychology associated with the names of Hartmann, Kris, Loewenstein, Rapaport, and a host of others. This once almost monolithic supremacy of the ego psychology paradigm of Freud's metapsychology has now given way to a whole array of divergent and revisionist theoretical positions, with contrapuntal, passionate defenses by its continuing adherents—what I have come to call the great metapsychology debate in our field.

The most succinct statement of the terms of this debate is in an opening paragraph of Holt's (1981) arrestingly titled article, "The Death and Transfiguration of Metapsychology." There Holt said:

> Beneath all this diversity may be discerned some strikingly different positions on basic methodological issues: Is psychoanalysis a science or one of the humanities, like history? If a science, is it or can it be a natural science or should it be a social–behavioral science, and what is the difference? Does it have one theory or two? If two, how do they differ, and what is the relation between them? [p. 130].

I cannot at this point spell out the detailed arguments around all of these questions, each of them, incidentally, a question with an implied negative bias about the status of psychoanalysis as a science. The names associated clinically with these questions are all well known by now—Home (1966), Rycroft (1966), and Klauber (1968) in England; Gill (1976), Klein (1976), and Schafer (1976) here in America. All in this group end with varying statements of adherence to the hermeneutic position.

In addition to all these empirically and theoretically based questions about our claims as a science, are the issues that arise from therapeutic considerations: we practice an applied clinical discipline with proud claims to being a healing profession, claims that are coextensive with our domain as a theory of mental functioning. The issue here is what the ongoing debate about our claims as science implies for psychoanalysis as a healing endeavor with necessarily a theory of therapy, of change, and of cure. Rapaport (1960) posed this question squarely with his assertion that however comprehensively explanatory psychoanalysis might be as a theory of personality development and functioning, and of psychopathology and its genesis, as a theory of therapy it was still a set of "rules of thumb" (p. 17) more than a theory at all. In fact, our own Psychotherapy Research Project at The Menninger Foundation was started in the early 1950s as an ambitious effort to take our theory of psychoanalytic therapy beyond that state epitomized by Rapaport. We sought to learn more not only about what changes take place in psychoanalysis and in analytic psychotherapy, but also about how these changes come about or are brought about, through the interaction of what factors in the patient, in the therapy, the therapist, and in the interacting (and changing) external life situation.

Here, then, is a capsulized presentation of the various realms of questions that frame the current debates about our status as a science and our possibilities for theory testing and theory extension on the basis of recognizably scientific endeavors. In what main directions are the current considerations of all these issues now going? McIntosh (1979) has summarized two opposite trends in what he calls the new revisionism in psychoanalysis. He says:

> At the cost of some oversimplification, one can discern two main opposing trends in this new wave of revision. First there is the view that psychoanalysis is a purely interpretive discipline, dealing wholly with the contents of subjective experience. Some of those advancing this view hold that the clinical theory (the psychology derived from and used in therapeutic practice) is sound and scientific, but reject much of Freud's instinct theory and often also the structural theory as invalid. . . . Others in this [same] camp hold that psychoanalysis is [nothing but] a humanistic and hermeneutic, not a scientific discipline [at all]. . . . The other main trend seeks to purge psychoanalysis of its putative metaphysical, anthropomorphic, and metaphorical elements, and to put it on a sound footing as a full fledged natural science . . . [pp. 405–406].

I would only add that what these opposite viewpoints have in common is a fundamental rejection of classical psychoanalysis as representing any kind of respectable or even possible *scientific* theory.

I will consider these various revisions by first discussing very briefly the far less influential and much more singular of these efforts, that in the so-called natural science direction, an effort that I feel to be almost brilliantly daring and yet fundamentally misplaced. This is the effort by Peterfreund (1971) and also by Rosenblatt and Thickstun (1977, 1984) to abandon what they declare to be the outmoded nineteenth-century mechanistic energy and structure model of psychoanalytic theory, condemned by them as merely pernicious metaphor. They would replace it with an information theory, systems, and cybernetics model of the mind as an information processing system functioning in a manner analogous to our high-speed computers, a model declared to be consonant with our rapidly expanding twentieth-century neurophysiological knowledge base. These authors have in common with some in the opposite, the hermeneutic, camp—Schafer (1976) for example—the intent to strip psychoanalysis of the putative theoretical mischief that they feel is created by its metaphors and reifications. I only want to point out here, in a painful oversimplification of my own perspectives on their major effort at total theoretical transformation of our science, that they have yet to establish the greater clinical, technical, or heuristic usefulness of their information processing model for our psychoanalytic work, or indeed that theirs is any less metaphoric a model of the mind than the energy–structural model that they abandon.

Let me now turn to a fuller consideration of what has become the major revisionist movement within psychoanalytic theory building and the major assault upon the claims of psychoanalysis to the natural science theory model: that is, all the varieties of hermeneutic, phenomenological, exclusively subjectivistic, or linguistically based conceptualizations of our field. This array of proposals comprises the most widespread and significant of what I have called in my title the "new challenges" to our accustomed willing conception of our discipline as properly a science. What all these perspectives, which I will embrace under the overall rubric, hermeneutic, have in common is an acceptance of the declared dichotomy in explanatory compass between a psychology based on reasons and one based on causes, put most concisely by Home (1966) as follows:

> In discovering that the symptom had meaning and basing his treatment on this hypothesis, Freud took the psycho-analytic study of neurosis *out of the world of science* into the world of the humanities, because a meaning is not the product of causes but the creation of

a subject. This is a major difference; for the logic and method of the humanities is radically different from that of science, though no less respectable and rational, and of course much longer established [p. 43, emphasis added].

This argument, drawing upon the *Verstehende Psychologie* of the German romantic school of philosophy spearheaded by Wilhelm Dilthey around the turn of the century, and with current sophisticated philosophy-of-science impetus in the works of Gadamer (1975), Habermas (1968), and Ricoeur (1970) in Europe, has seemed to carry an almost instant plausibility within much of current psychoanalytic theoretical thinking. Some, like Home (1966), Rycroft (1966), and Klauber (1968), have seemed persuaded that psychoanalysis should indeed not be considered a scientific discipline at all, but rather a humanistic one like history, or literary criticism, or the Biblical exegetical interpretation from which the term *hermeneutic* derived in the first place, all of these clearly governed by the logic of their own internal conventions, as Home put it in the passage I have quoted. Others, like Gill (1976) and Klein (1976) and I think also Schafer (1976), have rather preferred to see psychoanalysis as still a science. They see it, however, as a science very different from the so-called natural sciences, bound and governed as it is by its own set of evidential standards. Its criteria for proof, they feel, are intrinsically related to the totally subjectivistic nature of its data base and are therefore putatively different from the usual canons of natural science. This is what Harrison (1970) called the tendency to describe psychoanalysis, in quotation marks, as "our science," implicitly our "peculiar" science, or declaredly in some way our different *kind* of science. And still a third group, including myself for a period (chapter 6) but also others like Modell (Panel, 1971) and Sandler and Joffe (1969), have tried to grapple with the issue of how to reconcile the search for *meaning* and *reasons* through the individual exploration of a *unique* human life with the effort to fit the findings derived from that search into the explanatory construct of a *general* science of the mind as elaborated within a natural science *causal* framework.

The overall hermeneutic argument has taken a number of forms. It has tried (as in the writings of Ricoeur [1977] and of Steele [1979]) to *cope* with the question of how psychoanalytic propositions are validated and proved. Alternatively, it has sought to reject these very questions of evidence and proof as reflecting unacceptable distortions of the essential nature of the psychoanalytic endeavor (as in the work of Schafer [1981] and Spence [1982] and to some extent also Sherwood [1969]). Ricoeur (1977) tried to deal with this question of proof by first outlining his fourfold criteria for the "facts" of psychoanalysis as they operate in the "analytic experience" (p. 836). The question Ricoeur then posed is "how to specify the truth claim appropriate to these facts in the psychoanalytic domain" (p. 858). His (hermeneutic) answer is that the truth claim resides *"in the articulation of the entire network: theory, hermeneutics, therapeutics, and narration"* (p. 863). He acknowledged that since everything, "theory, method, treatment, and interpretation of a particular case" (p. 865), is to be verified at once, this does open the way to charges of circularity in the validating process, exposing the propositions to the risk of being ultimately irrefutable and therefore unverifiable. His response to all this was to piece together what he called "the confirmatory constellation" (p. 866), the criteria of coherence, of inner consistency, and of narrative intelligibility. According to Ricoeur, it is "these criteria of validation [that] constitute the proof apparatus in psychoanalysis. It may be granted," he added, "that this apparatus is extremely complex, very difficult to handle, and highly problematical" (p. 869).

All of this was encapsulated by Steele (1979) in a widely remarked article essaying to interpret the European hermeneutic position to the American psychoanalytic world. In essence, explanations in psychoanalysis are offered in terms of the framework of the "hermeneutic circle" (p. 391). In this conception, knowledge of the parts is required to understand the whole, but the parts in turn can only be understood as aspects of the whole which envelopes them with meaning. Nine key postulates are stated by Steele as constitutive of this hermeneutic circle, all being variants or implications of the constant circular or dialectical movement between the parts and the whole. What is sought is again the harmony of the parts with the whole in terms of coherence, consistency, and configuration. This, to Ricoeur, is constitutive of "proof" in psychoanalysis; Steele declares it to be the distinctive "hermeneutic method." "As the natural sciences are defined by their use of the scientific method so the cultural sciences are defined by their use of the hermeneutic method" (p. 389). Among these "cultural sciences," psychoanalysis is central, since man, after all, is the "hermeneutical animal" (p. 394).

This language of Ricoeur and of Steele is thus a language of evidence and of proof, albeit by hermeneutic–interpretive canons declared to differ radically from the usual canons of natural science. Others within the hermeneutic camp have tried to eschew the language of proof and truth altogether as itself a miscasting of the essential issues of the psychoanalytic dialogue. The distinction posed by them is of the quest for narrative fit rather than for so-called historical truth. In this view, psychoanalysis becomes the telling and retelling of stories of a particular life, until analyst and analysand finally come to a consensus on a better story or on their best possible story. This would be the one that more widely encompasses the previously repressed and disavowed, one that makes better sense of the puzzling motley of symptoms, behaviors, and dysfunctions with which the analysand had initially presented himself for treatment.

Sherwood (1969), in his book, tried to propose criteria of appropriateness, of adequacy, and of accuracy to evaluate these story lines that progressively emerge out of the psychoanalytic interplay. His third criterion, accuracy, constitutes, of course, a "truth claim," and in trying to set out its evidential base, he, too, like Ricoeur, was searching for a logical and "scientific" basis for preferring one narrative, one psychoanalytic explanation, over another. Spence (1982), in his book a dozen years later, took a more uncompromising stance. Spence squarely challenged the guiding assumption of psychoanalytic work that the words of the analytic text of the consulting room are in themselves sufficient clues that *can* lead to the unraveling of the psychoanalytic (i.e., historical) truth, in accord with Freud's archaeological or historical model of the mind. Spence's counterargument starts with the inevitable difficulties that even the most verbal and articulate among us have in putting thoughts and feelings and images into precise words. Combine this with the inevitable slippage between the intended meaning of the speaker and the supposedly shared or imputed meaning inferred by the listener. Bring all this together, and it is easy to come to the disconcerting conviction that it is through the happenstance of the choice of a particular linguistic construction, participated in by analyst and analysand, that we have fixed in a shareable language the form of the event or the memory we are explaining or seeking. Once we have decided on that particular construction, we come to see, and we in fact determine, the so-called historic past in a particular manner. Pushed to its logical extreme, the verbal construction, the narrative, that we create not only shapes our view of the past, but indeed it, a creation of the present, *becomes* the past.

The logic of all this can lead us—according to Spence—to a whole series of transformations of our usual analytic thought conventions: of reconstruction into new construction, of acts of discovery into acts of creation, of historical truth into (only) narrative fit, of pattern finding into pattern making, of veridical interpretation into creative interpretation, of all interpretation into a species of (more or less) inexact interpretation, of analysis as a science of recovery of the past into merely a dialogue of choice and creation in the present and future, and of psychoanalyst as historical scientist into psychoanalyst as only poet and aestheticist.

To summarize this exposition: The hermeneutic movement in psychoanalysis arose in response to our difficulties in establishing our credibility as a natural science in the face of the mounting positivist philosophical attack (Hook, 1959; Blight, 1981). Some leading theoreticians and clinicians came to conceptualize psychoanalysis as, anyway, only an uneasy amalgam of two separable, utterly different traditions, the projections of the two strands of Western intellectual history embodied in Freud (cf. Holt, 1972). There is the clinical psychological theory that seeks to interpret the reasons for human actions, the answers to "why" questions; and there is the general metapsychological theory that seeks to establish the causes of human behaviors, the answers to "how" questions (cf., especially, Klein, 1976). Klein's proposed "theorectomy" (1976) would sever and cast out the general theory as the outmoded mechanistic construction that the positivist critics have anyway already presumably successfully demolished. What is then preserved is the clinical theory, hermeneutic in method and logic, humanistic in its image of man.

This total movement, staking out a new ontological position for psychoanalysis, which Gill (1983) calls a "hermeneutic science" (p. 534), has clearly appealed to many. Others have seen it rather as a massive abdication of our scientific responsibility as a discipline; Blight (1981) labels it a misguided and an unnecessary "retreat to hermeneutics" (p. 150). What, then, are the counterarguments to the hermeneutic position? I will marshal them around the discussion of three sets of issues that the hermeneuticists claim distinguish psychoanalysis from natural science. There are: (1) issues of the *logic* of the theory; (2) issues of its *epistemological* base; and (3) issues of its *methods* of discovery and validation.

In regard to the logic of psychoanalysis as a theory, Habermas (1968), a leading hermeneutic proponent, has made two pivotal and differentiating contentions. The first is that as opposed to the causality of nature, operative in all natural science, psychoanalysis operates via the "causality of fate" (pp. 256, 271), a phrase taken from Hegel. What this purports to mean is that the neurotic's undoing of his pathogenic repressions in the analytic process actually *dissolves* the very causal connection that had previously linked the underlying pathogenic conflict to the neurotic illness structure. Of course, no counterpart to this alleged *overcoming* of a causal connection "as such" can exist in the domain of nature as explained by the laws of natural science. Grünbaum (1983b, 1984), in his current incisive critique, point out how Habermas slides easily from the conception of therapeutic effect through uncovering the pathogenic cause to the conception of the dissolution of the causal linkage between underlying pathogenic conflict and the erupted neurosis. As Grünbaum (1984) says: "Overcoming an effect by undercutting its cause is hardly tantamount to dissolving the causal connection that links them" (pp. 11–12). To the contrary, "the patient achieves his therapeutic gain precisely by *making use* of a causal connection rather than, as Habermas would have it, by 'overcoming' such a connection!" (p. 12).

Habermas's (1968) second contention, equally sweeping and equally wanting, is that causal accounts in psychoanalysis are always embedded in, and determined by, the uniqueness of history and of context, whereas causal accounts in natural science are always generic, free of relationship to either history or context (p. 273). Again, Grünbaum demonstrates convincingly that this is but a pseudocontrast. He uses an example from electrodynamic theory to point out that the electric and magnetic fields produced by an electrical charge moving with arbitrary acceleration depends on the particular (entire, infinite) past kinematic history of the charge. He also gives more homely examples of history and context-dependency in physical laws in the phenomenon that is called "hysteresis" (1984, pp. 18–19). The response of magnetizable metals to a magnetic field depends on the prior magnetization history of the given sample. Or in elastic hysteresis, the response of a rubber band to stretching depends on its past history of having been stretched. Consideration of both of these issues involving the logic of the construction of psychoanalysis as science—that of the "causality of fate" and that of dependence on context—shows that psychoanalysis, despite the hermeneutic claim, is clearly not distinguishable in theory from other sciences.

What, then, of the epistemological argument? Spence's (1982) whole book is a substantial effort to build the argument that the analysand has a peculiarly "privileged competence" in relation to the understanding of his internal mental states based on his exclusive knowledge of his own historical development, a privileged competence that his analyst can come to share over time out of their joint immersion in the analytic work. This is in contrast to the merely "normative competence" of the trained psychoanalyst who brings only his theory-grounded understanding to the report of the analytic interaction if he is not party to the entire prior history and current context. The two are obviously widely different. Again, Habermas has advanced this argument to the claim that therefore only the patient has the required privileged access to the ultimate validation or refutation of psychoanalytic hypotheses. This would make the patient, in Grünbaum's phrase (1984, p. 21), "the ultimate epistemic arbiter" of psychoanalytic postulates. If this were indeed so, it would constitute a radically different epistemological base than that of other sciences which rest on observations made by trained *observers* using methods relevant to the data of observation in ways that test them against the predictions of the theory.

Again, however, Grünbaum adduces many persuasive arguments counter to this claim of epistemological separateness; that we can and do interpret against the patient's judgments and in the face of his denials; that his acknowledgment is only one of the criteria that we use in assessing the heuristic or the veridical status of our interventions; that his agreement can indeed be a compliance contaminated by suggestion; and that no human memory, let alone the neurotically conflicted patient's, is infallibly reliable. Grünbaum (1984) ends by declaring the patient's so-called cognitive monopoly not only "cognitively myopic . . . but also demonstrably untenable" (p. 38). And indeed it is. Sampson (1985, personal communication) pushes the counterargument even further. He, too, finds Spence's position contradicted, in important respects, by observation. Sampson acknowledges that someone inside a situation has a "privileged competence" that, at least in some circumstances, allows an understanding denied to outsiders. He nonetheless points to our common observation—on which our whole educational and supervisory apparatus rests—that the outside consultant colleague is often able to understand events within the treatment situation, which those inside have found incomprehensible, precisely *because* of his distinctive

vantage point *outside* of the analysis. Here we are involved with all
the familiar issues of countertransference distortion and blind spots.

If the epistemological argument does not decisively demarcate
psychoanalysis from the body of natural science, what then of the
recurring statement of the so-called different "hermeneutic *method*"
(Steele) which to Home is a method "radically different from that
of science" (1966, p. 43)? Holt (1972), in a paper assessing the
antithetical images of man, the mechanistic and the humanistic,
that contrapuntally pervaded Freud's own philosophical and ontological perspectives over his lifetime of theorizing, has tackled this
issue most comprehensively. He calls the possibility of making a
science out of subjective human feelings and meanings one of the
major issues still argued in the methodology of the behavioral sciences. He accepts that

> [I]f behaviorism were the only possible scientific psychology, then we
> should have to agree with Home, Schafer, and Klauber that psycho-
> analysis cannot be a science but must be one of the humanities, like
> history. Science, however, is not procrustean. Home to the contrary
> notwithstanding, it is not defined by its subject matter but by its
> method; therefore, it is in no way enjoined from dealing with mean-
> ings, qualities, or unique individuals. To be sure, methods do differ
> somewhat from one science to another, depending on the nature of
> the subject matter; but, since the death of vitalism, there have been
> no biologists of any scientific stature who claim that studying living
> instead of non-living objects requires a method . . . fundamentally dif-
> ferent from that of the inorganic sciences [pp. 18–19].

And he adds further on:

> As to the claim that it requires a different logic to deal with motives
> as compared with physical causes, it remains just that—an empty
> claim, not backed up by any detailed demonstration of what is lacking
> in the logic of the scientific method, or what the new and different
> logic might be [p. 19].

At this point, Holt refers back to two earlier expositions of his
(1961, 1962), which portrayed in detail how the *methods* used in such
humanistic disciplines as literary criticism and history are indeed
substantially identical with those of proper science. The time-honored idiographic–nomothetic methodological dichotomy simply

does not hold; with all the developments of the *Verstehende Psychologie* propelled by Dilthey and his followers, "no idiographically personalistic research methods [as such] were developed" (1962, p. 14), nor does the so-called hermeneutic criterion of internal consistency really differ from predictive validity as a truth-criterion in the hard sciences. In fact, Holt emphasizes "the test of predictive validity is nothing more than establishing the degree of internal consistency within the combined body of (1) the data (and theory) on which the prediction was based, and (2) the newly obtained data" (1961, p. 52).

Eagle (1973, 1980, 1984) has also dealt with this issue of the—failed—search for distinctive idiographic or hermeneutic methods in science. What does not get resolved in the hermeneutic exposition is the "problem of intersubjective reliability—that is, the question of what happens when my notion of a good gestalt and when my empathic, intuitive understanding are radically different from yours" (1980, p. 340). For at this point, empathy is not enough and the criterion of "goodness of fit" (Schmidl, 1955)—empathically understood—on which the hermeneutic framework for understanding ultimately rests, has become, in the words of Ramzy and Shevrin (1976), "a shoe, unlike the glass slipper, that can fit any foot" (p. 157).

None of this means that the hermeneutic movement in psychoanalysis has run its course or that what Blight (1981) has labeled "the retreat to hermeneutics" is over, though some of its staunchest advocates have indeed retreated from its extremes. Actually, the philosophical coup de grâce to the designation of psychoanalysis as a special "hermeneutic science" was delineated by Blight through drawing paradoxically on the arguments of Karl Popper and what he calls Popper's "evolutionary epistemology" to describe the effective destruction by Popper, on epistemological grounds, of the conception that there is a great and unbridgeable divide between the methods of natural science and those of historical or so-called hermeneutic science. Popper's argument is simply that inductive justification is logically impossible since some theory or conception must precede observation and give meaning to observation, and that therefore "objective knowledge is also conjectural knowledge . . . [and] all theoretical or generalizing sciences make use of the *same* method, whether they are natural sciences or social sciences . . . the 'method of hypothesis,' the active attempt to grasp a situation and to solve a problem by advancing a hypothesis and trying to test it" (p. 189). In the end, both natural science and history use the *same* method to solve different kinds of problems—a "unity of method and diversity of interest" (p. 192).

At this point, of course, the constantly posited dichotomy between reasons and causes (Home, 1966; Rycroft, 1966; Klauber, 1968; Gill, 1976; Klein, 1976; and Schafer, 1976) has simply collapsed (Rubinstein, 1973, 1975, 1976; Eagle, 1980, 1984; Holt, 1981; Hopkins, 1982; Holzman, 1985). A single quotation from the literature should make this point well enough. Holt (1981) pointed out that there are causes that are reasons and there are other kinds of causes as well, and this should occasion no confusion at all. He put it thus:

> For years, I have operated on the assumption that a reason is one kind of cause, a *psychological* cause, and that various types of causes can be handled in the same study without confusion. Anyone who does clinical work . . . knows that just because one is a psychoanalyst . . . one is not restricted to a person's reasons for his behaviors, whether stated or empathically sensed or rigorously inferred. . . . Whenever you are confronted by a new patient and have to make realistic predictions of her prognosis or his analysability, you probably consider the person's motives for seeking treatment, fantasies about what psychoanalysis is, intellectual limitations, financial situation, place in a family configuration, and state of physical health, and treat this mixture of reasons and causes together in an informal predictive system with no difficulty in principle [p. 135].

This is the argument that Holzman (1985) has summarized as follows: "Reasons can be causes when such reasons make a difference to the occurrence of the event for which it is the reason" (p. 753). With all these putative distinctions between reasons and causes thus reduced to nothing more than different domains of inquiry approached by the selfsame (scientific) methods, with, at most, differences of degree and emphasis, the entire hermeneutic enterprise set forth as a different set of logical and epistemological assumptions, and expressed via a different set of (hermeneutic) methods for a supposedly different *kind* of science ("our science," our hermeneutic science), has collapsed into itself, no longer a real alternative to an empirical approach to psychoanalysis. This major effort at a revisionist reconstruction of the nature of psychoanalysis has in the end failed to alter the requirements upon psychoanalysis as a science, and in that sense—to revert back to the title of this paper—has failed as a challenge and as an alternative to the claimed status of psychoanalysis as science.

None of which means, however, that psychoanalysis has now a sufficiently secure position as science. Not only do the self-same empirical and clinical questions that I set forth at the beginning of this paper still exist as major and still unsatisfactorily resolved issues for psychoanalysis as science, but another, newer, and seemingly even more powerful challenge to the scientific credibility of our discipline has arisen from the opposite side. This, the other major challenge, to which I will devote the remainder of this paper, is expressed in the comprehensive philosophical examination of Freud's works and his theories by the philosopher of science, Adolf Grünbaum. Elaborated first in a sequence of closely argued, incrementally building papers (1979a,b, 1980a,b, 1982, 1983a,b,c) and then brought together as a full exegetical criticism in his book, *The Foundations of Psychoanalysis* (1984), Grünbaum's complexly developed argument simultaneously defends psychoanalysis as science against an array of its critics—both the hermeneuticists and Popper's falsifiability standard—while in turn essaying to fundamentally fault psychoanalysis on the internal logic of its own epistemological rationale, which he finds totally untenable. I undertake now to review this critique and to try to respond to it.

First, what is the essence of Grünbaum's position? The first third of Grünbaum's book is designated as introduction. It is a detailed critique of the hermeneutic conception of psychoanalytic theory and therapy, mostly directed at Habermas and Ricoeur, with a lesser focus on George Klein and Schafer. I have already detailed Grünbaum's arguments against the Habermas conceptions of the logic of the theory of psychoanalysis; I will not repeat them here. His critique of the others are equally incisive. To Grünbaum, the hermeneuticists have simply created an "antiscientific" vision of psychoanalysis on the basis of what he sharply castigates as a "Stone Age" (1983b, p. 11) conception of the nature of science as a human endeavor.

Grünbaum's next target is Popper's opposed claim that psychoanalysis should be a science but is not science enough; that in fact it is not science at all, despite its pretensions to that status, but is rather a "metaphysic" that fails utterly to meet the test of falsifiability that Popper sets as the demarcation line between proper science and nonscience. Grünbaum also counters this argument head-on.

In effect, he states that psychoanalysis clearly does fulfill the falsifiability criterion, and on that basis cannot be put down as a pseudoscience. Grünbaum adduces several well-known instances from Freud's own writings in which Freud clearly—on the basis of contrary accumulating evidence—did significantly change his theoretical conceptions. The best known is, of course, Freud's major shift from his original traumatic theory of the neuroses to his subsequent inner psychology of the vicissitudes of drive and defense, with attendant conflict and anxiety, as the source either of healthy character formation or of the deformations of mental disorders. Freud's shift in theory was predicated on his accumulating embarrassing and painful discoveries that the ubiquitous sexual seductions were so often fantasy elaborations, not facts of history. Grünbaum gives additional supporting examples from Freud's work, some indicated even through a casual perusal of the mere titles of the papers in the *Standard Edition*. One is "A Case of Paranoia Running Counter to the Psycho-Analytic Theory of the Disease" (1915); another is the lecture, "Revision of the Theory of Dreams" (1933, esp. pp. 28–30). Grünbaum (1984, p. 110) refers as well to Glymour's (1974) demonstration from Freud's Rat Man case of how Freud's specific etiological hypothesis on the Rat Man's obsession was falsified through disconfirming the retrospective prediction that Freud had based on it. Grünbaum (1979a) summarizes this overall response to Popper as follows: "Upon looking at the actual development of Freud's thought, one finds that, as a rule, his repeated *modifications* of his theories were clearly motivated by evidence and hardly idiosyncratic or capricious. Why, I ask, were Popper and his followers *not* given pause by their obligation to carry out some actual exegesis of Freud?" (p. 135).

Having thus, I think very persuasively, countered the attacks on psychoanalysis as science from the two opposed sides, from the hermeneuticists' efforts to draw psychoanalysis away from science via whatever variant of hermeneutic or humanistic stance they individually propose, and from the Popperian efforts to drive psychoanalysis away from science through trying to demonstrate the falsity of its scientific credentials, Grünbaum then seeks to mount his own, and different, assault upon the logical foundations of psychoanalytic theory: it fails to establish a probative (i.e., a scientifically verifiable) basis for itself; it fails to do more than to establish its remarkable heuristic value. This is the agenda that Grünbaum has so vigorously pursued in his succession of papers (1979b, 1980b, 1983a,b,c) culminating in his book (1984), an effort which has been to varying degrees acclaimed by several psychoanalytic theoreticians (Holzman, 1985; Eagle, 1984; Holt, 1984).

What, then, is Grünbaum's argument? It is simply that the entire claim of psychoanalysis as a method of clinical investigation that can yield verifiable data about mental functioning rests on one "cardinal epistemological defense" (1984, p. 127) that Grünbaum feels went entirely unnoticed until he called attention to it (1979b, 1980b). He dubbed this pivotal defense "The Tally Argument," from Freud's original statement of it in 1917. This is a passage from the *Introductory Lectures* (1916–1917) where Freud was trying to deal with the recurring charge—and the major epistemological pitfall—that psychoanalysis is "nothing more than a particularly well-disguised and particularly effective form of suggestive treatment" (p. 452). Freud stated of this, "Anyone who has himself carried out psycho-analyses will have been able to convince himself on countless occasions that it is impossible to make suggestions to a patient in that way" (p. 452). For, and this is the critical statement, "his conflicts will only be successfully solved and his resistances overcome if the anticipatory ideas he is given *tally* with what is real in him. Whatever in the doctor's conjectures is inaccurate drops out in the course of the analysis; it has to be withdrawn and replaced by something more correct" (p. 452; emphasis added). Freud then went on to state that the "fundamental distinction between analytic and purely suggestive therapy, and which frees the results of analysis from the suspicion of being successes due to suggestion" (p. 453) is the thoroughgoing resolution of the transference and with it of all transference-based suggestive changes. At the end when transference is cleared away, "if success is then obtained or continues, it rests, not on suggestion, but on the achievement . . . of an overcoming of internal resistances, on the internal change that has been brought about in the patient" (p. 453).

This tally argument of Freud's rests in turn on the conjunction of two causally necessary conditions: (1) that only psychoanalytic treatment yields veridically correct insights into the unconscious conflicts that determine the neurosis; and (2) that these correct insights are in turn causally necessary for the therapeutic conquest of the neurosis. Grünbaum (1984) then describes what he regards as Freud's central epistemological claim—that the entire edifice of psychoanalysis rests probatively on this tally argument. He writes:

It is of capital importance to appreciate that Freud is at pains to employ the Tally Argument in order to justify the following epistemological claim: actual *durable* therapeutic success guarantees *not only* that the pertinent analytic interpretations *ring* true . . . to the analysand *but also* that they *are* indeed veridical. . . . Freud then relies on this bold . . . contention to conclude nothing less than the following: collectively, the successful outcomes of analyses do constitute *cogent* evidence for all that general psychoanalytic theory tells us about the influences of the unconscious dynamics of the mind on our lives. In short, psychoanalytic treatment successes as a whole vouch for the truth of the Freudian theory of personality, including its specific etiologies of the psychoneuroses. . . .

As a further corollary, the psychoanalytic probing of the unconscious is vindicated as a method of etiological investigation by its therapeutic achievements. Thus, this method has the extraordinary capacity to validate major causal claims by essentially retrospective inquiries, *without* the burdens of prospective longitudinal studies employing (experimental, [i.e., nontreated]) controls. Yet these causal inferences are not vitiated by *post hoc ergo propter hoc* or other known pitfalls of causal inference. Magnificent, if true [pp. 140–141].

But Grünbaum points out at length that early on it became clear to analysts and nonanalysts alike that a unique therapeutic effectiveness could not be claimed for psychoanalysis, at least not in terms of the ways that such outcomes can be reliably judged. And he cites Freud's "Analysis Terminable and Interminable" (1937) to show that Freud himself retreated from his claims for the unique quality and durability of psychoanalytic treatment outcomes to a point that Grünbaum calls "bordering on a repudiation of treatment success" (p. 160). Freud's more limited therapeutic claims as of 1937, as well as the separation of analytic claims of therapeutic effectiveness from convictions about the explanatory value of the theory, have indeed become the conventional wisdom of the field. Anna Freud (1976) put it succinctly in a way that reflects the shared consensus of us all—that we have given up (albeit not necessarily happily) the idea "that understanding a mental aberration implies automatically the possibility to cure it" (p. 258). In other words, we no longer necessarily link the standing of the theory to the outcome of the therapy.

The observational basis of this separation of therapy and its outcome from explanatory theory derives, of course, from multiple sources which need only be mentioned. There are the seemingly spontaneous remissions of neurotic illness, which Grünbaum asserts that even Freud conceded—in 1926a (Grünbaum, 1984, p. 160); there are the therapeutic cures from rival treatment modalities, including the behavioral therapies based on an entirely different and totally unpsychoanalytic understanding of the mind and of pathogenesis; there are the comparative studies of treatment outcomes from rival therapies that have failed to reveal any sort of superiority for psychoanalysis within the overall array of therapeutic modalities (Smith, Glass, and Miller, 1980); and there are the claims that perhaps all the different therapies achieve the degrees of success that they do by virtue of common nonspecific effects, placebo effects, mobilizing hope and supportively counteracting psychic demoralization (Frank, 1961).

The tally argument as the road to confirmation of the theory has indeed clearly collapsed; it is not now—if it ever was—therapeutic success that gives us warrant to sustain our convictions about the value of psychoanalysis as theory, as method, and as clinical endeavor. To Grünbaum, who feels that he has successfully demonstrated that all the psychological understandings of psychoanalysis have been built on this argument, this means that there is no longer any viable epistemological or logical warrant for belief in the probative value of the psychoanalytic enterprise. He concedes that psychoanalysis has been remarkably fruitful heuristically and continues to be so, but he distinguishes that sharply from its lack of probative value; according to him, we can no longer accept that its propositions can be satisfactorily tested and validated within the psychoanalytic situation. He further says that all of psychoanalysis, all of its propositions, even those that are nonclinical and not explicitly linked to the therapy, are ultimately "epistemically parasitic" (1984, p. 167) on the therapeutic results, since the tally argument was "the epistemic underwriter of clinical validation" (p. 170). Once clinical validation has been bereft of the legitimation drawn from therapeutic success via the tally argument, in Grünbaum's words, "the menacing suggestibility problem, which . . . [Freud] had held at bay by means of this argument, comes back to haunt data from the couch with a vengeance" (p. 172).

This brings us to what Grünbaum (1984) calls the ineradicable "epistemic contamination" of the data of psychoanalysis by the now rampant possibilities for suggestion, operating even "the more insidiously under the pretense that analysis is *non* directive" (p. 130).

Involved here, of course, are all the issues of transference suggestion, of patient compliance, of spurious confirmations of our theory-
influenced interpretations, with any seeming therapeutic gains
wrought not by true, insightful self-discovery but by all these varieties
of nonspecific and suggestive placebo effects. Finally, to make matters even worse, since much of the clinical authentication of the
etiologically relevant early history in the lives of neurotic patients
must rely on recovered memories of childhood experiences, we
come to the issue of the reliability—or rather the fallibility—of
memory and Grünbaum's commonsense assertion that "such early
memories are surely more fragile epistemically than ordinary recol-
lections from adult life" (p. 242). This is especially so since, according to Grünbaum, "the analyst is doing exactly what a cross-
examining attorney is forbidden to do in the courtroom: leading
the witness" (p. 242). Here Grünbaum additionally asserts that psychoanalytic treatment cannot "be regarded as a bona fide *memory-
jogging* device" (p. 243), since it has been well established experi-
mentally that human memory is so malleable it can be readily bent
by beliefs, expectations, and preconceptions; and that human beings have a penchant, when under the influence of leading questions, to fill amnesic gaps by confabulated material (p. 243; see, in
this connection, Loftus, 1980).

Grünbaum's main point in all this is that "clinical findings—in
and of themselves—forfeit the probative value that Freud had
claimed for them," although, he acknowledges, "their potential
heuristic merits may be quite substantial." However, he also states:

> To assert that the contamination of intraclinical data is *ineradicable*
> without extensive and essential recourse to *extra*clinical findings is
> *not*, of course, to declare the automatic falsity of any and every ana-
> lytic interpretation that gained the patient's assent by means of prod-
> ding from the analyst. But it *is* to maintain—to the great detriment
> of intraclinical test-ability!—that in general, the epistemic devices
> confined to the analytic setting cannot reliably *sift* or decontaminate
> the clinical data so as to identify those that qualify as authentic [p.
> 245].

Grümbaum's final call at the end of his book is, then, for well-
designed extraclinical studies, prospective comparative studies, ex-
perimentally controlled studies, and epidemiological studies, all vital, he feels, if Freud's theories are ever to be validated, if
psychoanalytic propositions are ever to move beyond their acknowledged great heuristic value to a position of truly established probative value (p. 278).

This is, in summary, Grünbaum's passionately argued challenge to the epistemological and logical status of psychoanalysis as a scientific theory that purports to carry within its own methods the possibilities for empirical testing and validation. The challenge is indeed a most serious one and in its turn requires an equally serious response, now that Grünbaum himself has marshaled so effectively all the counterarguments against the hermeneutic effort to draw psychoanalysis away from its claim as science, and the logical positivist as well as Popperian efforts to drive psychoanalysis out of the ranks of science—both of them opposite challenges that he has helped so decisively to blunt.

An effective response to Grünbaum must relate to what I consider to be his two central theses: (1) that the whole of the claim of psychoanalysis to legitimacy as a science rests on Freud's so-called "Master Proposition" built out of and based on the designated tally argument; and (2) that should the tally argument not hold, the whole psychoanalytic edifice collapses as science, since any other avenue to clinical validation within the psychoanalytic situation is hopelessly contaminated epistemologically by the ever-present possibility of suggestion in its multiple forms and so can yield only heuristic and not probative values. Corollary to these two central theses is Grünbaum's further argument that the only way to rescue psychoanalysis as an enterprise—since, after all, its heuristic values may indeed reflect accurate conceptions of human mental functioning—would be via the validation that must come from extraclinical testing, prospective, controlled experimental, and epidemiological studies (the obvious designs for which Grünbaum indicates at a number of places in his book).

In response, then, to Grünbaum: To begin with, we have all long ago conceded that the tally argument, derived from Freud's earliest convictions that specific symptoms in his original hysterical patients disappeared with the uncovering of the repressed pathogenic trauma specific to each (Breuer and Freud, 1893–1895)—that this specific argument has not held up. Freud was the first to acknowledge this when he pointed to the sudden shifts in transference that could seemingly undo these therapeutic gains so abruptly and allow the return of full-fledged symptoms. In fact, the entire tally argument represents (in today's terms) a simplistic theory of neurosogenesis, as per psychoanalysis circa 1895–1905. Psychoanalysis has long since ceased to rest on a theory of neurosogenesis based on specific repressions of specific traumatic events or on a concomitant theory of therapy based on uncovering those repressions, that is, simply making the unconscious conscious.

Today, our theories of neurosis, of neurotic character and symptom formation, reflect a more complexly figured developmental process. A life course must be traced through the individual's successive facing of sequentially unfolding developmental tasks, with all the possibilities for dysphoric affect and attendant conflict at each turn in the interplay between maturational unfolding and the happenstance of (more or less potentially traumatic) experience. All of this eventuates, via endlessly reinforcing repetitive lifetime experiences, in particular healthy or neurotic, adaptive or maladaptive, character formations and behavior dispositions. Correspondingly, the psychoanalytic ameliorative and curative process is no longer viewed simply as the successive lifting of repressions through correctly timed veridical interpretations, until id has been everywhere replaced by ego. Again, it is much more complexly configured in terms of repetitive interpretive working over of endlessly recurrent themes linked to the infantile pathological resolutions of the individual's preoedipal and oedipal vicissitudes—the process that we call working through. What I am maintaining in all of this is that, in his assault on the credibility of the tally argument, Grünbaum has been pushing through an open door, one that has been widely open for more than half a century. The disappearance of the tally argument from psychoanalytic discourse is not news to either psychoanalytic theorists or psychoanalytic researchers.

However, if we have now given up the beguiling simplicity of the tally argument as the linchpin in our efforts to seek validation of our heuristically valuable constructions, then we are indeed faced with Grünbaum's next and more consequential challenge. How will we deal with his charge that, absent the tally argument, we are faced with irremediable difficulties of potential contamination of our assessments of therapeutic interventions and therapeutic changes by the power of suggestion? This is what Grünbaum calls "the menacing suggestibility problem" which Freud had tried to hold at bay with his invocation of the tally argument. Grünbaum feels this task to be impossible, which is why he talks so repeatedly of the "hopeless epistemic contamination" of all the data derived from the psychoanalytic situation. Holt (1984) has stated the response for most of us with the remark that though the problem is real enough and serious enough, the point may indeed be much overstated by Grünbaum, since contamination of clinical data by suggestion is not necessarily an "all-or-none affair" (p. 11).

For example, Glymour (1974) developed what he called the concept of "logical pincer movement" (p. 17) for the piecemeal testing of particular propositions within the overall theory, which, when applied sequentially, becomes a "logical pincer-and-bootstrap strategy of piecemeal testing," as Grünbaum (1984, p. 98) dubbed it. This strategy can work if the propositions under scrutiny are strong enough, as Glymour felt he demonstrated in his case exemplar, Freud's write-up of the Rat Man. Of this Glymour said:

> The kind of testing a theory admits depends largely on the strength of that theory itself. Weak theories which embody no putative laws, which concern only causal factors or correlations, may perhaps have to be tested with great regard for statistical methods and experimental controls. But the theory Johannes Kepler proposed long ago was strong enough to be tested in the observatory, and the theory Sigmund Freud developed at the turn of this century was strong enough to be tested on the couch [p. 29].

In answer to Grünbaum's vigorous critique (see especially Grünbaum, 1982, 1984, pp. 97–103) that Glymour's treatment of the problem of suggestion was overly sanguine, perhaps even naïve, Glymour responded in an afterword to his paper, written a decade later. I will quote it at some length because it encompasses much (but not all) of my own response to this challenge of Grünbaum's to our possibilities for a true science of psychoanalysis.

In his afterword, Glymour (1974) said:

> Knowing that clinical evidence is subject to suggestion should make us cautious in using that evidence, and it should make us sensitive to indicators that the therapist is determining the responses he receives. I do not see, however, that the experimental knowledge we now have about suggestibility requires us to renounce clinical evidence altogether. Indeed, I can imagine circumstances in which clinical evidence might have considerable force: when, for example, the clinical proceedings show no evident sign of indoctrination, leading the patient, and the like; when the results obtained fall into a regular and apparently law-like pattern obtained independently by many clinicians; and when those results are contrary to the expectation and belief of the clinician. I do not intend these as *criteria* for using clinical evidence, but only as indications of features which, in combination, give weight to such evidence. . . . The knowledge that clinical

evidence is liable to suggestion and confounding does not, I think, of itself recommend the policy of dismissing all such evidence, nor does the knowledge that astronomical observations are subject to error recommend the policy of dismissing the evidence of astronomy. In the latter case it is relatively easy to find out something about the limits of error and its dispersion; in the former case it is more difficult [p. 30].

In following upon this quotation from Glymour's afterword, how can we indeed satisfy ourselves that we are adequately coping with Grünbaum's challenge? Glymour spoke about the careful search for evidence of overt or covert suggestive manipulation or compliance; of the emergence of comparable patterns independently in the observations of multiple researchers with their different emotional predilections, styles, and theoretical preconceptions; of the emergence of results contrary to expectations and belief. This last argument has been significantly elaborated by Edelson (1983, 1984) under the rubric of "surprise" and the evidential value that surprise can provide for hypothesis testing. He stated (1984):

It is neither general explanations nor obvious positive instances of psychoanalytic hypotheses that appear to be especially important to either psychoanalyst or analysand. Rather, what is given special weight by both is the emergence of circumstantial detail, having an astonishing degree of specificity and idiosyncratic nuance. . . . Such details have not previously been remembered by the analysand . . . and almost certainly have not previously been imagined or guessed in advance by the psychoanalyst. A psychoanalysis without surprises cannot properly be termed a psychoanalysis at all. One cannot regard as plausible that such data have been suggested in any ordinary sense of that word. It is these data that may in the end prove to be most relevant to the search in the psychoanalytic situation for probative evidence providing support for psychoanalytic hypotheses [pp. 136–137].

This same valuation of the central place of surprise in the psychoanalytic enterprise was enunciated by Theodor Reik (1937) from a clinical perspective almost a half century earlier. His book on the subject was titled *Surprise and the Psycho-Analyst*.

Put another way, though all serious researchers recognize the ever-present vulnerability to suggestive compliance in all clinical therapeutic settings, many do not regard it as an insuperable epistemological liability. As Edelson (1984) put it:

It might be possible . . . to reduce the adulteration of data by suggestion in the psychoanalytic situation—perhaps to a vanishingly small
degree, or at least to a degree it ceases to be a *plausible* alternative
explanatory candidate. Many features of the psychoanalytic situation,
in contrast to those of other psychotherapies, are in fact designed to
control extraneous external influences on the analysand's productions [pp. 129–130].

What such authors emphasize is that, as I earlier quoted from Holt
(1984, p. 11), contamination by suggestion is not an "all-or-none
affair," that there are various circumstances in which suggestive
influence is far less likely, and that there are varieties of strategies
for assessing its impact, or for otherwise minimizing its distorting influence.

And if Grünbaum's sweeping charge that suggestion hopelessly
contaminates all data from the consulting room can be reasonably
countered by a measured assessment of the impact of such contamination and the strategies by which it can be contained and mini-
mized, then what becomes of Grünbaum's proclamation? What
becomes of his notion that in order to give psychoanalysis the opportunity to pass from the heuristic to the probative realm, the scientific
investigation of its hypotheses must move out of the clinical psychoanalytic situation and into the extraclinical world of the objective
clinical trials experimental model, with untreated control groups,
random assignments, and all the other accoutrements of that research strategy? Simply put, that argument is no longer overriding.

Which is not to denigrate the values of clinical trials research
or other varieties of controlled experimental or epidemiological
testing of psychoanalytic propositions. They, too, have their value
but they, too, have their methodological and logical problems, different from those that beset research efforts within the psychoanalytic situation which Grünbaum has so painstakingly laid open for
us, but equally real and perhaps equally serious. This is not the place
to elaborate all the well-known research problems of comparative
outcome studies. These include different treatment modalities conceptualized within different theoretical frameworks, with differently
conceived outcome criteria and employing differently understood
interventions, all applied to patient populations presumed to be
equally matched in all the relevant dimensions of personality functioning and illness structure. These problems are indeed well
known. Here, I want only to add one less often remarked perspective

on the *limitations* of extraclinical testing of psychoanalytic hypotheses, this from Thomä and Kächele (1975). Their point is: "If the psychoanalytic method is not employed and the process takes place outside of the treatment situation, only those parts of a theory can be tested that do not need a special interpersonal relation as a basis of experience and whose statements are not immediately related to clinical practice" (p. 63). This leads them to state that psychoanalytic practice must be "the crucial place where the proof of its explanatory theories is to be rendered—we would not know where else they could be fully tested" (p. 63), a conclusion that is the diametric opposite of Grünbaum's. Erdelyi (1985) has described this as the issue of "ecological validity."

Let me at this point summarize my overall response to Grünbaum's multifaceted challenge to the credibility of psychoanalysis as a scientific enterprise:

1. If the tally argument is no longer seriously held as the evidential wedge by which the whole of the structure of psychoanalysis must be validated, and if rather, the theory and its propositions concerning development, personality functioning, and psychopathology consist of a far more richly and complexly configured fabric, then its appropriate scientific testing becomes a more complexly and subtly nuanced process than the simple tallying of where the tally argument holds and where it does not. By the same token, the demise of our reliance on the tally argument no longer heralds the necessary downfall of the entire explanatory edifice. To hold otherwise is to hold psychoanalysis to the theory and the methods that go back to the early Freud of the turn of the century.

2. If all the possibilities for epistemic contamination via theoretical predilection, circular reasoning, *post hoc ergo propter hoc,* suggestion and compliance, are not all-or-none phenomena, are grave though not fatal handicaps to the hypothesis-testing effort, then ways must and can be found to account for, to contain, to diminish, the impact of inadvertent suggestion, compliance, or other contamination and the possibility that such factors might comprise a *plausible* alternative explanation of the observations being used as tests of particular psychoanalytic hypotheses.

3. If extraclinical testing of psychoanalytic propositions, though useful and important and not to be denigrated, itself carries its own burden of major conceptual and methodological problems, as I have cursorily indicated, and itself may be limited in just that area of most concern to us—how psychoanalytic treatment acts to effect

change and cure—as Thomä and Kächele (1975, p. 63) have reminded us, then it behooves us to turn in an intensified way to the systematic testing of our propositions within the crucible of the data derived from our consulting rooms, and in ways that are consonant with the requirements of empirical science. We can neither leave that whole burden to the extraclinical testing held out for us by Grünbaum and his supporters as the only proper proving ground, nor rely on the vestiges of the ill-fated tally argument that may still linger in our minds as a conceptual back-up to try to render such testing superfluous.

In concluding, I shall not try to state how, in the light of all the considerations adduced to this point, we can best proceed now with this enterprise of testing psychoanalytic propositions in a way that subjects heuristic contents to truly probative inquiry. That would be another, an empirical research paper, and not my central purpose here. Suffice it to say that I feel it can be done and that my own book, *Forty-two Lives in Treatment* (Wallerstein, 1986), is a full accounting of one such endeavor, the Psychotherapy Research Project of The Menninger Foundation. In that research program the concept of prediction was the central research principle as well as operational tool. In an article published back in 1964, I spelled out at length the crucial role of prediction in relation to theory-testing in psychoanalysis. In recent years Rubinstein, in a succession of methodological articles (1975, 1980a,b), has laid out the whole range of issues around the use of prediction as an effective theory-testing tool in psychoanalysis.

I will not try to develop any of that at this point. I have simply tried to indicate that there is sufficient *warrant* for such empirical testing in ways that are alert to the subtlety and complexity of subjective clinical phenomena while simultaneously loyal to the canons of objective scientific method. Indeed, this *has* been pursued as an activity, albeit a grossly insufficiently developed activity, within psychoanalysis both before and since the rise of the challenges from the different quarters I have addressed in this paper, the hermeneutic–phenomenological challenge in its various expressions, that of the logical positivists, that of Karl Popper, and now the latest, that posed in the writings of Adolf Grünbaum. Although there is much to be pondered in regard to each of these serious philosophical critiques of the scientific credentials of our psychoanalytic enterprise, I hope I have persuaded the reader that our credibility as science—or at least our potential credibility as science—has survived these challenges.

Our task as science, then, as I now see it, is to get on with our development as a body of science. We have always been vulnerable to the charge articulated by Sherwood (1969) that "in perhaps no other field has so great a body of theory been built upon such a small *public record* of raw data" (p. 70; emphasis added). If we wish to realize our possibilities for the kind of scientific position that our field warrants and that I have tried to demonstrate is inherent in it, this situation described by Sherwood becomes increasingly difficult to tolerate—and to date, grossly insufficient efforts have been directed toward its remediation. The cadre of serious psychoanalytic researchers who engage in systematic inquiry and in the testing of propositions through the accumulation of a public record of data that can be studied and checked by multiple, independent observers is still pitifully small, considering the numbers in our ranks and the magnitude of the task. Again, I will not dwell on all the difficulties created for those of us who undertake this task. Here I want rather to end with a credo. In words borrowed from Arlow (1982):

> We are approaching a *postapostolic* era in psychoanalytic history. In a few years, we will no longer have with us colleagues who had direct or indirect contact with the Founding Fathers. Our confidence in our work will have to rely not on the memories of bygone heroes, but on solid observational data, meticulously gathered in the analytic situation and objectively evaluated, for *it is upon this set of procedures that the claim of psychoanalysis to a place among the empirical sciences is based* [p. 18; emphasis added].

I believe that this statement sets as well as any other our vital present agenda for psychoanalysis as a discipline and a science. I hope that I have in some measure persuaded my readers likewise. For it is not enough just to respond conceptually, as I have tried to do in this presentation, to the challenges posed to our status as a science from various quarters.

8.

Psychoanalysis and Academic Psychiatry—Bridges

Psychoanalysis and psychiatry (especially academic psychiatry) have developed over the years an alliance that has been intimate but always problematic and uncertain, and periodically grossly troubled and strained. On the one hand, psychiatry has been the source of the greatest part (and in America, of the overwhelming part) of the manpower recruited to psychoanalytic training and activity. It has been the locus of the greatest application of psychoanalytic knowledge both as basic psychological theory infusing and informing the conceptual framework of academic psychiatry under the banner of psychodynamics, and as central psychotherapeutic technique under the rubric of psychoanalytic or psychoanalytically oriented psychotherapy. On the other hand, psychoanalysis has always, most ambivalently, asserted itself ideologically and conceptually as a discipline completely distinct from psychiatry (and having many nonpsychiatrists sharing fully in its work and its achievements). At the same time, pragmatically and opportunistically it has been a heightened specialization of psychiatric education, entitled, via this organic linkage to psychiatry and thus to the central body of medicine as a discipline, to the many symbolic and tangible advantages of physicianhood.

My own long-time concerns with the nature of this relationship between psychoanalysis and academic psychiatry have of course

213

been much more than academic. Like many psychoanalysts and psychiatrists of my generation who occupy positions of influence in the psychoanalytic and the psychiatric worlds, my own career—and the justification of my career commitments—has been built precisely on this relationship, or this bridge, between psychoanalysis and academic psychiatry. It is this bridge which is, in fact, the intersect of my own professional preoccupations over a lifetime, as a psychoanalyst, as a psychotherapy researcher—an investigator into the process, the how and what, of change in psychotherapy. It has influenced my work as a chief of a psychoanalytically grounded department of psychiatry in a community general hospital, and now as an academic psychiatrist, responsible for helping chart the destiny in the sense of the future, the very uncertain future, of psychiatry, of academic psychiatry, as a discipline in itself and as an enterprise within a separate hospital and psychiatric institute, a medical school, and a university. I say uncertain future because academic psychiatry is today in great flux and in a very self-conscious state of searching reappraisal of what it is about and what its proper place in the scheme of things should be.[1] It is central to the theme I will be developing that the currently unsettled relationship between psychoanalysis and academic psychiatry is a major representation of the uncertainty of destiny of academic psychiatry today, and that the reflective elaboration of a conceptually sound bridge or interface between psychoanalysis and academic psychiatry can exert a powerfully clarifying and corrective pressure toward the resolution of the current flux of multiple indecisions within and about academic psychiatry.

To begin to develop my theme, I will have to interweave two main strands, the one something of the nature and the relevant history of American academic psychiatry and the other something of the nature and the relevant history of psychoanalysis as its focal power and scientific leadership was transplanted from its European origin and base to its new American homeland—and by relevant, in this context, I mean, of course, that which bears upon the shifting vicissitudes of the relationship between the two, psychoanalysis and academic psychiatry.

As is usual in psychoanalytic discourse, I begin with Freud, who actually wrote very little on issues of education and the educational

---

[1] Marked, for example, by the currently ongoing activity of a special Josiah Macy Jr. Foundation Commission on the Present Condition and the Future of Academic Psychiatry of which I am privileged to be a member.

enterprise per se. From the small number of his statements in this area, I will quote only his best known, which touches, at least by implication, some of the roots of the array of issues that are my concern here. In *The Question of Lay Analysis,* Freud states his prescription, as of that time (1926b), for the ideal curriculum for the new profession of psychoanalysis that he had single-handedly created:

> If—which may sound fantastic to-day—one had to found a *college of psycho-analysis,* much would have to be taught in it which is also taught by the medical faculty: alongside of depth-psychology, which would always remain the principal subject, there would be an introduction to biology, as much as possible of the science of sexual life, and familiarity with the symptomatology of psychiatry. On the other hand, analytic instruction would include branches of knowledge which are remote from medicine and which the doctor does not come across in his practice: the history of civilization, mythology, the psychology of religion and the science of literature. Unless he is well at home in these subjects, an analyst can make nothing of a large amount of his material. By way of compensation, the great mass of what is taught in medical schools is of no use to him for his purposes [that is, for the purposes of the clinical practice of psychoanalysis] [p. 246; emphasis added].
>
> [A few pages further on, Freud restated his prescriptive advice even more tersely.] A scheme of training for analysts has still to be created. It must include elements from the mental sciences, from psychology, the history of civilization and sociology, as well as from anatomy, biology and the study of evolution [p. 252].

In these prescriptions of Freud's, more than a half-century ago, for what he considered the requisite or the best possible training in the theory and practice of the new profession of psychoanalysis we can discern implicitly, perhaps even explicitly, Freud's views on the proper context for psychoanalysis, its proper relationship to academic psychiatry and the medical school, and even, though less clearly, its proper relationships to the wider academic university world for which Freud always yearned, in Walter Lippman's words, the university "that ancient and universal company of scholars" (1966).

But this idealistic prescription for education and training in psychoanalysis is a description neither of how psychoanalysis started nor of what it could ever become, at least till now, in its European

homelands. Its origins and history in Europe are indeed broadly
known, and it is something that I have written about in considerably
more detail (Wallerstein, 1974). Here I only want to state the salient
aspects of that historic unfolding in grossly telescoped form in order
to set the historical context for the subsequent American developments. The elements that I single out are these: (1) There was the
gradual spread of the psychoanalytic idea through the educated and
intellectual strata of European society with at the same time bitter
and often scornful opposition to that idea both within the general
medical practitioner community and also within the academic university medical community with its attached teaching hospitals and
clinics. (2) The clinical growth of psychoanalysis in the first instance
resulted from the outpatient consulting room practices of neurologists (like Freud and his handful of early medical followers), dealing
with the mass of neurotic patients, prototypically the hysterical
(Freud's first psychological clinical work was *Studies on Hysteria*)
[Breuer and Freud, 1893–1895]. Hysterical patients were at that
time the special province originally of the neurologist concerned
with differential diagnostic distinctions between organically and psychogenically based disorders of the motor and sensory apparatuses.
(3) The very secondary and far more limited inroads of psychoanalysis into the understanding of the psychotic and organic patients who
were in turn then the special province of the psychiatrists, caught
up in the organically and descriptively centered tradition led by
Freud's great contemporary, Kraepelin.[2] (4) There was the development out of all this of psychoanalysis as an essentially private practice
and self-sufficient clinical enterprise that never had the academic
entrée into either the medical school, as a branch of the healing
arts, or, through it, to the university more broadly, as a system of
thought. It was an entrée to which Freud lifelong aspired and in
which he was lifelong disappointed. (5) There was the need for
psychoanalysis to create its own scientific and academic structure.
The concept which thus arose of the independent psychoanalytic
institute, the original vehicle for psychoanalytic scholarship and
training, can be viewed both in Europe and in America where likewise it took root and flourished, both from the standpoint of its
accomplishments and, at the same time, in the limitations and constraints of those adverse circumstances, the pursuit of a major intellectual–educational enterprise at a night school carried on the tired

---

[2] This inroad into the sphere of the psychotic patient came in the first instance with the
adherence of Bleuler and Jung and their colleagues at the Burghölzli Sanitarium in Switzerland to psychoanalysis.

energies of part-time men and women after daytimes of full-time practice.

Such are the highlights of the historical development of psychoanalysis in its European homelands where it had no place, and for several generations actually never won a place, never really penetrated into the medical schools or into academic psychiatry, which remained firmly planted in the organicist and nosologically descriptive world of Kraepelin and his followers. In effect, in Europe, bridges did not exist between psychoanalysis, as a quintessentially psychological understanding of the mind and the behavior of man, and academic psychiatry, as an organically conceived effort to understand the functioning of the brain and the behaviors linked thereto via biological mechanisms exactly analogous to those that were beginning to achieve such stunning success in the understanding of the functioning and malfunctioning of the body. Bridges could not in that historic–social context to which I have been referring be built. In fact, despite the several generations' headstart of psychoanalysis in Europe over its development in America, it is only in the most recent years—quite a while after it was a commonplace in America—that, in Europe, avowed psychoanalysts could become professors in medical schools and directors in psychiatric clinical centers.

In overall summary, and this is my main point, for various reasons of historical and social context, and with whatever degree of credit or blame we wish to attribute to the defensive responses of Freud and his followers or to the hostile reactions of an unreceptive academic and intellectual milieu, the fact is that psychoanalysis in Europe essentially grew up outside of psychiatry, of medicine, and of academia. By contrast, the relationship between psychoanalysis and psychiatry (including academic psychiatry) has almost from the beginning been sharply different in America than in Europe. This has played, I think, its major role in the differing initial conceptualization in America of the overall nature of the (academic) psychiatric enterprise, a conceptualization which now, in reverse flow, is developing and picking up momentum in Europe and around the world as well. I should insert the caveat that I am not completely sure of all my historical grounds, especially of whether it was the role of psychoanalysis itself in its transplantation to America and in its penetration into American psychiatry, which importantly influenced or even to a major extent determined the way in which the clinical and the academic psychiatric enterprise have been delineated in America. Or whether, conversely, it was the nature of the conceptualization of psychiatry in America that made it such a receptive soil for the implantation of the psychoanalytic viewpoint in its very midst—in such marked contrast to the European development. Such questions usually are not susceptible to either-or explanations, but rather are resolved into studies of propitious interactions between powerful ideas, receptive (because prepared) soils, and fortuitous timing, with idea and soil and timing each conjoining in some measure from both sides of the interaction.

What, then, is this conception of the nature of the academic psychiatric enterprise in its peculiarly American stamp that makes for such productive bridge building with psychoanalysis? Psychiatry, like all the branches of the healing arts, is, of course, a *clinical* discipline dedicated to the amelioration of human disease and distress, in this instance, that caused by mental and emotional conflict and illness. Like all clinical healing disciplines, psychiatry as a branch of scientific medicine rests on and is the clinical application of a base of knowledge in the preclinical or basic science realms, the clinical application of this basic science knowledge in relation to the ills and distresses of the variety of patients within its purview. This preclinical knowledge base for psychiatry is clearly in *three* realms, biological, psychological, and social science, since man is a biological animal individually thinking and functioning within a socially organized and constrained setting. It is the task of clinical psychiatry, of the psychiatric clinician, to integrate the data and the organizing concepts from each of these three knowledge realms into the total understanding of the functioning and malfunctioning of the individual patient in distress and then to translate that comprehensive understanding into an ameliorative effort directed toward remediation and change within any or each of these realms as appropriate. This psychiatry, at its best, encompasses the understanding of the mental and emotional conflicts and illnesses of human beings over their entire unfolding life-span, from infancy through old age.

Perhaps I should digress for a moment to state the truism that in theory this characterization of psychiatry as an applied clinical science resting on integrated data and conceptualizations from the three coordinate basic science realms is *in principle* not different from that of any of the other medical disciplines, each with their different arenas of clinical application. There is thus the present renewed and intensified concern with teaching medical students the psychosocial aspects of health and disease, especially to those headed for the various primary care or generalist areas covering the span of children, adolescents, and adults, and the families in which they grow up, which is but one current expression of that conception. The difference is that in the medical and surgical specialty areas, the data and conceptualizations from the biological basic science realm for the most part have fundamental primacy, with modification, of course, with the so-called psychosomatic diseases. For the most part the psychosocial data and conceptualizations, though useful and even necessary, can be only secondarily or less immediately vital. To give a trivial example, the first urgent order of business with the victim of lobar pneumonia and complicating pneumococcal meningitis is the institution of proper life-restoring antibiotic therapy and life-supporting physiological reequilibration. It becomes then a secondary concern, but one that of course needs also to be addressed when the life-threatening acute illness is conquered, that the pneumococcal infection, pneumonia, and meningitis developed in the setting of chronic deteriorating alcoholism, inclement weather, and despairing exposure.

However, the data and conceptualizations from the three knowledge base realms are more *coequal* in importance, in psychiatry, a tripod with three more equal legs, though these vary of course in emphasis with each specific clinical instance. Corollary to all of this is the statement that more than any other clinical discipline or branch of the healing arts, psychiatry is a boundary discipline living on the understanding and the integration of its three interfaces, into the biological, the psychological, and the social science realms with an overall concern across all of these for the processes of human development. In this sense, psychoanalysis has as its *main bridge* to the world of psychiatry and to the teaching of it and the accrual of new knowledge in it that we call academic psychiatry, not its position as a specific therapeutic modality with its implications for all the psychoanalytically related psychodynamic therapies that are taught to psychiatrists (as well as to other, allied mental health professionals), but rather its position as a psychology, that is, as part of the underpinning basic science base of the psychiatric enterprise.

Opinions will differ at this point, not just outside but also within psychoanalysis, as to the proper reach or limitation of psychoanalysis as a psychology and the extent to which it can try to lay claim to being the totality of the psychological theory of psychiatry. Psycho-analysis was born out of the study of conflict in the behaviorally and emotionally disordered (i.e., born out of psychopathology). In its first generations of expansion it progressively extended its reach into the study of normal behavior and emotion, and normal devel-opment, that is, toward the universalisms of a general psychology. This was built on Freud's fundamental insight into the continua between the normal and the abnormal, the abnormal as the inap-propriately exaggerated normal. Anyway, this was Freud's dream, of psychoanalysis as a comprehensive psychology, a dream carried to its logical furthermost in the endeavors of our great systematizers and architects of modern-day ego psychology, most especially Hart-mann (1964) and Rapaport (1967).

This claim of psychoanalysis to be ultimately a completely en-compassing and explanatory general and developmental psychol-ogy, to be reached finally (at least in Rapaport's view) when it had achieved a satisfactory psychoanalytically integrated learning theory was, however, one never accepted outside its ranks in academic psy-chology, not even by those academic psychologists benignly dis-posed to the psychoanalytic contribution. Put simply, even those most friendly to psychoanalysis in academic psychology's ranks have seen it primarily, or only, as a psychology of conflict and of motiva-tion, relevant and illuminating in those realms of psychological is-sues, but only partially relevant and illuminating in the realms of nonconflict-born, nonmotivation-determined psychic phenomena. To Ernst Kris's well-known aphoristic definition of psychoanalysis as *nothing but* human behavior considered from the viewpoint of con-flict, they have added the counterview that it is also *nothing more.*

Even within psychoanalysis, however, there is, as one (and not necessarily as the most central) aspect of the great metapsychology debate raging in our theoretical literature (e.g., Gill, 1976; Holt, 1976; Schafer, 1976), the falling back from the claim that psycho-analysis can be a completely comprehensive general and develop-mental psychology, and especially from any pretension that it can be the kind of general and developmental psychology expounded in terms akin to those that operate in natural science or biological science. At this point of major theoretical flux within psychoanalysis, our prevailing ego psychology paradigm is being subjected to search-ing criticism and efforts at fundamental revision (Rosenblatt and Thickstun, 1977; Rubinstein, 1976) or even total replacement, as, for example, by the action language model (Schafer, 1976), or by a feedback-regulating, information-processing model (Peterfreund, 1971). There is no agreement, not even within psychoanalysis, as to its scope and reach, the validity or not of its claim, or pretension, to generality and universality, and therefore no consensus possible with those outside, as well, on this issue. We will at this point perhaps have to rest more modestly on our well-established positions within the scope of the view of analysis propounded by Kris. We can then claim for psychoanalysis its place as a psychology in itself, a central developmental psychology and psychological base for psychiatry, interacting productively with the psychological understandings from the other realms of academic psychology. We see already some such productive interactions with the cognitive developmental psychology of Piaget (Wolff, 1960). This then leaves open, properly so for the present, the extent to which all these perspectives and paradigms from the realms of psychological phenomena can and ultimately will be subsumed within a larger, more encompassing, I hope, and comprehensive psychoanalytic psychological framework.

A last point should be added to this part of my statement of the bridges between psychoanalysis and academic psychiatry, or rather of the placement of psychoanalysis as *a* major psychological basic science undergirding clinical psychiatry: psychoanalysis as a therapy, both a specific therapy and a model therapy. This brings us back to Freud's well-known threefold categorization of psychoanalysis, first, as a fundamental theory of the mind, as a psychology, that is, and this is the sense in which I have been considering it to this point; second, as a method, an investigative tool, a way of research and of unraveling the reaches of the mind, especially its not conscious or its unconscious depths; and third, as a specific therapy originally derived from studies with neurotic patients, who are still those most amenable to it, but by now varyingly extended to those with wider and deeper ego disorders, the narcissistic (Kohut, 1971), the borderline (Kernberg, 1975), and by some (e.g., Searles, 1965) even to the openly psychotic. All of this depends on one's position in relation to the issue of the properness, the validity of, and the readiness for "widening scope," as against, let us call it, narrowing or focused concentration (A. Freud, 1954; Stone, 1954).

Considered from this standpoint, as a specific therapy, psychoanalysis is a specific clinical application of psychoanalysis as a basic science, as a psychology, applied to a specifically indicated patient population, and requiring rigorous specific training—as carried out in our various institutes. Other specific clinical applications of psycho-analysis as theory, as basic science, are the whole range of psychoana-lytically based or psychoanalytically oriented or psychodynamic psychotherapies. These range from the expressive insight-aiming through to the supportive ego-strengthening that are derived from the theory of psychoanalytic psychology. These have their specific range of indications for their defined appropriate patient popula-tions, partially overlapping with each other and with psychoanalysis per se as well. They are a chief subject of teaching in our psychiatric academic university centers and our psychiatric teaching hospitals and clinics—in fact, for many of our students in psychiatry, what they most want to learn in our field.

But now let me return to the thread of my main argument, the nature of the conceptualization of psychiatry in America as a clinical discipline resting on a tripartite basic science base. It is clear from this conception that psychoanalysis in the transplantation of its focal power from Europe to America, borne on the tide of refugees from Hitler, found a very different set of contextual circumstances and therefore a very different opportunity available to it in America than had ever been dreamed possible in Europe.

The psychoanalytic beginnings in America actually go back to before World War I, and took firm root in the interregnum between the two World Wars. This led to the establishment and evolution in America of the first training centers and institutes in the established European institutional form of the independent institutes in New York, Boston, Chicago, and Baltimore-Washington—alongside these another even more compelling current was gathering, and intensi-fying, less in defensive, more I think in adaptive response to the accession to psychoanalytic ranks in America of the large numbers and the established psychoanalytic prestige of the psychoanalyst Eu-ropean refugees. Whether self-consciously thought out and planned in terms of the full array of consequences that subsequently eventu-ated or, as is more likely, more the result of only partial and partisan perspectives imposed upon events, leading through the clash of con-tention and compromise to outcomes in part unforeseen and for the rest only dimly thought out, and to that little extent entitled to be called planned, however this was, certainly in retrospect it is as if a major strategy was deliberately evolved and pursued. But psychoanalysis was to follow a different path in America from the proud and at the same time lonely isolation that marked it in Eu-rope, to penetrate into the receptive soil of American psychiatry. It was to capture, in a sense, academic psychiatry and its formal training centers and to become its prevailing psychological theory under the banner of dynamic psychiatry or psychodynamics, and thus to be firmly planted in the midst of medicine, the medical school, and, at least via this route, the university as well. Here I speak not specifically of the university-based psychoanalytic institute, which was a subsequent development, but of the more basic effort to transform the departments of psychiatry in the various medical schools and teaching hospitals of our nation into bulwarks of psychodynamic thinking and of dynamic psychiatric practice.

The success of this effort, in the sense of the radical transformation of American psychiatry, reached its high watermark through the decade of the 1950s. During that period in one after another of the major departments of psychiatry in the country, the retiring chairman, characteristically an Adolf Meyer-trained psychobiological psychiatrist, was replaced by a psychoanalytically committed and psychoanalytically trained psychiatrist (Wallerstein, 1974). I will not digress more than briefly to refer to some of the concomitants of that effort, the decision arrived at after such bitter and divisive debate within the American Psychoanalytic Association to effect what was called the 1938 rule, the barring henceforward of training of nonmedical candidates under the auspices of the American and barring membership in it to nonmedical analysts unless trained before that date. It was as if to strengthen its claim to psychological hegemony within psychiatry that psychoanalysis felt it had to divest itself of its nonmedical cohorts, no matter how glorious the contributions from these rich and diverse nonmedical sources had been. Whether it was a sacrifice that was necessary to the waging of what turned out to be so successful a campaign, and whether the campaign would have been more difficult or less successful if this sacrifice had not been made, is hard to know so categorically in hindsight. But certainly it was a heavy sacrifice and one that so many of us have felt to be unwise. The story of our long, slow, and painful efforts and by now partial success in the undoing of this total restrictiveness against the training of nonmedical people in psychoanalysis is one with which personally I have been long identified in the affairs of the American Psychoanalytic Association and have written about (Wallerstein, 1974), but the telling of it would be tangential to the main thrust of my exposition here.

The main point is that of the intimate penetration of American psychoanalysis, strengthened enormously by the infusion of numbers and of intellectual leadership of the European refugee pre-World War II transplants to America, in the decade or so after that war, into the central fabric of American academic psychiatry, both as psychological theory, becoming *the* prevailing psychological science underpinning academic psychiatric understanding and teaching, and as derived psychotherapy, psychoanalytically informed and oriented psychotherapy, which in turn became *the* prevailing psychotherapeutic approach taught and learned within most psychiatric training centers. Many departments of psychiatry with psychoanalyst chairmen and heavily psychoanalyst faculty became avowedly psychoanalytic in orientation. Almost all, with only a few conspicuous exceptions, explicitly acknowledged their resting on what they called, a little more euphemistically, a psychodynamic base. This was officially recognized in 1952 at the very influential NIMH-supported American Psychiatric Association Conference on Psychiatric Education held at Cornell University. In the book of proceedings of that conference the chapter on "The Role of Psychoanalysis in Residency Training" states in the very first paragraph that "it is now almost universally agreed that a necessary part of the preparation of a competent psychiatrist is the development of and understanding of principles of psychodynamics" and that "it seems obvious that an understanding of psychodynamics presupposes—indeed, necessitates— . . . knowledge of Freudian concepts and of psychoanalytic theory and practice" (Whitehorn, Braceland, Lippard, and Malamud, 1953, p. 91).

Such is what I have called the high watermark during the decade of the 1950s, of the capture, if you will, of the main bastions of American psychiatry by the psychoanalytic idea and its praxis, and of the intimate intermingling and in some locales even efforts at actual fusion of the two, psychoanalysis and psychiatry. But history did not stop here, and my accounting, rather than drawing to its close at this point must now turn to the bewildering complexity of the changes and the growths in academic psychiatry which have transpired since the fateful turning point year of 1954. The consequences of these changes in psychiatry have led to what has become a necessarily much more complex as well as much more problematic (in the sense of needing to be continuously readdressed and redefined) relationship between academic psychiatry and psychoanalysis.

Since I spoke of a high watermark it is natural to think of the receding of the tide, and in many places people have characterized the relationship between academic psychiatry and psychoanalysis during the two decades since the 1950s in just such terms, that the tide has indeed receded, that the era of psychodynamic dominance in American psychiatry is over. As a reflection of this conceptual as well as programmatic shifting of emphasis, during the 1960s it was no longer the commonplace assumption that open chairmanships in the major influential departments would be automatically offered only to individuals with psychoanalytic credentials. In fact, new breeds of chairmen arose; for example, those identified with the stunning successes in expanding, clinically and in research, the whole area of biological psychiatry, which they came incidentally to identify in many eyes with scientific psychiatry and research psychiatry.

The major dimensions of change and growth in academic psychiatry between the 1950s and 1970s have made for an increasingly complex and problematic relationship between academic psychiatry and psychoanalysis. These dimensions of change and growth seem to fit quite well into the tripartite division I have advanced of the basic science realms, basic to the undergirding of the psychiatric clinical enterprise, and I will therefore categorize and briefly discuss them in that order.

First, of course, there has been an explosion of biological knowledge, of brain–behavior interrelations within the field of psychiatry, in the domain of mental and emotional disorders. There are advances in neurophysiology and in neurochemistry, in knowledge of neurotransmitter mechanisms and of catecholamine metabolism, in psychophysiology and in psychopharmacology. Both in fundamental investigation and in direct or at least potential clinical application, there are studies of average evoked potentials and the conditions of electrical activity in the brain; of split-brain preparations (both experimental and clinical) and the derived studies of cerebral lateralization phenomena. There is biofeedback and the control of involuntary autonomic mechanisms, of REM states and sleep–dream research. Biological psychiatry has rapidly become a most significant and most respectable scientific arena and is now the clinical and research focus of many academic psychiatric careers and major psychiatric space and money resources.

The second and related major development, also in the biological realm, is the modern era of psychoactive drugs as a central therapeutic modality in the management and treatment of the psychiatrically ill. We psychodynamically trained psychiatrists have tended to avoid the sicker, psychotic patients who have been historically such a heavy, collective, undischarged social responsibility of our profession. Historically, they have been warehoused in large public mental hospitals, often neglected at best, and badly abused at worst. Here is where the date 1954 represents so sharp a turning point. Prior to that, and in the time when many of us chose psychiatry as our specialty within medicine, our drug armamentarium was limited essentially to sedatives and hypnotics with all the potentials for barbiturate abuse and addiction and for bromide poisoning. It was 1954 that brought Largactil, a drug developed in Switzerland, via Canada, to the United States, where Smith, Kline and French marketed it as Thorazine and inaugurated the era of the modern antipsychotic, major tranquilizer drugs. I do not need to recount the great proliferation of psychoactive drugs and of classes of such drugs in the years since. There are the major tranquilizers or antipsychotics, the minor tranquilizers, or so-called antianxiety drugs, the several classes of antidepressants, including the tricyclics and the monoamine oxidase inhibitors, and the very special drug lithium with its so poorly understood effects in relation to manic and depressive disorder. Suffice it to say that the existence of all these drugs has vitally changed the practice characteristics of psychiatrists (not to speak of the ministrations to emotionally and behaviorally troubled individuals by nonpsychiatric physicians). It has forced accommodations in the psychotherapeutic arena where adjuvant or concomitant use of psychoactive drugs has become a commonplace, again especially with the less well-integrated patients, for the most part those outside the normal-neurotic range. Understanding of drug–behavior interactions and of the psychological meanings of such chemically induced mood and behavior changes has become part of what we must know and teach in our psychotherapeutic endeavors—very much even in our psychoanalytically guided psychotherapeutic endeavors.

The third major dimensions of change in the field of psychiatry is in the psychological arena. Here I need only point out that psychoanalysis is no longer the unquestioned prevailing psychological theory guiding and illuminating our understanding of the human mind and its aberrations. It has now been challenged by the astonishing (astonishing to us, anyway) growth of two fundamentally different and competing psychological paradigms, the one the learning theory and stimulus-response conditioning model (partly classical, partly operant), with the behavior modification technology derived from it. The other, attacking both psychoanalysis and behavior modification as being mechanical and stripped of essential subjectivism and humanism, the so-called third force, is the existentialist–phenomenological tradition of European philosophy and letters brought to America as humanistic psychology and leading to the whole encounter and human growth and potential movement both within our profession and, with a larger force even, without. The point at issue here is that these are competing and, despite the efforts at reconciliation or at least at finding common ground (Wachtel, 1977), antithetical paradigms that make it much more difficult now when most departments of psychiatry, no matter how psychodynamic, also have their behaviorists and their humanists, so readily to link psychoanalysis and its theoretical understandings as *the* psychological basic science of the derived psychiatric clinical enterprise.

The fourth major dimension of change is in the social science (and social policy) arena. Here I want to mention another influence, as potent as the psychoactive drug industry in transforming the character of modern American psychiatric and mental health practice, and that is the community mental health center movement and ideology inaugurated by the Kennedy legislation of 1963. This community mental health center movement is clearly the new center of gravity in political power and in access to funding mechanisms in the whole field of mental health and illness, but it is also a succession of linked conceptualizations and ideologies, not necessarily all politically inspired, and many of them developed both before and outside the official community mental health movement. I refer to the concepts of the open hospital and the therapeutic community pioneered by Maxwell Jones in England, and of milieu therapy as designed by D. Ewen Cameron in Canada and further developed with psychoanalytic sophistication by Will Menninger and his colleagues at the Menninger Clinic in Topeka, Kansas. There is also the very current and very fashionable concept of deinstitutionalization that has already carried us from the era when most of our sicker patients were kept, or rather, incarcerated, in our large public mental hospitals for very long periods of time, even for their whole lifetimes. Today, hospitalization is by and large very short and mainly for acute and unmanageable life crises and psychological decompensations. Even the very sick, chronically psychotic patients are managing (or not managing) in outpatient lives in the outside world. We now see the new, untoward consequences of the deinstitutionalized life, the patients once neglected and abused in the state hospitals, now often neglected and abused in board and care homes and cheap inner-city hotels. There is the impact of chronically psychotic patients, as parents living at home, upon the children they are trying to raise. At any rate, a host of major problems and issues stamp the whole face of current mental health practice and are necessarily a major concern of academic psychiatry in preparing its students for their professional life ahead!

Fifth, and last in this cataloging of major dimensions of impact upon psychiatry in these past two decades, are the correlated developments of theory that relate to the changes in emphasis from the therapeutic to the preventive ameliorative models and from the idiosyncratically individual to the socially controlled family and group and social system concerns that characterize the philosophic thrust of the community mental health movement. Some of this theory was developed within psychoanalysis, such as crisis theory as innovated originally by Lindemann (1944); most of it has been developed outside psychoanalysis, in academic sociology and social psychology, such as role theory, theories of deviance, theories of small group behavior, and social systems theory. Again, the main point is that there are other bodies of knowledge, social science knowledge, which are being brought to bear as explanatory frameworks upon many of the phenomena that are within the purview of psychiatry and of psychiatrists. In terms of the issues that have surfaced by the emphases of the community mental health center movement, these are putatively better, in the sense of more broadly encompassing or more directly relevant, or perhaps are just more easily understandable or commonsensical explanatory frameworks. There have been efforts to link these theoretical understandings from the side of social science to the more centrally traditional psychoanalytic psychological understandings of the phenomena of mental illness, pioneered first by Talcott Parsons (1964) and continued into a current very lively ferment within our field (Wallerstein and Smelser, 1969; Weinstein and Platt, 1973) but such endeavors are at present, and with all due respect, but a programmatic promise, and not an accomplished fulfillment.

So much for a tabulation of some of the major trends of development within and around psychiatry in but the last two fast-moving decades. Where does that leave us today, and what are the implications of all this for the relationship between psychoanalysis and the academic psychiatric enterprise? Basically it is a statement of the diversification of psychiatry as a *variety* of fields of interrelated endeavors, all more or less closely interdigitated in their various partial, and varyingly overlapping comprehension of and ameliorative influence upon the central phenomena of the field, the range of mental and emotional disorder. In contrast with the post-War period today there are multiple, equally honorable, equally honored, and at least equally appealing career paths open to the student in psychiatry, and it is no longer a foregone conclusion that the most or the best will be drawn to psychoanalysis. It is not that this multiplicity of options and the internal glamour and external support that some of them seem to enjoy in higher measure than does psychoanalysis has in any sense pressured psychoanalysis into a diminished posture and status. It is just that psychoanalysis is now only one among several, or one among many, and only in some eyes, primus inter pares, the first among equals. It has both to compete for its share of the allegiances of psychiatry students and to justify itself in new terms, including its capacity to relate meaningfully to the conceptualizations and the data that derive from the other basic science realms. It must then in turn relate meaningfully (and comprehensively) to the phenomena in the patients that must be comprehended in terms of the synthesized understanding that derives from the perspectives brought to bear upon those clinical phenomena from each of the three major basic science realms. This is one way of stating what I feel to be the present-day challenge and opportunity in the continually evolving relationship between psychoanalysis and academic psychiatry and is also the arena in which I think the future of that relationship rests.

To spell out this terse and bald conclusion somewhat more, I turn to a variety of the very contemporary, very current, concerns of academic psychiatry and will delineate briefly the particular problems as well as opportunities that they pose for the relationship of psychiatry to psychoanalysis. I will discuss these current concerns under four headings: (1) the remedicalization of psychiatry, a now popular catchword in the field; (2) the evolving relationship of academic psychiatry to the behavioral sciences; (3) the dilemma of what makes basic research basic in our field; and (4) of such central interest to those of us in psychoanalysis, who after all stand first of all for a clinical enterprise, the new questions of the proper relationship of psychiatry to psychotherapy.

1. The theme of remedicalization indeed has several interrelated aspects, adding up in cumulative impact to perhaps the most powerful thrust on the present-day psychiatric scene. Included here are all the developments in biological psychiatry in the most recent decades, the advances in all the facets of neurobiology that I have already enumerated, as well as in genetics and the influence of inborn genetic loading upon subsequent behavioral disorder (most notable with manic–depressive illness but also seriously implicated with schizophrenia). A corollary also included here is the renewed growth of somatic therapy in psychiatry, the varieties of psychoactive (mood- and behavior-influencing) drugs that are so large a part of the learning experience and of the employed therapeutic armamentarium of today's psychiatrist. These drugs are also important, incidentally, to today's nonpsychiatric physicians who in their daily medical generalist practices over the entire developmental life course see so many emotionally and behaviorally troubled individuals. Linked to the new growth in the realm of the biological aspects and interests of psychiatry is the great revival of interest in the psychosomatic–consultation–liaison function and activities, an arena given much of its original impetus in the first decade after World War II under psychoanalytic auspices (Alexander and French [1948] and many others). This aspect is now being importantly renewed after the relative decline into which it earlier seemed to recede, as a complexly integrated biobehavioral research investigative enterprise and a humanistic biopsychosocial clinical science enterprise in hospital ward and clinic.

Concomitant with the surge of knowledge growth in these more "medical" areas and interfaces is the current heightened teaching attention of departments of psychiatry to medical students and to undergraduate medical education, that is, to the total medical student population, only a fraction of whom (and currently it is a rapidly declining fraction) will seek specifically psychiatric careers. There is special emphasis in this teaching to the training of future primary care physicians (the new majority among today's medical students) in the psychosocial dimensions of health and disease: all this, by the way, is in contrast to the scene but a few short years ago when departments of psychiatry tended to concentrate their primary efforts not upon medical students or nonpsychiatric physicians, but rather on their own residents, those who had opted for careers in psychiatry, and alongside the psychiatric residents, students from the other clinical mental health disciplines, like clinical psychology and psychiatric social work.

In all of this, I am speaking here under the heading of remedicalization only of the clinical, educational, and research aspects of present-day psychiatry. I have not mentioned the obviously linked, more practical, and political considerations. (a) The main extramural funding mechanisms for the academic psychiatry enterprise are flowing the same way, with overall available NIMH monies actually declining, but within that, sharply increased gradients of support to psychosomatic–consultation–liaison programs and to undergraduate medical student education programs. (b) The economics and politics of health care mean that some form of national health insurance is reasonably near, with massive third-party payment and reimbursement formulas already the ongoing reality of practice. These livelihood considerations are driving so much of psychiatry and so many psychiatrists back into an intensified "medical" identity and medical allegiance.

What are the implications of this massive and many-pronged, conceptual as well as practical, remedicalization of psychiatry, what are its implications for our concern here, with the bridge or interface between academic psychiatry and psychoanalysis? Clearly, all this has made the biological science knowledge base of psychiatry and the biobehavioral interface with medicine immensely more important within psychiatry than it had been just a decade or so earlier. The risk for us is that of the swing of the pendulum. Need we attend to the voices of gloom that assert that the dominant psychodynamic era of psychiatry that so characterized the field during the 1950s and 1960s is now decisively over, or can we still hold onto the central importance of the psychosocial dimensions of the phenomena in our field, alongside of and in interacting accommodation with the biobehavioral and the biomedical? Can there be here, in these interactions, an even more vital continuing role for the psychological and specifically for the psychoanalytic, for the undiminished importance of its perspective upon human behavior no matter what the growth in cognate realms?

2. Seemingly at the opposite end of the spectrum, we have witnessed the intensifying patterns of relationship between modern-day psychiatry and the array of the so-called behavioral sciences. The issue here is usually posed as that of the proper place of the behavioral sciences, mostly anthropology, sociology, social psychology, and personality and experimental psychology, all now increasingly recognized as part of the proper basic science preclinical

knowledge base for the physician in training alongside of the heretofore wholly biomedical or molecular biological basic science knowledge base. What is the proper place of these behavioral sciences
within the medical school setting? Should it be as a separate department of behavioral science, a preclinical basic science department,
charged to teach for the entire medical student body the behavioral
science base for all of medicine, for clinical medicine, and for clinical psychiatry? Or should the behavioral sciences (basic sciences to
the phenomena of health and disease though they be) be incorporated as part of the clinical department of psychiatry charged to
teach its clinical phenomena, psychopathology, psychiatric diagnosis, and psychiatric treatment, but also its own behavioral basic science base, for its own phenomena and for medicine in general?

Viewed pragmatically, one can say that where separate medical
school departments of behavioral science have been established,
they have characteristically not fared well; and where some degree
of success in behavioral science teaching has been achieved, it has
characteristically been from within the umbrella of the department
of psychiatry, with this marriage, where most successful, often
marked by an actual change in name to Department of Psychiatry
and Behavioral Science. Whatever the location, the point is the dialectical one that side by side with the remedicalization or the medical–biological turning of present-day academic psychiatry is the
other growing imbrication of psychiatry with the other sciences of
behavior. Psychoanalysts will certainly see the parallels to these
trends in the issues I have already alluded to surrounding the efforts
to link the theoretical understandings from the side of (psychoanalytically informed and sympathetic) social science to the more centrally traditional psychoanalytic psychological understanding of the
mind, and in the counterpart organizational or structural concerns
that linkage to the department of psychiatry of the medical school
not be the exclusive avenue of access of the psychoanalytic idea to
the academic university world. Here many will recognize the oft-
repeated call of David Shakow for another model of psychoanalytic
inclusion in the university, that of the separate psychoanalytic institute, linked to the department of psychiatry of the medical school,
to be sure, but also to all the various other graduate departments
in the social sciences and the humanities that can profitably share
mutual discourse. Given the structure and funding base of the American university system, Shakow's dream seems a utopian vision, but
perhaps the opportunity to realize it will come after all in a new,

more relevant version via the very departments of psychiatry, to which Shakow has been fearful to accord such a monopoly, as more of those departments of psychiatry become in practice as well as in name departments of psychiatry and behavioral science. Situated in that setting, psychoanalysis can then perhaps find its fullest opportunity at realization of its academic–intellectual ambitions and of its linkages to related realms of knowledge of the mind. At least with rare exceptions, such as in the English Department at Columbia University in the days of Lionel Trilling and Mark Van Doren or in Social Relations at Harvard under the leadership of Talcott Parsons (1964), or more currently again in English at the State University of New York in Buffalo with the Group for Applied Psychoanalysis led by Norman N. Holland (1968), psychoanalysis to this point has not secured a substantial place in organized academia—except within departments of psychiatry.

3. The confusing arguments continue over what constitutes "basic" research in our field or whether the investigation of the psychological or the psychosocial dimension can be basic. This is not merely a semantic or definitional quibble but rather is, to my mind, a fundamental conceptual stance concerning the nature of our field. Here there are two major positions. The one, which I mean nonpejoratively to call the reductionistic, is the prevailing model in much of the medical science and natural science enterprise, that the psychosocial is a complexly higher but also epiphenomenally organized level of understanding which can ultimately, and therefore causally, be reducible to the biological level of understanding. In accord with this conception, basic research in psychiatry, as in every other clinical branch of medicine, is ultimately biological, and the research quest then is to search out what genetic complexity (including behavioral aberration) can ultimately be "explained" by an altered placement of a hydroxyl group on a vital organic molecule. Within psychiatry this has been specifically expressed in the oft-quoted statement, "Behind every twisted thought there is a twisted molecule."

It should be abundantly clear from the body of this whole presentation that my own position is exactly the opposite one. If we take seriously the conceptualization that psychiatry is a clinical discipline in medicine, a branch of the healing arts, and that it rests equally on three basic science knowledge bases in the biological, psychological, and social science realms, then it follows that it is a field in which one needs to be able to do both applied research (clinical application to the phenomena of mental health and illness) and equally basic research in each of the three basic sciences. Put this way, basic does not mean just biological, and is not counterposed to the psychosocial since psychosocial investigation can be and should be equally basic, namely, concern with fundamental mechanisms within the level of discourse, be it biological or psychosocial.

This I would like to assume would be a congenial and an uncontroversial statement at least within the ranks of psychoanalysts with their own appreciation of the fundamental psychological contributions of Sigmund Freud to our knowledge of how the mind of man functions. Yet, as part of what I have earlier called the great metapsychology debate raging in psychoanalysis today, one of the most thoughtful and provocative participants in that debate, Peterfreund (1971), has called for the total abandonment not only of the structure of current metapsychology but of all ego psychological or psychological-level thinking as an explanatory, causal theory of the functioning of the mind. He calls a purely psychological theory of the mind an "anachronistic vitalistic position" (p. 41) and further elaborates:

> I am abandoning any attempt to theorize about psychological phenomena from a psychological standpoint, as is the rule in current psychoanalytic theory. And I am abandoning the idea implicit in much of current psychoanalytic theory that the mind is an entity with an independent existence, capable of interacting with the body. No simple or direct equation can be made between current psychoanalytic theory and the information-systems frame of reference which I am attempting to present. The focus for theory shifts *away from* psychological experience or behavior to the larger world of information processes and their links to neurophysiology. The world of man's mind will be viewed from the *larger world* of biology and evolutionary time [p. 148; emphasis added].

I have quoted at this length from a contemporary psychoanalytic theorist merely to underline the importance of this issue as a fundamental focus of current debate within both academic psychiatry more broadly and psychoanalysis more narrowly. The clarification of this issue is of fundamental importance to both disciplines since it is so critical to the conceptualization of the research enterprise in both arenas, within psychiatry and within psychoanalysis, and thereby to the impact of the research findings on the theory and practice in each of the fields. Here I think academic psychiatry and psychoanalysis stand on common ground; they have a shared and common problem, and conceptual clarification in the one realm will be directly reflected in the other.

4. The last of the major themes preoccupying current academic psychiatry is the central one of the relationship of *psychotherapy* as an activity to academic psychiatry. At one time, some ten to twenty years ago, this was not an issue. Psychotherapy was universally and unquestioningly regarded as a central, and mostly *the* central, clinical and therapeutic activity of the psychiatric practitioner and therefore the central pedagogic activity of the academic psychiatric teacher and clinical supervisor. Not an officially or legally recognized discipline in itself, psychotherapy was rather looked at as the central skill that marked the mental health practitioner and therefore central to psychiatry, but also to the allied mental health disciplines, clinical psychology and psychiatric social work.

Today all of that is under question in a confusing babel of ideological, social, and political cross-currents. There is the attack by political opponents on the shibboleth of the "medical model," which they declare to be the outmoded symbol of psychiatry's anachronistic bondage or allegiance to (antihumanistic or even antihuman) medicine. There is the rise of alternative therapeutic paradigms (behavioristic or existential-humanistic) and their derived alternative therapies (behavior modification, Gestalt, and transactional therapies, etc.). There is a further extreme, the human potential and encounter movement dealing with issues of growth and of actualization, not of health and illness. All of these together have served both to meld various interpersonal helping processes into a more amorphous and a less technically differentiated mix of human helping services and at the same time to push these now less professional helping processes out of the orbit of psychiatry as a clinical helping profession, and one suspiciously linked to medical hegemony via its so-called medical model. This feat of attempting to thrust the center of gravity of psychotherapy out of psychiatry can indeed be accomplished fairly readily if most of mental and emotional illness, except for the organic syndromes and perhaps the major psychoses, is transformed into merely "problems in living," and this one can also recognize as a trend abetted in part from within the center of psychiatry itself (Szasz, 1961).

Put somewhat differently, the question can readily become one of why any therapist would need or want to be a psychiatrist these days. Psychiatry, for its part, has experienced a tremendous new surge of biological knowledge and pharmacological therapeutics in the realms especially of severe mental disorder, which everyone acknowledges to be an exclusive province of psychiatry. So perhaps psychiatry should attend more exclusively to those very severely ill for whose care it has an unchallenged prerogative, a social argument for which can be made out in terms of society's greatest need of psychiatry. Psychotherapy or the psychotherapies would then be the province of all the various practitioners of various theoretical and school persuasions, and all the instant intimacy and self-help movements, to deal with all the many individuals with acknowledged "problems in living."

Stated this way, it is an extreme and a fringe argument, and few of us in psychiatry or in the main professional centers of the other traditional mental health professions would subscribe to it. Most of us are more than a little aware of not just the antipsychiatric but also the antiprofessional and ultimately the anti-intellectual tenor of the whole movement. Certainly psychiatry, and just as certainly academic psychiatry, is in no serious risk of turning its back on psychotherapy, though there are a few psychiatrists who, as I have indicated, are ideologically committed to getting psychotherapy (or rather interpersonal helping) out from under psychiatry. There are more psychiatrists who in their personal commitments within the field are working primarily in the biological arena and eschew psychotherapy as a professional activity that they themselves carry out.

The real danger within psychiatry is a subtler one, that the current melange of helping movements, therapies, schools, encounters, and self-actualizations can in their total impact tarnish the coin, can undermine dynamic psychotherapy—read psychoanalytic psychotherapy—as a principled scientific activity and thus weaken the fabric of something which is central (theoretically and practically) to both psychiatry and psychoanalysis and is a main common ground between the two. Here again, then, psychiatry as an academic and professional enterprise and psychoanalysis as a discipline indeed have common cause in the continuing assertion of a scientific psychotherapy built on a scientific theory of the mind as the essential centerpiece in the continuing psychiatric enterprise, even as its biological science and behavioral science components grow in their importance.

This overview of the many dimensions and issues of relationship between academic psychiatry and psychoanalysis, has followed the historical route that is psychoanalytically so congenial, starting with Freud, as is our wont, but concentrating on the period since World War II and the changing vicissitudes of that relationship over that period as I have been witness to those changes and participated in them. I am sure that my own particular historical perspectives and the emphases that I have accorded to particular issues will not be equally agreed to by all. But I do hope that I have at least persuaded any who have been wavering, or who have been openly skeptical, to my own conviction that academic psychiatry and psychoanalysis are indeed linked together in multiple ways in shared conceptual and clinical endeavor and that the future of each will only be the brighter the more it is shared on broadly traveled bridges with the other.

9.

The Future of Psychoanalysis

ROBERT S. WALLERSTEIN, M.D. AND
EDWARD M. WEINSHEL, M.D.

An invitation to write an article on the future of psychoanalysis evokes a response that is both personal and speculative. Our personal response is derived, for each of us, from almost four decades of the clinical work of psychoanalysis and also from years of intense involvement in the organizational life of the American Psychoanalytic Association and the International Psychoanalytical Association. Our speculations are inevitably colored by these experiences, both national and worldwide.

Any discussion of the future of psychoanalysis can be approached from a variety of perspectives: the nature of psychoanalysis as a science; its nature as a discipline; psychoanalytic education and its relationship to the wider academic world for which Freud always yearned; the nature of psychoanalytic research; the nature, and scope, of professional practice; and the institutional expression of psychoanalysis in the International Psychoanalytical Association and its component organizations. Space constraints dictate that we deal with these issues selectively; we cannot devote equal space to each, and some we may scant almost completely or defer altogether.

PSYCHOANALYSIS AS A SCIENCE

The nature of psychoanalysis as a science is perhaps the most fundamental of all these questions. It is also the issue that may be beset by
the most intense theoretical controversy and the most fundamental
cleavage. On the one hand, there is the natural science model in
all its variations, ranging from those that claim lineage from
Freud—ego psychology and the interpersonal, object relational, self
psychological, Kleinian, and Bionian conceptions—to their replace-
ments by information theory, systems, and cybernetic models. On
the other hand, there are the varieties of humanistic (i.e., hermeneutic, phenomenological, subjectivistic, or linguistically based)
conceptualizations, including, of course, the Lacanian. This is a scientific debate that is far from resolution; to the contrary, it is an
arena of widening differences, focused on by one of us (Wallerstein,
1988a) as the problem of our increasing theoretical diversity, or
pluralism, as we have come to call it.

    Within this arena, our own commitment is to a natural science
model and our own allegiance, by training and practice, is to the
ego psychological, now the post ego psychological, paradigm. The
basis for this commitment and allegiance has been spelled out by
us at length elsewhere (chapter 7; Wallerstein, 1888c; Weinshel,
1990) and will not be repeated here. The path toward coming to
terms with this range of theoretical differences (albeit within the
natural science model) has at least been pointed out in one of the
articles referred to (Wallerstein, 1988c).

PSYCHOANALYSIS AS A DISCIPLINE

Inextricably linked to the nature of psychoanalysis as a science, but
also clearly distinct, is our conception of its nature as a discipline.
Here we feel that we are in the midst of a fundamental shift in our
vision, a real sea-change, particularly in America, but one which
most of us are aware of only occasionally. This is an issue usually
conceptualized as the controversy over nonmedical or "lay analysis," which we see rather as a controversy over the very nature of
our discipline. Is psychoanalysis a branch of the medical healing
arts, a subspecialty, as it were, of psychiatry? Or is it a fully independent discipline, with an important interface, to be sure, with natural
science, but with equally important interfaces with academic and

clinical psychology, with the behavioral and social sciences, and with philosophy, law, and other relevant domains of human thought?

This controversy has been central (again, most intensely in America) ever since Freud published *The Question of Lay Analysis* (1926b) in defense of Theodor Reik who had been arraigned in a Viennese court on charges of "medical quackery" for practicing psychoanalysis (putatively a branch of medicine) without a medical license. Freud's defense of Reik was followed a year later by the publication of twenty-six responses (pro and con) from analysts from just about every one of the existing psychoanalytic centers with final remarks by Freud and Eitingon (Jones et al., 1927). A political resolution of this controversy was attempted at the 1938 Paris IPA Congress. The American analysts (solidly opposed to lay analysis) demanded that the IPA's International Training Commission be abolished, so that the American Association could wrest total autonomy in regard to training standards; it would then be free to bar psychoanalytic training for nonphysicians within the United States. The Europeans (mostly open to parity for training of qualified physicians and nonphysicians alike) strongly objected, and the issue was put off for final decision at the next Congress, scheduled for 1940. World War II intervened, and when the next Congress met in Zurich in 1949 after an eleven-year hiatus, it was taken for granted that the "1938 Agreement" was operative, constituting the American as a Regional Association of the IPA with exclusive jurisdiction over official psychoanalytic training in the United States and full autonomy over training standards.

From this "1938 Regional Association Agreement," psychoanalysis as a discipline took two different developmental paths for the next half-century, although the controversy over lay analysis was never stilled. In Europe the development everywhere was one of total openness of training to all qualified applicants, regardless of disciplinary background. In practice, this worked out to physicians comprising from half to two-thirds of the trained analysts in each psychoanalytic society, with nonphysicians from a great diversity of backgrounds (though more from psychology than from any other) comprising the remaining third to a half. In the United States, to the contrary, during the same half-century psychoanalytic training was restricted to physicians, except for the opening up (in the late 1950s) of "research training" to a very limited number of academic research scholars. These scholars undertook psychoanalytic training within the context of their careers in their original disciplines, their scholarship and research activities presumably enhanced by psycho-analytic knowledge and perspective. In Latin America, the most re-cently developed of the three major regions of psychoanalytic activity worldwide, the trend was not uniform, but was at first more in keeping with the United States exclusionary model.

We all well know the events of the past few years, and they will not be discussed in any detail here. There was the lawsuit, leading to three-and-a-half years of litigation, brought by four clinical psy-chologists against the American Psychoanalytic Association and two of its affiliated institutes, with the International named as a codefen-dant. The plaintiffs charged that the barring of full clinical psycho-analytic training to nonphysicians by the American constituted restraint of trade and a violation of the antitrust laws. The final, out-of-court settlement of the suit was on terms that we feel were in the best interests of psychoanalysis as well as of the plaintiffs and the defendants. Concomitantly, by two-thirds vote the American passed the Gaskill Committee proposal, opening a pathway for full clinical training in psychoanalysis for nonphysicians. Bylaw changes were voted by the IPA at its Business Meeting in Montreal in 1987 and subsequently ratified in a mail ballot of the whole membership. The changes altered the 1938 Regional Association Agreement: the American retained its internal control over training standards but relinquished its exclusive jurisdiction within the United States. Thus, nonmedical psychoanalytic training centers that had developed out-side the American Association would now be eligible for direct affil-iation with the IPA, provided they met IPA standards of training and practice.

What this all adds up to is the opening of two main channels of psychoanalytic training under IPA auspices for nonphysician, qualified mental health professionals, in the United States. One channel lies within the established institutes of the American (the implementation of the Gaskill proposal). The other is in institutes to be directly affiliated with the IPA but outside the framework of the American. These are long existing or newly developing nonmedical institutes in the United States, twenty-seven of which have already made formal inquiry of the International. Five of them have now been judged to be sufficiently developed and sufficiently in accord with IPA standards to warrant IPA site visits, which are currently underway. If the evaluations are positive, these institutes will be proposed for IPA affiliated status, as official Study Groups or Provi-sional Societies, at the 1989 Rome Congress. Clearly, as these trends continue over the next decade, the institutes of the American will be training increasing numbers of nonphysicians, and their percentage within the ranks of trained analysts within the American will rise significantly. At the same time the newly admitted nonmedical societies and institutes in the United States will be competing for medical candidates, since they, too, will offer a channel of access to IPA membership for their graduates.

Coextensive with what has been happening in the United States, but in a totally different historical and political context, have been developments in Latin America. The past decade has seen an increasing political democratization, including in the largest countries, Brazil and Argentina, with a curiously parallel democratization in the governing structure of some of the largest psychoanalytic societies in those nations. An aspect of this has been the abrogation, in Argentina, for example, of a law which had restricted the practice of psychoanalysis to physicians, and the opening of the doors of one psychoanalytic society after another to the training of nonphysicians. At this point, analytic training is restricted to physicians in only two of the societies in Latin America (these, among the smallest), and we understand that it is in the process of being opened up in one of them.

What all this means is that we are now approaching worldwide the situation that has all along existed in Europe, and that the divisive struggle over lay analysis is beginning to be surmounted everywhere. As we see it, the full implication of this (when finally achieved) will be a fundamental shift in the conception of the nature of psychoanalysis as a discipline; a shift in the nature of the psychoanalytic identity. To put it succinctly, the shift will be from "I am a psychiatrist who practices psychoanalysis," which, for many North and Latin Americans, has been the prevailing conception, to "I am a psychoanalyst whose original discipline was psychiatry"—or clinical psychology or whatever.

This major shift in the identity of the analyst and in the nature of psychoanalysis as a discipline was actually both pleaded for and presaged by Maxwell Gitelson (1964) in a plenary address to the American, aptly titled "On the Identity Crisis in American Psychoanalysis." There, in the context of a discussion of his call to "cast a wider net for students of psychoanalysis" (p. 474) in America, which he said was a return to the "question of lay analysis," Gitelson stated:

I have been turned in this direction by my consideration of the history of psychoanalysis in America. *I think the time has come for psychoanalysis to accept its identity as a separate scientific discipline,* whose practitioners can be various kinds of intellectually qualified persons who are humanly qualified for the human experiment that is the psychoanalytic situation [p. 474].

Apropos the shift in student body that would reflect this identity shift, Gitelson said:

The emotional qualities that ensure the fulfillment of the human obligation to patients are basic to the practice of medicine. But in the psychoanalytic field the practitioner must also have the intellectual qualities and scope which will bring to it the necessary scientific sophistication. . . . The prevailing tendency to place exclusive value on antecedent psychiatric training as such may need to be revised in respect to the barrier it erects against scientists with other qualifications who might advance the conceptual horizon of psychoanalysis [p. 474; see also Weinshel, 1979, pp. 81–82].

None of this has to mean any weakening of the biological embeddedness of psychoanalysis as a natural science theory of the functioning of a mind within a body. Nor need it mean any weakening of the powerful interface between psychoanalysis and psychiatry (for psychoanalysis *is* the dynamic psychology of psychiatry), or medicine (the whole area of psychosomatics), or biology (especially neurobiology). It does not have to mean any lessening of psychoanalysts' involvement in academic medicine and academic psychiatry, including, of course, the teaching of psychoanalytic concepts and psychotherapy in psychiatry residency programs. On the professional (and political) level, the psychoanalysts with strong medical and psychiatric roots and identities may continue to play active roles in the organized medical and psychiatric associations. Scientifically and theoretically, this will include the continued cultivation of the interfaces between psychology and physiology (more specifically, between psychoanalysis and neurobiology) in the ways described, for example, by Reiser (1984), in *Mind, Brain, Body,* although this is still more a promise made than one fulfilled (Wallerstein, 1985). And, of course, it is far from clear how the rapidly increasing knowledge in neurobiology, molecular biology, and molecular genetics will interdigitate with our psychoanalytic understandings of mental functioning, and whether this new biological knowledge will (or can) add to our psychoanalytic clinical effectiveness.

Alongside this continued cultivation of the biological–medical interface with psychoanalysis, there will be a more formal legitimation of other natural interfaces—those with academic psychology and clinical psychology, and those with all the behavioral and social sciences and the humanities as they relate to our understanding of the individual human mind. As part of this, we also wish to point out another recent and continuing shift in our conception of the nature of psychoanalysis as a discipline. This pertains to the kind of psychology that psychoanalysis is and, pari passu, to its limitations as a psychology. In *The Question of Lay Analysis,* Freud (1926b) made his most specific statement on this subject:

> It will not have escaped my readers that in what I have said I have assumed as axiomatic something that is still violently disputed in the discussion. I have assumed, that is to say, that psycho-analysis is not a specialized branch of medicine. I cannot see how it is possible to dispute this. *Psycho-analysis is a part of psychology;* not of medical psychology in the old sense, not of the psychology of morbid processes, but simply of psychology. It is certainly not the whole of psychology, but its substructure and perhaps even its entire foundation. The possibility of its application to medical purposes must not lead us astray. Electricity and radiology also have their medical application, but the science to which they both belong is none the less physics [p. 252; emphasis added].

Here Freud was clear in his mind on two points: he did not consider psychoanalysis to be a part of medicine but rather a part of psychology; and he considered it only a part, not the whole of psychology. Those who came after him, particularly those who developed the (American) ego psychology paradigm (Hartmann, 1939, 1964; Hartmann, Kris, and Loewenstein, 1964; Rapaport, 1967), were far more ambitious for psychoanalysis as a psychology. Hartmann and his coworkers were intent upon spreading psychoanalysis beyond its clinical beginnings in the study of the minds of the mentally and emotionally disordered. They wished to make of psychoanalysis a general psychology of the total mind, seen as the organ of adaptation via proper maturational unfolding in an "average expectable environment." An autonomous ego differentiates out of an original id–ego matrix; its conflict-free spheres of functioning are developmentally elaborated alongside its apparatuses born of conflict, with areas of primary, then secondary autonomy. In 1956, in one of his best known papers, Rapaport (1967, pp. 594–623), the great systematizer of the ego psychology paradigm, sought to synthesize Hartmann's contributions with Erikson's focus on the *psychosocial* developmental unfolding via an epigenetic ground plan. In Rapaport's last years, he was turning his attention to the experimental study of psychoanalytic propositions. He was convinced that psychoanalysis lacked only a sound learning theory to achieve the ego psychologists' dream of psychoanalysis as a general psychology encompassing all the realms of normal and abnormal mental functioning.

Current, post ego psychological psychoanalysis has been marked by a general retreat from the hegemonic vision of Hartmann and Rapaport, to a position which Kris had enunciated as long ago as 1947: that psychoanalysis is, after all, nothing but human behavior considered from the point of view of conflict (i.e., that it can only truly illuminate and influence those aspects of mental functioning that are born of conflict).[1] In keeping with this more modest assessment of the overall place of psychoanalysis within the larger domain of general psychology, there is also a more modest assessment today of the ability of psychoanalysis to eradicate neurotogenic intrapsychic conflict thoroughly and permanently. One of us (Weinshel, 1990) has articulated just this current view of the limitations in how much we can expect to modify intrapsychic conflicts and ameliorate the behaviors and symptoms through which they are expressed.

In summary, we feel that psychoanalysis, considered from the point of view of its nature as a discipline, is clearly coming into an era of a crystallized independent identity. It will be separate from but closely linked to natural science, to general psychology, to the social and behavioral sciences, to the humanities—in short, to all of the relevant realms of the study of the human mind. As an independent psychological discipline—and here Freud's view (1926b) is completely in accord with our current evolution—we see it as but a partial psychology, a psychology of the mind in conflict, with a suitably realistic therapeutic reach in the overcoming of conflict and the behaviors and symptoms that reflect it.

---

[1] It would be a digression to discuss here self psychology's posited distinction between its theory of psychological formation as born not of conflict but of deficit or deficiency, and "classical" psychoanalysis, prototypically considered a psychology of conflict. We feel this to be a spurious distinction, and each of us (Wallerstein, 1983a; Weinshel, 1990) has counterposed a broadened construction of the concept of conflict in psychoanalysis. Within these constructions, the so-called deficit phenomena described by self psychology can be at least as fruitfully considered as manifestations of conflict. Similar critiques of self psychology have been advanced by Segel (1981) and Treurniet (1980).

TRAINING FOR PSYCHOANALYSIS

These considerations lead us to our views on psychoanalytic training and the proper context for it. Two basic models for training have taken hold in America. The model employed until the end of World War II was the one developed by Eitingon for the first formal psychoanalytic training institute, in Berlin, started in 1920:the tripartite scheme of personal (or training) analysis, didactic curriculum with theoretical and clinical seminars, and the conduct of several analyses under supervision. This is the model of the independent psychoanalytic institute, a part-time, usually a night school, with a student body engaged in full-time clinical practice to earn a livelihood and to defray the costs of psychoanalytic training. The well-known advantage is the total autonomy in the pursuit of psychoanalytic training, with no constraints imposed by nonpsychoanalytic influences or forces. It was the model historically imposed on psychoanalysis in its beginnings in central Europe. There, Freud and his followers were denied formal access to academic medicine or to the university at large, partly because of the revolutionary and shocking nature of Freud's ideas, and partly because of the official anti-Semitism that would yield no place in academia to the followers of this "Jewish science."

The other psychoanalytic training model developed in the wake of World War II, the period marked by the psychoanalytic idea's successful capture of American psychiatry and its training centers in the nation's medical schools. Actually, part of the American fervor to limit psychoanalytic training to psychiatrists derived from the self-conscious intent to identify completely with medicine and to make American psychiatry thoroughly psychoanalytic, thereby making the teaching of psychoanalytic psychotherapy the central clinical activity of psychiatric residency training. This campaign succeeded brilliantly in the post-World War II days through the decade of the 1950s, as one after another medical school department of psychiatry sought an analyst chairman who would bring analysts and analytic teaching to academic center stage.

One major product of this campaign was the creation of a succession of new psychoanalytic institutes within medical school departments of psychiatry at Columbia, Downstate, Cleveland, Pittsburgh, and Denver in the first wave. The institutes were accorded, to begin with, all necessary autonomy by the department chairmen, who were either analysts themselves or analytically sympathetic psychiatrists. What was asked in return was that the institute—its faculty and its candidates—play a major role in the department's clinical psychiatric teaching (i.e., teaching psychoanalytic principles and psychotherapy to the psychiatric residents). It was hoped that this would stimulate interest in full psychoanalytic training in the brightest and best of the residents, a process looked upon as mutually beneficial by the department of psychiatry and the psychoanalytic institute. Even where the local psychoanalytic institute was fully autonomous, as in the first model, many of its most active members played similar roles in medical schools or teaching hospital departments of psychiatry, volunteering their time to teach psychoanalytic principles and therapy. Everywhere, the atmosphere was heady with visions of psychoanalysis being ensconced in academia in a way always denied to Freud—even though only through the medical school and not the university at large.

There was a third psychoanalytic training model proposed, but one that was never fully actualized. This was the far more sweeping and innovative proposal by Shakow (1962) for the creation of autonomous psychoanalytic institutes within the university, independent from but affiliated with both the medical school and the graduate faculties in the behavioral and social sciences. This is in keeping with our discussion of the concept of psychoanalysis as an independent academic discipline (not a subspecialty of psychiatry), but one with its ultimate proper place within the university. According to its idealistic proponents, only then could psychoanalysis truly flourish in fruitful interaction with the other scholarly disciplines, and only then could its own scholarship and research find the proper academic stimulation and nourishment.

More practical (in the sense of more immediately feasible) was the variant proposed by Anna Freud (1971) in her "The Ideal Psychoanalytic Institute: A Utopia." She envisioned a full-time institute where scientific work and educational work would not be the part-time and night-time activities of tired men and women, an institute where there would be salaried positions with major time commitments, as in the university tradition, even if necessarily outside the university structure. In her Hampstead Clinic and Child Therapy Training Centre, Anna Freud approximated that model as best she could within the constraints of her limited resources, which were dependent upon philanthropic donations. In October 1974, the

American held a week-long Conference on Psychoanalytic Education and Research assessing "the current situation and future possibilities." That conference, via the work of nine commissions, discussed these various training models at length, with the implications and the potentialities of each for our psychoanalytic educational and research enterprise. A book of the proceedings was published (Goodman, 1977).

These are, then, the various educational models for psychoanalytic training that have been vying for place and favor over almost the whole of our professional lifetimes. As to which one would—or should—win out in our preferred psychoanalytic future, we have had, over much of that time, somewhat different perspectives. One of us (Wallerstein, 1972) has long felt the historic imperative of a university-centered psychoanalysis. This does not necessarily have to be within a medical school department of psychiatry, although that has so far seemed the only practical pattern. More ideally (or idealistically), it would entail some version of the Shakow or Anna Freud proposals. Only then would the relative isolation of psychoanalysis from the wider scientific and intellectual world be overcome, and only then could we truly upgrade the scholarliness and seriousness of the academic aspect of our enterprise.

The majority analytic sentiment, however, has been with the other one of us. While such analysts wish to continue strong links with academic psychiatry and psychiatric residency training, they are wary of the price that could be exacted—the subtly coercive pressures that could control or dilute educational content and form if the psychoanalytic institutes were to give up their independence and move into the seductive embrace of the proffered academic homes. Unhappily, the trend of almost two decades has, at least for the time being, borne out these misgivings. With the explosive growth of neurobiology and its applications in psychopharmacologic therapy of the major mental disorders, the psychoanalytic tide within psychiatry has receded far from the high-water mark of the 1960s. Psychiatry has become increasingly biological, its basic research increasingly focused in the areas of molecular biology and molecular genetics, and its new rallying cry that of "remedicalization." Crisis intervention, consultation-liaison, substance abuse programs, and geriatric services are the new clinical centers of activity, with a heavily biological—and often enough a subtly antipsychological or overtly nonpsychological—emphasis. Chairmanships of medical school departments of psychiatry now rarely go to analysts, and psychotherapy teaching has a much diminished place in residency training programs. Coincidentally, in at least some university-based psychoanalytic institutes, the once mutually advantageous interaction between institute and parent department has deteriorated, in one instance disastrously.

The apogee of this trend is in an ongoing debate over whether psychotherapy training should continue to be required or whether it should be converted into an elective within the overburdened psychiatric residency training program. Even further, there is the call on the part of a very distinguished chairman of a medical school department of psychiatry and university provost that neurology and psychiatry be reunited into a combined department of neuropsychiatry. Having separate departments and separate domains of inquiry is stated by him to be as anachronistic as it would be to have a department of ear, nose, and throat separate from a department of hearing, smelling, and breathing.

None of this fact or rhetoric means, however, that the university is lost to the psychoanalytic idea. Quite aside from the penetration of psychoanalysis into psychiatry and its training centers over a span of several decades, psychoanalysis—and this was a mark of Freud's genius—has always been far broader than its therapeutic and training functions. In the celebratory words of W. H. Auden (1940) upon Freud's death, "To us he is no more a person now but a whole climate of opinion." Psychoanalysis in this sense is now an integral part of the intellectual climate of our time, coloring the way we see our world and our place in it as profoundly as Darwinian or Marxist thought or Einstein's thought. Specifically, psychoanalytic perspectives have everywhere entered the university world, from the pioneering of Lionel Trilling at Columbia and Norman Holland at Buffalo in English literature and literary criticism, to departments of comparative literature, French, philosophy, sociology, anthropology, and, of course, psychology. Whatever the fate of psychoanalytic teaching within psychiatry and the medical schools,[2] the university

---

[2] We have neither space nor time to discuss, in this connection, the relationship of psychoanalysis to psychiatry in other countries. Mention should be made, however, of the very interesting German postwar evolution. The departments of psychiatry in West German medical schools have been continuing, in the tradition of Kraepelin, the nonanalytic, biological treatment of psychiatric disorders, primarily the functional and organic psychoses. Alongside the psychiatrists who deal thus with the major mental disorders (increasingly in psychopharmacological terms), the psychoanalysts have entered about half of the medical schools in the country, via separate departments of psychosomatics and psychotherapy. They are attempting to bring psychoanalytic understandings and psychotherapeutic treatments to the range of psychosomatic and neurotic disorders. The two departments, psychiatric and psychoanalytic, seem, for the most part, to exist peacefully side by side.

will increasingly be a place where psychoanalytic ideas will help illuminate the problems of human mental functioning, and will do so
in fruitful interaction with the perspectives of cognate disciplines.
Actually, we are confident, too, that the pendulum will self-correct
over time in academic psychiatry and that psychodynamic and bio-
logic thinking will be able to coexist as complementary perspectives
on the phenomena of mental illness and behavioral disorders. But
in terms of the psychoanalytic institute as a center that trains candidates for a profession as well as educating them for a science, perhaps the university cannot, at least in the foreseeable future, fulfill
Freud's dream or Shakow's or Anna Freud's. Perhaps (regrettably
for one of us) the original psychoanalytic institute training model
forced on us by exclusionary necessity will continue to be the
most viable.

This does not mean, however, that the format and the content
of psychoanalytic institute curricula do not need critical review. The
whole tripartite educational system has remained essentially unchanged since its beginnings in 1920, despite the fact that the formal
didactic seminar has been the object of unremitting criticism and
has always been looked upon as the least essential component.[3] For
example, we have always taken the training analysis and supervised
analyses with the utmost seriousness, and analytic careers have been
held up or have foundered completely at these vital points. But how
often have we heard that someone has actually failed a course or
been made to repeat it, let alone have a whole training jeopardized
over issues of achievement and nonachievement in seminars?

The criticisms of our formal curricula have been many. From
our research candidates, but also from our regular clinical candidates, too often do we hear complaints that their teachers seem
narrowly professional and overly dogmatic. Rather than the classroom and seminar being experienced as a place for critical challenge of espoused viewpoints for purposes of comparison and
contrast, the students complain that they become arenas for the
mastery of material presented by teachers who brook no questions
and make no effort to set their presentations within the context of
the problems of the field and the limitations of the theory.

---

[3] For a number of years Vann Spruiell chaired a COPE Study Group on Formal Didactic
Teaching in the Institutes of the American Psychoanalytic Association. It would be of great
interest and usefulness if some of the findings of that Study Group were available to all our
institute curriculum committees.

Aside from these issues of the general trade-school approach in what should be a graduate academic training program are issues of content and format. Almost unique among intellectual disciplines, psychoanalysis is almost everywhere still taught as it was in the earliest days—chronologically, in the unfolding of Freud's views and those of selected others who have come after him. Clearly, there are not just reasons of history and convenience for this, but reasons related to the nature of the psychoanalytic edifice and how it can best be comprehended. Nevertheless, only a few among us, and Arlow[4] and Gill are notable among these, have called for the intellectual effort of rethinking the curriculum to see how it might be restructured along thematic lines, the themes to be presented in terms of today's understandings, with prior perspectives called upon as they help in illuminating today's positions. This is the way any other scientific discipline, whether natural science or social science, is taught.

The issue is, of course, not as stark as here stated, but it is nonetheless real. Chemists, by contrast, do not start with immersion in phlogiston theory as a preliminary to the understanding of oxidation. Needless to say, this, perhaps like much else in this paper, can lend itself to misinterpretation of our meaning. We, of course, are not chemists, and we deal with a science in which the unique history and development of individual human minds are central keys to understanding. There is virtue in understanding the origin of psychoanalytic concepts and why changes have occurred in them. But it is also true that our students need not repeat the whole evolution, step by step, in our curriculum. The challenge would be to fashion a curriculum that fully reflects our present-day knowledge while inculcating an appreciation of its historical derivation to illuminate how and why our knowledge base has developed the way it has.

Related complaints center on the psychoanalytic parochialism of our curricula. With few exceptions around the world (and the British Institute is a good example of such exception) because of special historical circumstance, our curricula have mostly rigidly reflected the dominant theoretical position of the particular training center, and there has been little incentive to explore the literature of other perspectives. Until the rise of Kohut's self psychology, institutes in the United States had been almost monolithically within the

---

[4] This was affirmed in Arlow's paper with Brenner (1988, pp. 6–8) in this series on the future of psychoanalysis.

dominant ego psychology paradigm. Until recent years, institutes in Latin America have been equally single-mindedly Kleinian and/or Bionian. Aside from the shared beginnings in reading Freud, there have been almost no points of correspondence in what is read and integrated into one's psychoanalytic understanding and identity between those trained in the North American and in the Latin American contexts.

None of these criticisms, some of them harsh and perhaps overstated, are new. What is new, we think, is that we are entering a period of both curricular flux and challenge. The challenge will come from the significant influx into the institutes of the American of new categories of students, many of them nonmedical and from university graduate backgrounds. On the one hand, they will be academically and perhaps theoretically more savvy; on the other hand, they will be less clinically immersed and technically focused than our traditional candidates who have come by way of medicine and psychiatric residency. They will pose a challenge to our faculties to fashion the kind of curriculum in that proper mix, adjusted to the differing needs of each category of students, so that all will emerge with the optimal integration of professional training for clinical practice and academic education for the advancement of the science. Curiously, this process may well be facilitated by the loosening of the exclusive ties to psychiatry and medicine, with a concomitant assumption of a new independent psychoanalytic identity and a more self-conscious effort in curriculum making to include the best and most appropriate elements of professional school and of graduate academic education without being the intellectual captive of either.

The curricular flux will come from the process we are finally beginning to see: the true internationalization of psychoanalysis. We are all more willing today to acknowledge the diversity of theoretical perspectives within psychoanalysis—the ego psychological, object relational, Kleinian, Bionian, Lacanian, and self-psychological—as well as the different regional, cultural, language and thought conventions within which psychoanalysis is expressed. We are more willing today to see each theoretical perspective as a legitimate framework within which respected colleagues can organize the clinical encounters in their consulting rooms and interact therapeutically with their patients. The 36th International Psychoanalytical Association Congress in Rome in July 1989, with the theme, "The

Common Ground of Psychoanalysis," was intended as an exploration of the clinical commonality and thus of the true psychoanalytic consensus that can be found within our theoretical diversity.

Inevitably, these considerations will have an impact upon our curricula. We all have individual theoretical allegiances fashioned out of our own training and practice experiences, and these will, of course, provide a central curricular focus. But at the same time, we will be trying to impart to our students a respectful understanding of other theoretical positions and of why, for many colleagues, those alternative positions are preferred as ways of understanding the phenomena of the consulting room. Put most simply, we will all be more knowledgeable about other theoretical perspectives and their special values, and about other language- and culture-determined psychoanalytic voices. The increased translation efforts, particularly from the French and Spanish languages into English; the ongoing efforts at cross-language dialogue between American and French analysts (Poland and Major, 1984); the more frequent worldwide travel for lectures and clinical consultation; and the activities of the International in its new publication venture (educational monographs in the four official IPA languages, with representatives of different major theoretical viewpoints discussing topics of significant analytic interest)—all these will facilitate this process. We would like to predict that our formal analytic institute curricula a decade from now will be more catholic in scope while remaining concentratedly analytic; that they will be more academic (in the best sense of that maligned word) while at the same time effectively professional; and that all this will make the institutes much more exciting as centers of learning and teaching. The time is propitious for this development, and the opportunity is here.

Again, we wish to guard against misinterpretation. We do not intend this to be read as a call for an uncritical ecumenicism that equates each psychoanalytic perspective in all particulars with every other. We are talking, rather, of a broadened, more "tolerant" curriculum in each of our educational centers (whatever the particular theoretical heritage and allegiances of each training center), a curriculum that would be nonetheless still integrated into an overall coherent theoretical perspective, or perhaps a creative amalgam of two or more. We will then be able to see more broadly and deeply how the same clinical phenomena are conceptualized within other theoretical systems with their differing idioms.

RESEARCH IN PSYCHOANALYSIS

Consideration of educational curriculum always brings up issues of scholarship and research, the more so as the training curriculum comes to transcend the narrow professionalism of purpose and parochialism of viewpoint we have discussed. For many reasons, psychoanalysis does not have an established tradition of formal and systematic research embracing a significant set of its membership. George Engel (1968) enumerated these reasons in great detail and with telling accuracy two decades ago—and a number of us (Beres, Kanzer, Wallenstein, and Zetzel, 1968) were invited to respond as best we could to his indictment. Some of the obstacles to which he pointed have to do with the issues we have discussed in this article: the institutional structures we have built and the way we have organized our educational system as private night schools set in the context of busy lives of full-time clinical practice; the essential isolation of most of our institutes from academia and its scholarship and research; and a curriculum that could in consequence become narrowly professional in the trade school sense. Considerations of this sort have impelled one of us, over many years, to look to the university as the proper home for psychoanalysis, where the very nature of the academic enterprise could help ensure that psychoanalytic scholarship and research would naturally be fostered.

This, of course, would all be ideal if it could have come to pass. But the disenchantment with psychoanalysis in the one part of academia to which it has had access, the medical school departments of psychiatry, and the growing independence of psychoanalysis as a discipline sui generis, require a rethinking of the place for research in psychoanalysis and how it can best be promoted. This situation will probably make the psychoanalytic research enterprise more complicated than ever, but perhaps such research will ultimately be truer to the essential nature of psychoanalysis, which Harrison (1970) called "our peculiar science."

For research in our discipline began with Freud's clinical case study method, and that is still the source of most of what we know in psychoanalysis. Almost two decades ago, one of us (with a collaborator) presented the issues involved in our research enterprise as follows:

There is no need to document the extraordinary reach of the traditional (specifically psychoanalytic) case study method innovated by

Freud. The whole corpus of psychoanalysis . . . comprehending the phenomena of both normal and abnormal personality development and functioning, attests brilliantly to the explanatory power of the theory derived from the data of the consulting room. It has flourished in the hands of its founding genius and of those who have come after and has provided a truly extraordinary range of insights into the structure of the mind, the organization of mental illness, the forces at work in the treatment situation, the processes of change and the requirements of technique. By contrast, it is the sobering appraisal of Strupp, a dedicated psychotherapy researcher (whose professional origins and commitments were fashioned primarily in the research rather than the clinical crucible) that whatever spectacular growth formal research method and research inquiry in psychotherapy have undergone . . . *to this point* these have exerted but very slight influence on the theory and practice of psychotherapy. He states the issue bluntly (Strupp, 1960): "clinical penetration and scientific rigor have varied inversely. . . . If the advances of psychoanalysis as a therapeutic technique are compared with the experimental research contributions, there can be little argument as to which has more profoundly enriched the theory and practice of psychotherapy. To make the point more boldly, I believe that, up to the present, research contributions have had exceedingly little influence on the practical procedures of psychotherapy" [Wallerstein and Sampson, 1971, pp. 11–12].

It is this productive stream of clinically derived insights and formulations, yielding new data and new or revised theory, that must not be allowed to dry up. It is not at all clear, as some aver, that the case study method can no longer be looked upon as yielding new knowledge. Edelson (1984, 1988) has devoted two books to a persuasive demonstration that, properly constructed, the clinical case study not only provides heuristic yield, but has evidential value as well. It can therefore advance the process of testing psychoanalytic hypotheses in full conformity with the canons of natural science—and this, despite the contention of Grünbaum (1984) and others that the data of psychoanalysis are inevitably hopelessly contaminated by suggestion and are thus useless for scientific hypothesis testing.

Given the exciting possibilities documented so impressively by Edelson for an enhanced research yield from the properly constructed case study, it is no loss to these research possibilities that the main locus of psychoanalytic scholarship is not shifting from independent institutes to the university. This kind of study can flourish in any setting that does not constrain the inquiring mind. Typically, it has been the product of solo practitioners or of small groups of colleagues working out of a private practice base and drawing their collegial and scientific nutriment from their own psychoanalytic societies as well as from meetings of the American and the IPA. In this context, Spruiell (1983, pp. 360–361) has written about the value of the small case conference or discussion group as a useful forum of clinical research; here, out of intense discussions and productive disagreements, heuristically valuable formulations have emerged and been added to our literature, as in the monographs of the Kris Study Group. On the other hand, this is the kind of scholarship that is typically not prized or well rewarded in (medical school) academia, although there are exceptions to this generalization.

At the same time, it is clear that the clinical case study method has many shortcomings qua research—described in detail by Wallerstein and Sampson (1971)—and that it must be supplemented by formal and systematized research inquiry if psychoanalytic research is to flourish maximally. Indeed, the main purpose of that article was to justify and to elaborate on the need to go beyond the clinical case study method as the central research instrument and research access to the therapeutic process in psychoanalysis. The article discussed the many problems involved in devising and executing such research in a manner that would be responsive to the subtlety and complexity of the subjectivistic phenomena in our field, and at the same time scientific in the best sense of that term (i.e., loyal to the reality principle as embodied in appropriate canons of scientific inference). This kind of formal and empirical research has always required and will continue to require an academic base or some other full-time clinical setting, such as The Menninger Foundation or the Anna Freud Centre. But it is also exactly the kind of research that has always been done and will continue to be done by those analysts who are full-time academics in medical school departments of psychiatry. Unhappily, such analysts are now few in number, and the new biologism is beleaguering their position and making their possibilities for adequate research funding more precarious. In the near future, there may be further decline in this small volume of such formal psychoanalytic research, not only on therapeutic processes and outcome but also in other psychoanalytically based research areas—in infant and child development, psychosomatics, psychophysiology (sleep-dream, etc.) and experimental studies (perception, cognition, etc.). In partial compensation for whatever falling off there is here, applied psychoanalytic studies in the fields of literary criticism, psychobiography, art and aesthetics, linguistics, history, and society may all be entering a new and exciting phase of expansion. There is clearly a wide range of psychoanalytic research and scholarship, from the precise laboratory study of subliminal stimuli to psychoanalytic studies of Shakespeare. This mirrors roughly (but not isomorphically) the spectrum from natural science to hermeneutic perspectives in psychoanalytic commitment.

PSYCHOANALYSIS AS A PROFESSION

We come now to the nature and scope of psychoanalysis as a profession, to the clinical practice and livelihood that it is for most of us. Here, the issues are legion, and the changes in the conditions of practice confronting the new generation of analysts are bewildering. They include:

1. A diminishing number of psychoanalytic patients;
2. Increasing numbers of mental health practitioners with little or no psychoanalytic training or knowledge;
3. Increasing numbers of nonpsychoanalytically based alternative therapies, some verging on the cultist, and of self-help groups;
4. A systematic retreat from adequate insurance coverage for long-term psychotherapeutic care (even in countries where national health insurance is advancing or has already been fully achieved);
5. The growing preoccupation everywhere with cost effectiveness and cost containment (with psychoanalysis losing out to psychopharmacologic approaches, not only to the psychoses but to some borderline and neurotic disorders as well); and
6. The growing necessity for peer review and utilization review systems, with their inevitable impingements on the privacy and confidentiality of the two-party therapeutic transaction.

Just to allude to this host of sociopoliticoeconomic issues in this cursory manner brings to mind varieties of consequences, some of which many of us are already encountering. The economic impact on the income potential of psychoanalysts is already clear—and adverse. Other consequences are not necessarily detrimental. Two worldwide studies of the effect of national health insurance coverage for psychoanalytic treatments, conducted under the auspices of the IPA and the European Psychoanalytic Federation (by Widlöcher and Groen-Prakken respectively), document clearly that psychoanalytic work and the psychoanalytic identity suffer in some aspects: while there is the benefit of insurance reimbursement, there is inevitably the constraint of the linked insurance controls.[5]

We will not attempt to discuss the many consequences and implications—professional, economic, political, and ethical—of the changes that are occurring worldwide in the clinical practice of psychoanalysis and intensive psychotherapy. Many of them are obvious and known to all of us, although we will assign to these shifts our own idiosyncratic, positive or negative affective valences. We want, rather, to discuss here a related but distinct aspect of the current changes as they affect the future of psychoanalytic professional practice: the relationship of psychoanalysis to dynamic or psychoanalytic psychotherapy.

This issue has preoccupied our field ever since World War II, particularly in America where psychoanalytic psychotherapy evolved in the effort to adapt technique to the clinical requirements of patients not suitable for the stringencies of proper psychoanalysis. It developed naturally as an expression of the close adherence of American psychoanalysis to psychiatry and to its clinical patient population.[6] One of us (Wallerstein, 1989a) has recounted a progression

---

[5] Two examples will suffice. In some western European countries with national health insurance, psychoanalysis may be fully covered for its usual duration. In the largest system of all (Germany), however, it is covered only for three hundred hours, after which the patient must bear the total cost. It occasions little surprise to hear that a great majority of the psychoanalyses under the German system manage to be satisfactorily concluded in under three hundred hours! In Great Britain, of course, psychoanalysis, as such, is completely excluded from the national health system, although less intensive, once-weekly psychoanalytic psychotherapies are available in some localities within the national health service. The other unhappy example comes from the practice in some countries (Canada and Sweden, for example) to cover the cost of psychoanalysis when carried out by physicians (as an aspect of the practice of medicine) but not when carried out by nonphysicians. The latter must obtain their patients in the private market outside the system. The impact of this differential treatment on the relations between physician and nonphysician analyst should be obvious.

[6] In fact, dynamic psychotherapy as a technical adaptation of psychoanalytic theory to a wider array of patients than those suitable for unmodified psychoanalysis has been the single specifically American contribution to clinical psychiatry, albeit a glorious one. Psychoanalysis was created by Freud in Austria; the descriptive nosology of the major mental disorders was the work of Kraepelin and his school in Germany; electroconvulsive therapy was inaugurated by Cerletti and Bini in Italy, insulin coma by Sakel in Hungary, and the ill-starred lobotomy by Egas Moniz in Portugal; the concept of the therapeutic community was developed by Maxwell Jones in England; the modern psychoactive drug era was inaugurated in Switzerland with Largactil, later brought to America as Thorazine; and lithium was first successfully employed by Cade in Australia.

of three main stages in the historical development of the relationship of psychotherapy and the psychoanalysis from which it derived.
The first, dubbed the *prehistory of psychotherapy,* was the era of Freud
and Glover and Jones. It comprised the development of psychoanalysis as a distinct therapy, with an attendant new psychological theory,
distinct from hypnosis and all other extant therapies which could
be collectively subsumed under the rubric of suggestion.

The second stage, called the era of *crystallizing consensus,* saw
its flowering—and its heyday—in the several panels of the early
1950s within the American, panels on the nature of the relationship
of, the similarities and differences between, psychoanalysis and psychodynamic therapy. The panels were all brought together in one
issue of the *Journal of the American Psychoanalytic Association* (Panels,
1954). The essence of that broad consensus (aside from the "deviations" represented by Alexander and his coworkers [Alexander and
French, 1946] and Fromm-Reichman [1950] and her coworkers)
was that psychoanalysis and the expressive and supportive psychoanalytic psychotherapies constituted a spectrum of technical approaches, all grounded in the theory of psychoanalysis and
differentially deployed in relation to specific sectors of the psychopathological spectrum. These approaches had clear-cut similarities,
but even more clear-cut differences, each being prescribed and carried out in relation to specific indications and contraindications
stemming from the different clinical configurations of the patient
population.

The third and current stage, which has developed over this
most recent decade, has been called that of *fragmented consensus.*
Where there was a well-established majority psychoanalytic consensus in the 1950s (and for a substantial period thereafter) on what
constituted psychoanalysis and what constituted the expressive and
supportive psychotherapies, this has now broken apart. The very
same individuals (e.g., Gill, Rangell, and Stone) who were so united
during the panels of the early 1950s separated widely in their reas-
sessments of the field in the symposium held a quarter-century later
in Atlanta, under the sponsorship of the Southern Regional Psychoanalytic Societies. The median and perhaps the majority position
in this renewed debate was neither the relatively unchanged views
of Stone (1982), nor the radical revisionism of Gill (1984), but the
moderately but significantly altered stance of Rangell (1981). This

involves a perspective of more porous boundaries, of more interdig-
itation of specifically therapeutic and specifically analytic interventions, with supportive maneuvers infiltrating even the most classical
of psychoanalytic treatments. Nonetheless, distinctive conceptualizations for psychoanalysis and for the analytic psychotherapies are
maintained, though more fuzzily than a quarter-century earlier. This
has also been a main message of the write-up by one of us of the
findings of over thirty years of the Psychotherapy Research Project
of The Menninger Foundation. That study has dealt with the long-
term processes and outcomes of forty-two cases, half treated in psychoanalysis, half in varieties of psychoanalytic psychotherapies (Wallerstein, 1986).

Put another way, what this assessment of psychoanalysis, the
analytic psychotherapies, and their relationship adds up to, in regard to the clinical practices in which we all engage, is that the
demarcations are much less clear-cut today than they used to be.
The questions then are: What constitutes psychoanalysis, modified
analysis, analysis with parameters, and even "wild analysis"? And
what is *only* psychotherapy, albeit psychoanalytic psychotherapy?
How close is it to the model of psychoanalysis and therefore mostly
"expressive," or how distinctively different is it from psychoanalysis
(in terms of clearly *psychotherapeutic* interventions) and therefore
mostly "supportive"? Or, put still another way, are we still following
the "widening scope of indications for psychoanalysis" (Stone,
1954), stretching what we call psychoanalysis (with increasing tolerance for technical modifications and perhaps unresolvable parameters) to cover ever wider arrays of patients toward what Stone called
the "nosological periphery" (1954, p. 593)? If we follow the thrust
of Kohut (1984) in his technical recommendations for work with
narcissistic characters and of Kernberg (1984b) for work with borderline personality organization, the answer to this question would,
of course, be yes. Or, oppositely, shall we follow Anna Freud's call
(1954, pp. 610–611), in her discussion of Stone's paper, for a narrowing scope? Proper psychoanalysis would then be reserved for
those most amenable to it, and the designation of psychoanalytic
psychotherapy would be given to all our therapeutic efforts with
patients who have wider and deeper ego disorders than the ideal
"normal neurotics" or the neurotics with Freud's "normal ego"
(1937). Such psychotherapy would be utilized even with so-called
normal neurotics whom we approach, for whatever reason, with
more circumscribed goals than in analysis. The state of the field, in

EDUCATION, RESEARCH, SCIENCE AND PROFESSION

our view, is such that both these opposed answers can be given today, and each can be staunchly and persuasively defended.

This current uncertainty on precisely how to define clinical psychoanalysis is in contrast to the elegant definitional clarity offered by Gill in his 1954 paper (p. 775). The uncertainty, of course, is but one aspect of our growing awareness and willing acceptance of our increasing theoretical diversity, a worldwide pluralism of theoretical perspectives, of linguistic and thought conventions, of distinctive regional, cultural, and language emphases in psychoanalysis. Given this diversity, with all our varying psychoanalytic perspectives all vying in the marketplace of psychoanalytic ideas, it is indeed far more difficult today than it was in Freud's (1910) day to delineate the proper boundaries of psychoanalysis from what is beyond it—from what is "only" but nonetheless proper psychotherapy, or from what is "wild" analysis and thus out of bounds in any psychoanalytically informed framework. Today, with our pluralistic conceptions, our varying theoretical perspectives and models of the mind, what may be conventional or proper psychoanalysis within one perspective may well be seen as wild within another. It is for these reasons that Schafer (1985), in his article on wild analysis, proposed abandoning that term altogether in favor of the more charitable and accommodating notion of "comparative analysis." As Schafer said, "Whereas once upon a time wild analysis referred to idiosyncratic violations of the theoretical premises and technical precepts of a simpler and solitary psychoanalysis, today recourse to the concept wild analysis [only] plunges us into theoretical debate" (p. 276; see also Weinshel, 1990).

We need belabor no more our thesis that, as with other aspects of the future of psychoanalysis that we have discussed, the world of our professional clinical practice is today also one of increased complexity and increased subtlety, with fewer of the simplifying guideposts that once seemed to cushion our professional activity so comfortably. We should here acknowledge, however, at least one area of (enforced) real simplification in the scope of our present-day professional work. That is our substantial retreat, forced by the advent of the plethora of psychopharmacologic agents, from the psychoanalytically guided therapy of the major mental disorders. There are, of course, still a few adamant clinicians among us continuing to work psychotherapeutically with psychotic patients, but they are now seen more as quaintly anachronistic rather than as courageously pioneering. Perhaps, though, as the therapeutic limitations of the new biological psychiatry become more clinically evident and acknowledged, there will be a place again, at least in an investigative context, for a revived intensive psychotherapeutic effort in the tradition once pioneered so proudly by Frieda Fromm-Reichmann, Harry Stack Sullivan, John Rosen, Marguerite Sechehaye, and others.

SUMMARY

We have tried, in a necessarily kaleidoscopic and highly condensed manner, to highlight our perspectives on the foreseeable future of psychoanalysis, along a number of interrelated but clearly distinct dimensions. Our discussion has dealt with the nature of our field as a science and also as a discipline, the nature of the training for it, the nature of its research, and the nature and scope of its professional practice. In all of these areas, matters seem both more complex and less clear-cut than they were in the immediate post-World War II period when we entered the field, which is now forty years ago in the approximately one-hundred-year-old history of psychoanalysis. We did not discuss in any detail the International Psychoanalytical Association or the American, its component through which we have our international membership. We have, however, via the IPA *Newsletter,* given voice to the organizational struggles of the International: the April 1989 issue of the *Newsletter* carries our account of the organizational changes within the IPA during the last four years and what we think they mean in relation to some of the issues discussed in this article. The fuller story of how our changing psychoanalytic life and identities are reflected in our institutional structures, as well as a more detailed specification of the future directions we have tried to chart in our inquiry, all deserve separate extended treatment and more complete justification.

10.

The Future of Psychotherapy

There is both great pleasure and real sadness in having been asked to give this plenary address to the California Psychiatric Association at the threshold of this decade of the 1990s on the suggested topic, "The Future of Psychotherapy." The pleasure is simple and deep, in that it provides an opportunity and a forum to address my fellow psychiatrists with my convictions about the central passion and central intellectual interest that has guided and motivated my career as a psychiatrist and psychoanalyst over more than four decades. It also enables me to express my views on the possibilities for preserving that central position for the like-minded colleagues who I hope will continue to seek out and pursue similar careers in psychiatry. The sadness is linked to the felt need to have a plenary talk on this topic under the conference banner, "Challenge of the '90s," with all the implications of the title that we must consider as well as the negative possibility of a diminished and problematic future, perhaps in extreme, the question of how best or even whether to try to preserve an endangered species, a soon-to-be anachronistic enterprise, which once had its day in the sun.

It is the very fact that we are having this talk today, with the range of manifest as well as tacit questions that I have just alluded to, that bespeaks the sea change in the psychiatric enterprise over the years of my formal involvement in the field, since 1949— in the immediate aftermath of World War II. At the time I entered formal psychiatric training, on January 1, 1949, a talk on my topic today would have been either totally gratuitous or, if given, the occasion for a utopian vision of ever-expanding human melioration and betterment, as more therapists were trained and became available and more individuals became sophisticated to the role that therapy could play in resolving their emotional and behavioral distress and in enhancing their lives.

PSYCHOTHERAPY TRAINING FOUR DECADES AGO

In 1949 psychotherapy was taken for granted as a human good, in the sense of being *the* road to the treatment of mental disorder and disturbed behavior, and therefore the overwhelmingly dominant learning goal of those who sought specialty training in psychiatry. There was, of course, a nationwide network of state hospitals housing the chronically and severely mentally ill, the openly psychotic, often for years and even lifetimes, but it was not uncharacteristic for only four physicians to be employed in such mental hospitals for up to 4000 patients, and they were not regularly psychiatrically trained; in fact, they often were older preretirement general practitioners or physicians, sometimes foreign educated, who had difficulty obtaining state licensure for private practice. These state hospitals were usually, and by design, removed from the major population centers, and they attracted few of the yearly quota of psychiatric residency graduates. Psychiatric units in general hospitals (and in major urban centers), of which that at Michael Reese Hospital in Chicago was an early exemplar, were just beginning to be established in the immediate post-World War II years. The same was true of the academic departments of psychiatry in the country's medical schools and their associated teaching hospitals. This time span was the period that consolidated the establishment of separate departments of psychiatry as major departments in our medical schools. The usual progression was from being combined with departments of neuropsychiatry, with the last such combined department existing even into the 1950s or 1960s at the University of Wisconsin. Less frequently, there was separation of the division of psychiatry from among the other specialty divisions of the department of internal medicine, the last such separation taking place at the University of Chicago in the 1950s. All these still-fledgling departments of psychiatry had very small full-time academic cores to begin with, and the formal psychiatric research enterprise was essentially still unborn.

Rather, the expectation of the beginning psychiatric resident of that early postwar era was to learn dynamic psychiatry, meaning psychoanalytic theory, a psychoanalytic conception of human growth and development and its varying deformations into psychopathology, and then the psychoanalytic psychotherapy fashioned to address that range of psychopathology, all euphemistically under the banner of "psychodynamics." This was indeed given its official psychiatric imprimatur in the very influential NIMH-supported American Psychiatric Association Conference on Psychiatric Education held in 1952 at Cornell University under the leadership of John Whitehorn, himself not at all a psychoanalyst but one of that outstanding generation of Adolf Meyer-trained psychobiologist chairmen (a psychobiologist in the then-Meyerian sense and not at all in the current sense of grounding in neuroscience and biological psychiatry). In the proceedings of that conference (Whitehorn, Braceland, Lippard, and Malamud, 1953), edited by a committee under Whitehorn's chairmanship, the chapter on "The Role of Psychoanalysis in Residency Training" stated in the very first paragraph that "it is now almost universally agreed that a necessary part of the preparation of a competent psychiatrist is the development of an understanding of principles of psychodynamics" and that "it seems obvious that an understanding of psychodynamics presupposes—indeed, necessitates— ... knowledge of Freudian concepts and of psychoanalytic theory and practice" (p. 91).

This agenda was very congenial to the large numbers who flocked to psychiatric training in the wake of their wartime experience. Many were an older group, medical graduates of the 1930s who were swept into wartime military service after but a few years of general medical practice. Because of the Army's voracious needs for insufficiently existent psychiatric manpower, they were converted into Army psychiatrists via three-month-long indoctrinations. They were then sent to cope with the vast numbers of wartime psychiatric casualties, the so-called traumatic war neuroses, the heirs to the shell-shocked psychiatric victims of World War I and the predecessors of the newly named posttraumatic stress disorders (PTSD) of the Vietnam conflict. It was these wartime psychiatric practitioners with only minimal formal psychiatric training who emerged from the Army, many of them in pursuit of the model of psychiatric training grounded in the theory of psychoanalysis and its derived technical interventions, including the hypno- and narcoanalytic techniques and brief, crisis-oriented interventions that had worked so stunningly well on the battlefield. They sought a more comprehensive grounding in psychodynamics in preparation for the private practice of dynamic psychiatry in the nation's large urban centers where the most motivated and ambitious would, in addition, swell the ranks of candidates in the then rapidly expanding and proliferating psychoanalytic institutes. In the country's largest psychiatric training center, the Menninger School of Psychiatry, where in the late 1940s, one hundred of the country's then eight hundred psychiatric residents were being trained—1 in 8 in the country in that one small town—forty of the one hundred applied simultaneously to the Topeka Institute for Psychoanalysis, which strained to accept eight to ten when it had been thinking to take only four to five. Most of those turned down scattered to apply elsewhere, some bearing letters of rejection that gravely informed them that they had "talents in other fields." Incidentally, that was the period when, in response to this overwhelming demand, psychoanalysis in the United States switched its modal frequency from five to four times weekly, on the basis that in each twenty hours of psychoanalytic work, five rather than only four patients could be seen.

But to stick to my main theme: the nature, the context, and the conditions of psychiatric training when I turned up in Topeka in 1949 as one of those one hundred residents. Although this may be in some sense too categorical and sweeping a statement, I think it is by and large true that the theory of psychoanalysis and its application in psychoanalytically informed and guided psychotherapy represented almost the totality of what was taught and learned. At the time, psychoanalysis was *the* prevailing psychology of psychiatry. The competing behavior modification paradigm based on academic learning theory psychology, in its earliest therapeutic beginnings, was mainly found in academic psychology settings. The client-centered Rogerian approach, which has never made a real inroad into psychiatric thought and practice, existed likewise mainly in clinics attached to clinical psychology programs in graduate psychology departments.

Contemporary neuroscience and the current explosive growth of molecular biology and molecular genetics were still part of an unknown future. The array of somatic therapies available in psychiatry at the time comprised only electroshock for psychotic depression, insulin coma and subcoma primarily for chronic severe schizophrenic illness, with the ill-starred lobotomy operation available for the even more intractable psychotically disabled, and malaria therapy for neurosyphilis. There were a variety of sedating and soporific medications, primarily chloral hydrate, bromides, and barbiturates (with all the potential for barbiturate abuse and addiction and for bromide poisoning from prolonged administration), plus such nursing measures as warm sedative tubs and cold sheet packs as general aids in the management of the overexcited and unruly. The contemporary era of psychopharmacology with its panoply of psychoactive drugs—neuroleptics, anxiolytics, and antidepressants—did not begin until 1954, with the introduction of the Swiss drug Largactil to the United States by way of Canada, marketed by Smith, Kline and French under the trade name Thorazine. Although there was an emergency room to be covered and a range of psychiatric consultations on the general hospital medical and surgical wards, there was no established psychiatric emergency service or consultation–liaison service in anything like the contemporary sense, nor were there specialized geriatric or substance abuse or forensic services with their specific clinical populations and their own bodies of theory and focused interventions.

What there was then at that time in psychiatric residency training—and, as I have said, almost the totality of it— was seminar instruction in psychodynamics and psychopathology with their applications in psychoanalytic psychotherapy, and almost all of that individual psychotherapy, with some adjuvant teaching of hypnotherapy (still in use) and group therapy, mostly *faute de mieux*, to help deal with the suddenly rapidly swelling mental hospital population, especially in the newly opened network of VA hospitals. These were taken over from wartime Army general hospitals, to accommodate the influx of the psychiatrically disabled among the 10 million demobilizing service personnel. What this meant for the average psychiatric resident in the then three-year residency program, after a separate rotating internship year, was a forty-hour scheduled workweek, with the expectation of twenty hours minimum for individual psychotherapeutic work with patients. The other twenty hours per week were consumed (probably more than consumed) by individual supervision for three to four hours, paperwork, general ward duties, the processing of admissions and discharges, meeting with patients' relatives, perhaps some work with groups (one or two). Depending on the program, there were from five to ten seminar and lecture hours. The concept, pioneered actually by The Menninger Foundation, was of the psychiatric residency as a school of psychiatry making up what the medical school had failed to teach of psychiatric theory and practice. A minimum of twenty hours of individual psychotherapeutic work for up to fifty weeks a year was close to one thousand hours of individual psychotherapy experience, which, multiplied by the three years of residency, meant that the psychiatric resident of my vintage logged around three thousand hours of psychotherapy during the residency training period. The only significant difference among the three residency years was that in the first year of primarily inpatient service, the psychotherapeutic work was with the hospitalized psychotics. These patients were hospitalized for months, if not years, and were thus available for efforts at intensive psychotherapy, along with the ECT or insulin coma that some received. Here, the writings of Frieda Fromm-Reichmann, Harry Stack Sullivan, and John Rosen in America, Gertrud Schwing and M. A. Sechehaye in Europe, and, among the British Kleinians, Herbert Rosenfeld, served as inspiring and inspirational guideposts. In the next two years of primarily outpatient service, the work was with ambulatory neurotic patients in the classical mold of the psychoanalytic psychotherapy identified in the writings of that time with the names of Knight and Gill and E. Bibring and Rangell and Stone. For that minority who went on into child psychiatry fellowship training, there was a gradual shift to include an increasing number of children and adolescents into the treatment mix.

Given an "average expectable" diligence, intelligence, and talent on the part of the resident, the psychiatric residency program of that day could graduate its trainees reasonably confident that they were equipped to practice a reasonably competent brand of primarily outpatient psychotherapy in the private practice market. Many residents, of course, used their training as a prep school for the psychoanalytic institutes in which they sought candidacy while pursuing their careers as dynamic psychiatrists practicing analytic psychotherapy. In those days, there was a widely receptive market of available and waiting patients eager for their services. There were few other mental health practitioners in the private sector. Clinical psychology as a professional discipline was in its infancy, with the very recent proliferation of clinical psychology training programs under combined university and VA hospital auspices, with the VA eager to offer internship and postdoctoral fellowship experiences to psychologists who could then be enticed into VA jobs dealing with the large numbers of hospitalized neuropsychiatrically impaired veterans. These were jobs that psychiatrists, intent on the private market, were more reluctant to take, at least not in anywhere near the numbers needed.

Some few clinical psychologists were starting in private practice, but often with a heavy emphasis on diagnostic psychological testing, then a more cultivated and honored activity than today. Although psychiatric social work, both in individual casework and in group work, was a well-established profession, almost all its practitioners worked at that time in social agencies, family service agencies, child guidance clinics, and so forth, supported by some combination of public and private philanthropic dollars. There they dealt with the social and psychological problems of the poor and other groups of the socially disadvantaged. Almost no psychiatric social workers were in private practice at that time, and the few psychiatric nurses were to be seen exclusively on the inpatient services in psychiatric hospitals and in the newly created psychiatric units of general hospitals. Other than intensive individual psychotherapy, the private practice market included some hypnotherapy, the flamboyance and showmanship of Moreno's psychodrama in New York, the beginnings of family therapy at the Ackerman Institute (also in New York), and, among social workers, in social agencies, the psychoanalytically oriented group therapy pioneered by Slavson. The real proliferation of bowdlerized psychoanalytic offspring (Gestalt, transactional analysis, primal scream, and so on) had not yet occurred, nor the many fringe and cult therapies—in which California has always had a leadership role—nor the real growth of the various self-help movements, of which only the original prototype, Alcoholics Anonymous, then existed on any scale. In effect, the psychiatrists practicing psychotherapy had the private practice market pretty much to themselves; they had plenty of patients, and by and large they were competent at what they did with them and confident that their training had equipped them to do it well enough.

CHANGES IN PSYCHIATRY OVER THE PAST FOUR DECADES

Presenting in this way the picture of the nature and conditions of psychiatric training and practice at the point at which I came into the field in 1949, just over forty years ago, clearly highlights the vast changes that have taken place when we compare all this with the nature and conditions of training and practice today. This is especially so as we follow the guiding thread of concern for the transformations undergone by the psychotherapy enterprise and its place in the overall psychiatric scheme of things over this time. I won't try to trace all these kaleidoscopic changes in the nature, scope, and content of psychiatry over these four decades but will merely state them here in very condensed form.

First, of course, is the literal explosion of knowledge in neuroscience and neurobiology, especially in its molecular biological and molecular genetic dimension, with the spectacular growth of intelligence of brain–behavior interrelations in the domain of mental and emotional disorder. There has been specific scientific focus on the elucidation of genetic markers of mental dysfunctions and on the multiplicity of interlocking and interacting neurotransmitters and cell receptors. Biological psychiatry has rapidly become a most significant and exciting scientific arena, and is now the research and clinical focus of many academic psychiatric careers and major psychiatric space and money resources.

The second and related major development, also in the biological realm, is the modern era of psychoactive drugs as a central therapeutic modality in the management and treatment of the psychiatrically ill, especially the sicker, psychotic patients whom we psychodynamically trained psychiatrists have tended to avoid anyway. Historically, they have been such a heavy, collective, undischarged social responsibility of our profession, long warehoused in large public mental hospitals, often neglected at best and badly abused at worst. I do not need to recount the great proliferation of psychoactive drugs and of classes of such drugs since the inauguration of the modern psychoactive drug era in 1954. Suffice it to say that the existence of all these drugs has vitally changed the practice characteristics of psychiatrists (not to speak of the ministrations to emotionally and behaviorally troubled individuals by nonpsychiatric physicians). It has forced accommodations in the psychotherapeutic arena, where adjuvant or concomitant use of psychoactive drugs has become commonplace, especially with the less well-integrated patients (for the most part, those outside the normal-neurotic range), and where the understanding of drug–behavior interactions and of the psychological meanings of such chemically induced mood and behavior changes has become part of what we must know and teach in our psychotherapeutic working.

The third major dimension of change in the field of psychiatry is in the psychological arena. Here I need only point out that psychoanalysis is no longer the unquestioned prevailing psychological theory guiding and illuminating our understanding of the human mind and its aberrations. It has now been challenged by the astonishing growth of two fundamentally different and competing psychological paradigms: the one the learning-theory and stimulus-response conditioning model (partly classical, partly operant), with the behavior modification technology derived from it. The other, attacking both psychoanalysis and behavior modification as being mechanistic and stripped of essential subjectivism and humanism, is the existentialist–phenomenological tradition of European philosophy and letters brought to America as humanistic psychology. It has led to the whole encounter and human growth and potential movement, to some extent within our profession and, to a far larger extent, outside it. Of more practical consequence to those of us practicing and teaching dynamic psychotherapy is the encroachment of the behavioral technologies into our clinics and training programs—for example, in the sex therapies and in the eating disorder clinics, both now popular arenas of subspecialization.

The fourth major dimension of change is in the social science (and social policy) arena. Here I want to mention another influence, as potent as the psychoactive drug revolution in transforming the character of modern American psychiatric and mental health practice, and that is the community mental health center movement, inaugurated by the Kennedy legislation of 1963. This community mental health movement is clearly a new center of gravity in political power and in access to funding in the whole field of mental health and illness; it is also a succession of linked conceptualizations and ideologies, not necessarily all politically inspired, and many of them developed both before and outside the official community mental health movement. I refer to the concepts of the open hospital and the therapeutic community pioneered by Maxwell Jones in England, and of milieu therapy as designed by D. Ewen Cameron in Canada and further developed with psychoanalytic sophistication by Will Menninger and his colleagues at The Menninger Clinic in Topeka, Kansas, as well as the current and dominant concept of deinstitutionalization. This latter concept of deinstitutionalization has already carried us from the era when most of our sicker patients were kept—or rather, incarcerated—in our large public mental hospitals for long periods (even for their whole lifetime) to the current time when hospitalization is by and large short and mainly for acute and unmanageable life crises and psychological decompensations. Today, even the very sick, chronically psychotic patients are managing (or nor managing) in outpatient lives in the outside world, and we now see the new, untoward consequences of the deinstitutionalized life. Patients, once neglected and abused in the state hospitals, are now often neglected and abused in board-and-care homes and cheap inner-city hotels, or worse yet, swelling the ranks of the homeless living on our streets. In any case, this host of major problems and issues stamps the whole face of current mental health practice and is necessarily a major concern of academic psychiatry in preparing its students for their professional life ahead.

Fifth and last are the correlated developments of theory that relate to the changes in emphasis from the therapeutic to the preventive ameliorative models and from the idiosyncratically individual to the socially controlled family and group and social system concerns that characterize the philosophic thrust of the community mental health movement. Some of this theory was developed within psychoanalysis, such as crisis theory as innovated originally by Lindemann; most of it has been developed outside psychoanalysis in academic sociology and social psychology, such as role theory, theories of deviance, theories of social group behavior, and social systems theory. Again, the main point is that there are other bodies of knowledge, social science knowledge, that are being brought to bear as explanatory frameworks on many of the phenomena that are within the purview of psychiatry, and that, in terms of the issues brought to the surface by the emphases of our crisis clinics and community mental health centers, are presumably better, in the sense of being more broadly encompassing or more directly relevant, or perhaps just more easily understandable or commonsensical as explanatory frameworks.

PSYCHOTHERAPY TRAINING TODAY

So much for the tabulation of some of the major developments within and around psychiatry in these last four fast-moving decades. All of them have found their way into the seminar sequences and the clinical rotations of the psychiatric residency training program. Although the typical residency is now a four-year sequence, at least half a year and up to a year in many of the programs is given back to what used to be in the separate internship year: rotations in general medicine, in neurology, and, for those who look to a future as a child psychiatrist, in pediatrics. In the remaining years of specifically psychiatric training experience, major rotations exist through inpatient services, which are no longer psychotherapy focused but rather are drug-management focused because lengths of stay are rarely (except in some specialized clinical centers) longer than thirty days. Rotations also exist through outpatient emergency rooms and crisis clinics and acute inpatient emergency units, with their length of stay usually a week, or less if forced by the pressure of new admissions; through substance abuse wards and outpatient detoxification and methadone maintenance units; through consultation–liaison services; and through specialized inpatient and outpatient geriatric units. Significant amounts of the outpatient years are devoted to community mental health centers, with their brief therapy and group therapy focus, and often to specialty clinics such as affective disorder clinics, chronic drug maintenance clinics, and sleep disorder and eating disorder and sexual disorder clinics, all with their drug treatment and behavior treatment focus. All of these significant time allocations and major teaching and learning foci have been carved from the time once given to the teaching and learning—from a psychoanalytic perspective—of psychopathology, psychodynamics, and psychotherapy. These were the activities that once consumed almost the entire residency training, and because they are anyway presumably more flexible in the more-or-less time that needs to be devoted to them.

And, of course, I should add to the many pressures that conduce to the diminution of the time and effort devoted to the teaching and the practice of psychotherapy, the pressures of the insurance carriers and the various governmental sources of third-party reimbursement, whose concerns for cost-benefit balances and for demonstrated therapeutic efficacy of the reimbursed services have led inexorably to the progressive shortening of the coverage afforded to long-term individual psychotherapy in favor of brief therapy models, group therapy, and psychoactive drug management. This, of course, has had an inevitably chilling effect on the readiness of mental health care providers, whether institutional or individual, to offer intensive psychotherapy to the extent that it is truly indicated and clearly useful in social and individual terms.

It would be a digression here to elaborate on the conceptual and technical complexities of the process and outcome research that would be necessary to establish the comparative efficacy of intensive psychotherapy vis-à-vis briefer or drug-centered approaches to the array of disorders in the psychopathological spectrum. Suffice it to say that in terms of the criteria central to governmental and insurance carriers (concern for the relief and amelioration of presenting symptoms and disturbed or disturbing manifest behaviors), it is unlikely that intensive psychotherapy will be (or can be) established to be indubitably superior. Its putative benefits lie rather in the subtler and less measurable realms of enhanced life satisfaction and more effective and adaptive life functioning consequent to inner character and personality shifts and alterations. And beyond this, much of what we treat people for in intensive individual psychotherapy—gross dissatisfactions with the course of their life, difficulties in the areas of interpersonal relationships or work adjustment, school or work inhibitions, and so on—are not considered by the third-party payers to be formal diseases for which they should be expected to carry the treatment costs. After all, the inability of a graduate student to complete a doctoral thesis in comparative languages or in anthropology, which will result in one less doctoral degree holder and one less academic career, is hardly considered a disease state for which an insurance program should provide treatment, no matter how tragic the career and life consequences for the disappointed and frustrated individual. And certainly the casting of disease criteria, reimbursable disease criteria, into DSM-III terms with specific symptom criteria for illness has further compounded this problem. Again, all these factors will chill even further the ardor of the potential long-term psychotherapy provider.

So where does all this leave us today in relation to our concern for the well-being and the vitality of the psychotherapy enterprise, both the education for it and the continuing practice of it? It is clear from everything that I have recounted to this point of the major new components of contemporary psychiatric education that the teaching of the theory and the techniques of psychotherapy has been progressively and severely eroded in our training program curricula, even in those programs that have tried to resist the current tides and to maintain time-honored commitments to psychodynamic thinking and practice. Typically, in today's psychiatric residency programs, the third year of the four-year sequence is designated as the "psychotherapy year." What this means in actual practice is that, given the other time demands, even in that year (even in the committed programs), the expectation will be at most for twelve hours per week of individual psychotherapy which, for a maximum fifty weeks (although almost nowhere are residents' vacations plus time away for educational leaves limited to but two weeks a year), would come to something a good deal less than six hundred hours of logged time (i.e., the very maximum twelve hours per week for fifty weeks). Although there may be a patient or two seen in psychotherapy prior to that psychotherapy year, and the continuing of some of those third-year patients into the fourth year (depending on other program pressures), except for that minority of residents within that minority of programs that have specialized psychotherapy tracks available for fourth-year electives, the basic less than six hundred hours of third-year psychotherapy experience, supplemented a little—often very little—in the second and fourth years, becomes the totality of psychotherapy teaching in today's residency training programs at their very most. Compare that with the three thousand hours of psychotherapy experience typically logged by the residents in just about every program in the immediate post-World War II era in which I was trained and which was regarded then as what was minimally necessary for the residency training programs to feel satisfied that they were graduating residents qualified and competent to enter independent practice with requisite skill and experience, individuals to whom they would be willing to refer private patients.

Lest you feel that this contrast is too stark and exaggerated, let me quote from two articles that have appeared just this year, 1990, in the *American Journal of Psychiatry*. The first is by Paul Mohl and six collaborators, the lead article in the January issue entitled, "Psychotherapy Training for the Psychiatrist of the Future." The article was the product of a joint task force of the Association for Academic Psychiatry and the American Association of Directors of Psychiatric Residency Training. It endeavored to lay out an *optimal* psychotherapy training program within the context of present-day psychiatry and its various parameters and constraints. In the PGY-1 year, the program emphasis would be on clinical care, that is, "diagnosis, crisis intervention, pharmacotherapy, and extensive history taking and treatment planning. Residents follow hospitalized patients with a primary focus on understanding the natural course and resolution with treatment [meaning psychoactive drug treatment] of major psychiatric illness, rather than the provision of psychotherapeutic treatment" (p. 9). This, incidentally, contrasts with my own initiation into psychiatry, where I was thrown into twenty hours a week of scheduled psychotherapy from my very first day on a psychiatric service, buffered as best as possible against all my anxieties by intensive and high-grade supervision by a senior psychoanalyst supervisor.

But to go on with this recounting. In the PGY-2 year, "Clinical care . . . largely involves hospitalized patients [meaning again, brief treatment via drugs and ward management, not psychotherapy], but assignments should also include at least two patients for whom outpatient psychotherapy is the predominant or exclusive form of treatment" (p. 10). Translated, this turns out to mean once-a-week psychotherapy, a maximum of two hours each week over the whole year, or one hundred hours in the hypothetical fifty-week working year, but in most cases it would work out to half of that, one hour a week, or up to only fifty hours. PGY-3 is of course the presumed big psychotherapy teaching year. Here the disappointing recommendation is, "Clinical care during PGY-3 consists of 4–7 psychotherapy hours per week and at least one patient who is seen more than once per week" (p. 11). Let's call that an average of six hours per week or up to three hundred hours per year in the big psychotherapy teaching year, an official statement of optimal intent that is only half of the six hundred hours that I had built into my word-picture of where we have come from the three thousand psychotherapy hours of my own psychiatric residency training experience.

And then for the final residency training year, the authors propose, "In PGY-4, most residents will not add new long-term cases but will add cases that provide the opportunity to use a subspecialty form of psychotherapy" (p. 11). And these they had specified earlier in the article—brief psychotherapy, hypnosis, cognitive therapy, sexual therapy, and so forth—all laudable perhaps, but not the same thing. They also say, "There should be some unsupervised cases during this year" (p. 11). Do those of us who have devoted many years to psychotherapy training and experience, both as students and as teachers, really feel that our residents are ready to do unsupervised work after so minimal an exposure to psychotherapy under supervision? I would submit that this is not an issue of mature adulthood and autonomy versus infantilization as some would have it, but of the kind of message it conveys of what we think constitutes adequate enough psychotherapy training and experience. Contrast that with the comment made to me recently by a senior psychoanalytic colleague who told me that now after some forty years of full-time clinical practice, he has at last attained to the comfortable feeling that he really knows what he is doing when he treats his patients and feels that he can be of maximal help to them. Put that down to hyperbole and feigned modesty if you will, but there is also much more than a kernel of truth in it.

What is to me the dismaying capstone to this article comes then toward the end, when the authors ruefully acknowledge that only some residency training programs will have the resources (let alone the will) to meet even these (to me, extremely meager) training demands. They therefore state that for all the rest there is also a "model curriculum for *minimum* training in psychodynamic psychotherapy" (p. 12; emphasis added):

> To meet these objectives, each resident must spend a minimum of 200 hours treating patients with psychodynamic psychotherapy. These sessions must be at least weekly and last at least 45 minutes, and the purpose of each session must be to engage in psychodynamic, expressive, exploratory psychotherapy. Preferably, these 200 or more hours of experience will extend over the entire training period of the general psychiatrist. Each resident should see at least four different patients, at least one for more than 50 sessions and at least one, preferably more than one, who is treated until termination [p. 12].

Given that the total four-year residency program constitutes up to eight thousand scheduled hours, and that the two hundred psychotherapy experience hours constitute only 2.5 percent of that time, one can well ask what other branch of medicine would consider as adequate specialty training the devotion of 2.5 percent of its total training time to the treatment of but four patients (only one to completion) by the most characteristic, distinctive, and widely used treatment modality at its disposal?

What can be seen as a codicil to the article by this task force is an article appearing three months later, in the April 1990 issue of the *American Journal of Psychiatry*, by Kenneth Altshuler entitled, "Whatever Happened to Intensive Psychotherapy?" Altshuler's article is based on a questionnaire survey of 212 psychiatric residency programs, from which he secured 163 responses. To introduce just one of his dismaying findings, less than forty percent of the respondent programs required any patients to be seen more than once a week within the total residency training period. This means that more than sixty percent of our programs graduate residents into careers of psychiatric practice who will never in their training period have seen any patient more than once a week. And of the 59 programs out of the 163 that do require some patients to be seen at least twice weekly, only 10 across the country require that there be at least three such twice-weekly patients—the others divide into 21 programs that require one such patient and 28 programs that require two.

PSYCHOTHERAPY AND PSYCHIATRY: CURRENT CONTROVERSIES

This in sum total is the picture of psychotherapy training, 1990 style, across our nation's psychiatric residency programs. In this context, it should be no surprise that the American Association of Directors of Psychiatric Residency Training can have panel discussions at their annual meetings, not on how much psychodynamic psychotherapy experience and teaching there should be in a contemporary psychiatric residency, but on *whether* psychotherapy training should still be required or be only optional for those who want to pursue what is now called a subspecialty within psychiatry as their career choice. Those who believe that psychotherapy training should be optional argue that there are so many knowledge areas in contemporary psychiatry that require full medical training for their proper understanding and utilization (like neuroscience and its clinical applications in the psychopharmacological treatment of severe psychiatric disorders). They say further, that dynamic psychotherapy is the one area of psychiatric expertise that can be shared with, and learned equally well by, nonmedical practitioners, who can then also practice it equally well and presumably less expensively. Thus, the psychiatrist's relationship to psychotherapy can properly be confined to understanding the range of its indications and contraindications and the appropriate prescription for it by referral to the nonphysician, in a manner similar to referrals by orthopedic physicians of physiotherapy to be carried out by allied disciplines. Of course, ultimate medical control should be maintained and the psychiatrist must assume administrative and supervisory responsibilities for this prescribed psychotherapy carried out by other mental health professionals. Quite aside from the inevitable political turf battles with our fellow mental health practitioners in other disciplines over this no-longer-acknowledged assumption of medical–psychiatric hegemony in the mental illness treatment area, there is also the irony, which seems to have escaped the proponents of this position, that the psychiatrist could be presumed to be in the position to *supervise* psychotherapy without ever having had the requisite training to himself or herself carry it out properly.

It is not much of an extension of this antipsychotherapy-for-psychiatrists argument to follow the voice of an eminent psychiatric educator, Thomas Detre, the former chairman of one of the country's major medical school psychiatric research departments and now the provost for all health sciences in that university, Pittsburgh. The proposal he has advanced is that, with the modern growth of neuroscience and biological psychiatry and all the technology of contemporary psychiatric laboratory and clinical research, psychiatry now has the historic opportunity to correct what he considers its fundamental mistake, made in the 1930s and 1940s, of splitting off into an independent specialty from the previously combined departments of neuropsychiatry. It is important to correct this mistake and rejoin with neurology into recombined departments, because after all, he states, there is absolutely no difference in this day and age between the training of a first-class psychiatric resident and the training of a first-class neurological resident. Thus, having separate departments of psychiatry and neurology is as fundamentally ludicrous as having a medical school department of hearing, smelling, and tasting apart from a department of otolaryngology. This talk by this major figure in American psychiatry, given at the grand rounds of another equally prestigious medical school's department of psychiatry (Yale)—the department in which he had begun his academic career—then detailed all the declared unhappy consequences for psychiatry of its unfortunate separation from neurology. These consequences included the opportunity for psychoanalytic theory and psychodynamic psychotherapy teaching to rise to a position of primacy within psychiatric training and practice, the long delay in the coming of age of proper (i.e., biological) psychiatric research, and so forth.

Detre expressed no confidence that his would be either a popular or a possible agenda; he is too savvy politically to harbor such illusions about the nature of the entrenched political and professional vested interests that would render turning back this particular clock no longer feasible. It was proposed rather as an effort at a rigorous intellectual rethinking of the real conceptual implications of the content revolution that has transformed the psychiatry and the psychiatric practice within which I was trained into the psychiatry and the psychiatric practice within which we train today. Clearly

282   EDUCATION, RESEARCH, SCIENCE AND PROFESSION

it is a vision that has quite completely removed dynamic psychotherapy from the present (and the future) psychiatric scheme of things.

And, of course, this line of thinking is substantially abetted by
the current and the predictable reimbursement trends for psychiatric practice that I have already partially spoken to earlier in this
presentation. The unmistakable trend, as I have indicated, is toward
the progressive sharp diminution of coverage for long-term psychotherapy, from the time ten to fifteen years ago when patients could
get entire long-term psychotherapies including psychoanalysis,
wholly or up to 80 percent reimbursed in some of the country's
major programs. These programs included the Federal Employees
Health Benefits Program, which sustained an entire psychoanalytic
and psychotherapy practitioner community in Washington, DC,
where the majority of the city's workforce is on the federal payroll;
the staff employees of the Veterans Administration, with its hospitals
in every major metropolitan area in the country; numerous private
insurance programs in many major industries and companies. The
current downward shift has resulted in twenty psychotherapy ses-
sions in a calendar year as the norm for outpatient psychotherapy
coverage. This is in contrast to continued sustained coverage for
psychiatric inpatient care (to a cap, of course, but one that does
cover the vast majority of hospitalized patients; in fact, almost all
except for the residue, in this era of deinstitutionalization, of the
remaining chronic, unrehabilitatable patients still publicly supported in our state mental hospitals). We are today, along with South
Africa, the only advanced, industrialized country in the Western
World still without universal health care coverage. As the inevitable,
long-delayed trend toward some kind of universal (probably combined privately and publicly supported) national health insurance
scheme picks up momentum out of our growing health care crisis
in America it seems likely to me, given the way things have been
going to this point, that intensive psychotherapy of any kind will be
squeezed out of the system, to be relegated to the private market
for those more affluent and sophisticated who can afford it and will
seek it on their own.

Mental health coverage is, of course, far from uniform in all
the industrialized countries of the world that have universal health
care coverage. In some, like Canada and Sweden, there is total coverage for long-term psychotherapy and psychoanalysis when provided
by a psychiatric practitioner; in others, like Belgium, there are significant copayments; in still others, like Germany, there is full coverage but with a cap on total duration—three hundred hours. But the

model to which I see the United States moving in terms of the restrictions being progressively put in place by governmental and privately supported insurance programs alike is the British model. In Britain, psychotherapy on an indefinite once-weekly basis is available within the National Health Service, at least at those NHS clinic settings like Tavistock in London that undertake to provide it. However, more intensive (i.e., more frequent) psychotherapy must be financed privately by those who desire it and can afford it. This means that in Britain, all psychoanalyses, for example, are privately paid for, and totally outside the tax-supported health care system. As a consequence, psychoanalysis in that country is largely limited to London, where the overwhelming majority of the requisite sophisticated and affluent patient population resides, and the fee structure is at a level far less than half of that prevailing for therapeutic hours in our country, despite the fact that living costs in London are not significantly different from those in New York.

THE FUTURE OF PSYCHOTHERAPY

This brings me up to the present moment and to the question with which I undertook this talk, my charge to prognosticate as best I could on the future of psychotherapy, intensive psychotherapy, and psychoanalysis, in this country circa 1990. Many of you will no doubt have concluded that the unspoken subtitle that I had in mind for this talk indeed has been what I alluded to in my opening paragraph, "Psychotherapy: An Endangered Species." In one sense, that could be read as an entirely fair conclusion, at least psychotherapy in the professional sense in which we came to know it in the heady days of the 1950s and 1960s in this country. This was a time when the hegemony of the psychodynamic psychotherapy enterprise as the central intellectual and therapeutic activity within psychiatry was almost unchallenged, when public acceptance, prestige, and esteem for us and our activity was at an all-time high, and when this was widely enough acknowledged by the social policy and economic planners, both in government and outside, who were responsible for the nation's health care.

Clearly, I have outlined the various scientific–professional and sociopolitical trends that together have conduced to so drastically alter that situation now as we have come into the 1990s. How then do I read the future of the psychoanalytic and the dynamic psychotherapy enterprise today in the light of this drastically altered current climate? First let me say that psychoanalysis, as theory and as practice the intellectual wellspring of dynamic psychiatry and psychotherapy, survives, and taking a broader and longer view, flourishes. Certainly, as a theoretical perspective, psychoanalysis has a very sharply diminished place within academic psychiatry, as compared with its position fifteen to twenty years ago, and this continuing trend of diminishing position and influence promises to continue for some time ahead before the pendulum will (inevitably) begin to swing back and self-correct. The promises of biological psychiatry and the promised therapeutics of genetic alteration and of psychopharmacologically corrected neurotransmitter imbalances are still in the first flush of enthusiastic expansion, much as psychoanalytic psychotherapy was in the 1950s and 1960s. The inevitable oversell, the raising of unrealistic expectations, and the ultimate tempered disillusionment and settling down to a more sober and modest statement of reasonable and realistic therapeutic expectation have not yet begun to take place and may not for ten to twenty years. But certainly we all know that the varieties of depressed people, in all life stages and subject to all varying circumstances, have myriads of psychological problems, traumatic happenings and losses, conflicted interpersonal relationships, and inner and outer disequilibrating pressures that will not be resolved just by mood-altering medications that take them out of dysfunctional despondency and render them more able to try to face and deal with life's difficulties. The George Engel biopsychosocial model of human psychological functioning and malfunctioning is still our collective scientific ideal, to which we all give allegiance, although for so many of the enthusiasts for each extreme position within psychiatry, it is too often but lip service that in practice is set aside from our practical therapeutic pursuits. And for now we are as surely in the era of one-sided biological ascendancy within psychiatry, and especially academic psychiatry, as we were a quarter of a century ago in the era of one-sided psychological (i.e., psychoanalytic) ascendancy. This is a theme that I have developed at great length in chapters 8 and 9 (the latter with a colleague, Edward Weinshel).

Nonetheless, looking beyond the confines of academic psychiatry and professional psychiatric practice in America to a wider purview, geographically and intellectually, we see that the picture is not at all so one-sided. Worldwide, psychoanalytic ranks (and as a rough corollary, psychodynamically interested and committed psychiatric ranks), although stable only in the United States and also, interestingly, in Great Britain, are in most other places on a remarkable accelerating upward spiral. Psychoanalysis is in fact a major growth industry all over Latin America and Europe, with truly explosive growth in such major nations as Argentina, Brazil, France, Germany, and Italy, to say nothing of the burgeoning interest and growth in Asia, with South Korea as the most recently emergent center of psychoanalytic ferment. With the collapse of the East European communist world and its pell-mell rush westward, there has been an intense new surge of psychoanalytic activity in Czechoslovakia and Poland and (former) East Germany and Lithuania and even in the Soviet Russian heartland, where after decades of being totally forbidden, Freud's major writings have been newly translated and published in Russian and sold out fully in the first week. What all this adds up to, including these different time trajectories within Latin America and the European continent, as compared with the United States and Britain, of scientific and professional interest in the Freudian idea and its therapeutic application in psychoanalytic therapy, is that psychoanalysis per se is growing in strength and influence worldwide, even as the American component, of course still the largest, is diminishing in its percentage role and has lost its erstwhile world dominance. A major indicator of this growing place of psychoanalysis in the intellectual scheme of things around the world is the extent, unthinkable in present-day America, to which the scientific and professional activities of psychoanalysis are foci of attention in the news media, influential daily papers, journals of opinion, and radio and television programs in all the other major centers of psychoanalysis around the world.

And even in America, there is rising psychoanalytic interest in the wider university world and its graduate academic departments today, across our country, although most notably at particular major research universities—including incidentally, the University of California at Berkeley—in departments of English, French, comparative literature, and philosophy, not to speak of cognate social sciences like sociology and anthropology. I must believe that this continued and growing psychoanalytic intellectual vitality within American university academia will provide a continuing nourishing current that will help foster that more balanced era I see ahead (although not at all in the immediate future) when organized academic medicine, and not just psychiatry, will again enlarge its vision of health and illness beyond the particular natural science perspective provided by molecular biology and molecular genetics.

In the meantime, psychoanalytically grounded psychotherapy training still manages to survive (perhaps even there, more as an ideological statement than as an adequate teaching and learning activity) in certain of our medical school academic residency training programs that have been its traditional prestigious bulwarks, such as Cornell, Yale, and Colorado and some of the other major centers in New York and Boston. This, however, is admittedly spotty and nowhere really adequate, and additionally, as compared with all the other disciplines in medicine, psychiatric training programs not only vary greatly in quality and prestige—which is true of all specialties—but, uniquely, vary equally greatly in their programmatic and ideological and intellectual emphases so that there have always been antipsychotherapeutic, even anticlinical, strongly and one-sidedly research-oriented programs (i.e., bench research in laboratories) and their numbers have clearly increased dramatically in recent years. This is to say nothing of the separate story of the gradual disappearance of the psychiatric residency programs in the community general hospitals of this country. For example, in the San Francisco bay area alone, there have been shutdowns of psychiatric residencies, once very major in size, scope, and influence, at Mt. Zion Hospital in San Francisco and at Herrick Hospital in Berkeley, and there are current moves in that direction at St. Mary's in San Francisco. These residency programs, once bulwarks of clinical psychotherapy training in this and other metropolitan areas over the country, are falling victim to the harsh economics that make primarily outpatient-centered residency training programs in psychiatry deficit enterprises to the point where community general hospitals find them unsupportable. This is in contrast to all other medical disciplines, which are primarily hospital inpatient centered, where the costs of residency training can be folded into the bed care costs of the hospitalized patients and covered adequately by the hospital's usual mix of governmental program support (including Medicare and Medicaid), private insurance coverage, and bearable out-of-pocket expenses by the patients. This economically driven trend is driving psychiatric residency training out of the community general hospitals all across the country and is pushing the training (apart from the medical schools that are of course committed to residency training in all medical disciplines) into exclusive reliance on governmentally funded institutions, the Veterans Administration and other federal installations, the large state hospitals, and the public county hospitals in the larger cities of this nation. With a few notable exceptions, these governmentally supported hospitals have not been significant bastions of dynamic psychotherapy training.

If this is our current academic and training situation for psychiatry nationwide today, then how do we as psychiatric practitioners of psychotherapy survive and hope to continue to survive in our activity? Actually, of course, there are still very many of us, trained in the heyday of psychodynamic training programs in our residencies, and now occupying positions of prominence in our professional communities across the country, to whom the practice of psychotherapy is a vital exercise, both as a way to help people suffering from mental and emotional disorders, and at the same time an exciting intellectual challenge and adventure, a way to understand even more about the fascinations of the human mind. I can note in this context a famous remark by Seymour Kety, one of the founding fathers of biochemical research within psychiatry, that he was very confident that some day we could have an adequate biochemistry of memory, but he doubted very much, in fact could not conceive, that we ever could have a biochemistry of memories. It is the personal store of memories that give each of our lives its individual richness of meanings and that is the central arena of the psychotherapeutic effort, to unravel and make coherent the development of a lifetime of experiences embodied in those memories, both those that are readily available to recall and those that we have had to disavow and banish via our various defensive and adaptive character forms and symptom formations.

It is my own conviction, really my credo and article of faith, that there will always be people who will be drawn to this psychiatry and to the practice of dynamic psychotherapy, and, some of them, to psychoanalytic training and practice, individuals who will be drawn to this particular intellectual challenge, the fullest exploration of and influence on the inner workings of the human mind. There will also always be people gathered together in at least some psychiatric institutions and training centers who will respond to the increasing emptiness of the so-called psychotherapy training offered in the great majority of our standard residency training programs these days by offering two-year postresidency fellowship training in *psychotherapy* of the kind that the Austen Riggs Center in Stockbridge, Massachusetts, was already pioneering in the late 1940s. And, of course, our psychoanalytic institutes will continue to offer the specialized training in psychoanalysis as the most intensive and extensive kind of psychotherapeutic work. Although they are being fortified now by the widened opportunities for nonmedical routes to psychoanalytic training, I would hope that sufficient numbers of graduating psychiatrists would keep coming for this training. In all the other countries of the world where psychoanalytic training is equally open to qualified medical and nonmedical applicants alike, psychiatrists continue everywhere to be the largest group, up to two thirds in most psychoanalytic institutes and societies around the world.

I have, of course, not yet spoken of the less sanguine economics of our coming psychotherapy practices. We are, all of us, painfully aware of the influences on our practices to which I have referred through the course of this talk, not only the diversion of so many psychotherapy patients into psychoactive drug treatments, often administered by general physicians and family practitioners (not even psychiatrists), but also the proliferation of the ranks of nonmedical mental health practitioners, the ever-growing involvement in the private practice arena of the ever-increasing numbers of clinical psychologists and psychiatric social workers and, more recently, of psychiatric nurses and pastoral counselors and marriage, family, and children's counselors (MFCCs). Many of the latter are aided in their quest for clients by the growing number of would-be patients who avoid psychiatrists precisely because they see them as too quick to resort to drug therapy rather than talk therapy. There are also the various self-help groups, growing more popular and drawing often on a variety of sources suspicious of and hostile to the professionally credentialed, who are so often disparagingly viewed as a self-serving and self-enriching establishment dedicated more to guild protection than to public service. Add to all of this the serious many-fold escalation of our hourly fee structure over these years as we psychiatrists have sought, actually vainly, to keep up with the income escalation of our medical and surgical confreres who can earn such large incomes from the many extensive and lucrative procedures of an increasingly technological medicine, not only surgery.

All of this is having its inevitable effects, slowly becoming more and more apparent, that those of us who will continue to do psychotherapy because it is the most exciting and challenging thing for us to do within psychiatry and within medicine, will have to gradually accommodate ourselves to a relative decline in remuneration as compared with all other physicians. The older and the longer established we are in our practices, of course, the less we will personally be affected by these trends and perhaps the more philosophical we can be about them. For the younger colleagues coming into our ranks, the issue is very real indeed, and it may sound like cold comfort to be told that, however much the theory and practice of psychotherapy can endure and even grow and continue to offer unparalleled opportunities for adventure and research, and even be restored at some point to a more balanced and appreciated position within the overall psychiatric pantheon, nonetheless, it is a future of relatively significantly diminished income and affluence, and it will have to draw those of us who continue to be drawn to it on the basis of other than economic considerations.

Which brings me to the end of my overall message about the present status and the future prospects of psychotherapy, as an intellectual activity and as a professional practice. It is clearly not an ebulliently expansive message, nor could it be in 1990. But it is a dedicated, as well as, I hope, a realistic message and a reasonably unblinking prognostication. I mentioned before a credo and an article of faith. I have been fortunate to have lived my scientific and professional career over what have been the expanding and halcyon days of the psychoanalytic and psychotherapeutic enterprise to which I have so contentedly dedicated my working lifetime. I would like very much to believe that I would feel the same curiosity about the human mind and desire to better understand it while trying to ameliorate its dysfunctionings that would draw me to seek the same training and to try to chart a similar career if I were several decades younger and just now making those lifetime career and work choices. I say this despite the more stringent economic prospects and despite the far greater difficulty today than it has been over my life span in pursuing the kind of career in psychotherapy research within psychiatric clinical and academic institutions that it has been my rewarding privilege to have enjoyed. At least I believe in all this enough to have been moved to prepare this address and to try to extract for us still hopeful possibilities from more problematic circumstances. I trust that enough of you in this audience also believe in it enough so that you want these issues appraised as realistically and comprehensively as possible, the better to help you deal with today's realities in the context of enduring hopes and an enduring vision of the high human worthwhileness of what we do.

11.

The Identity of Psychoanalysis: The Question of Lay Analysis

It is a pleasure and a privilege to give this keynote address on a topic that has centrally concerned me in my more than four decades of involvement in psychoanalysis, and that has troubled our discipline for the greater part of this century until its negotiated resolution in 1988 at least within the American and the International Psychoanalytic Associations. It is also a topic on which the American Academy of Psychoanalysis has taken its own principled stand over its decades of existence, a stand which I believe should be reconsidered in the light of the history of the issue and of the much altered dynamic of today, psychoanalysis in the mid-1990s. I am referring to what Freud (1926b) called *The Question of Lay Analysis,* which is not just the parochial or guild issue of which disciplines should have access to the psychoanalytic marketplace, but rather a question of the identity of psychoanalysis itself. It is this issue of the identity of our discipline, what it is all about in the intellectual scheme of things, that to me is the core consideration, and it is this that I want to present by way of a historical unfolding of the question within our discipline.

I take this method, the history of the matter, as my vehicle, because the theoretical arguments, pro and con, as to whether a medical training and identity is essential to the proper practice of analysis have been repeated many times, are well known to this readership, and by themselves seem not to have persuaded individuals on either side to alter their views. Perhaps then, a historical recounting of the controversy over time, the way in which events unfolded, and the probable reasons for them taking the course they did, can put the whole matter into a fresh enough perspective to foster serious reconsideration of once compelling convictions about the matter. At least that is my intent in the story to follow.

I begin with the year 1910, marked for our purposes by two events, seemingly totally unrelated. The one, in Europe, was the publication of the paper, " 'Wild' Psycho-Analysis" (1910). It was Freud's first cry of alarm that the psychoanalytically untrained, in this case a physician claiming an expertise that he did not have, would impart pseudo-analytic advice hurtful to the patient. Indeed it was just this kind of happening, which was occurring often enough as our nascent science was beginning to gain some adherents and some credibility, that impelled Freud to establish the International Psychoanalytical Association (IPA), actually two years earlier, in 1908, with Carl Jung as its first president. It was for the same reasons that some years later, after the defections of Stekel and Adler and Jung, that Freud created the famous committee of the seven ring holders to try to guarantee the stability of his central analytic doctrines as well as the loyalty and the capacity of those who carried the psychoanalytic imprimatur.

The other event in 1910, this one in America, was the issuance of the famed Flexner Report, that startling expose of the shocking state of medical education in the United States, with its widespread proliferation of so-called medical schools that were little more than diploma mills, and with even the best organized schools sadly deficient in full-time faculty and in basic science education. The hue and cry raised by this devastating critique led to an extraordinarily rapid sea change in American medicine with about half the existing medical schools driven to close their doors over the following decade and the remainder shaking down into the approximately one hundred class A medical schools in the nation by the 1930s. The watchword was to exorcise the charlatans and the quacks from the therapeutic activity, and to make the proper medical degree, obtained in the now fully upgraded schools, the hallmark of proper training and competence in the healing arts.

From these beginnings in 1910, two diverging developmental paths can be traced for psychoanalysis, the one in the Central European heartland where Freud lived and was personally influential, and the other in America where as early as the teens of the century some doctors became interested in psychoanalysis, went to Europe for variable periods of personal analysis and some rudiments of training, and then returned to establish the new science in North America. The much larger numbers were with Freud in Europe; the Americans were no more than 20 percent of the world numbers as late as 1930.

The European development was of course heavily colored by Freud's personal fate. Because of the more-or-less official anti-Semitism of Freud's Vienna, and because as well of the scandalous sexual nature of his theories, Freud never achieved the recognition he aspired to throughout his life, from the university and the scientific and medical worlds. Despite his growing worldwide fame, he had only a clinical faculty appointment at the University of Vienna, and his only recorded lecture series there was given during the academic years 1915 to 1917, in the midst of the First World War—the series published as the famed sequence of twenty-eight *Introductory Lectures on Psycho-Analysis* (1916–1917).

For the most part psychoanalysis had to exist and grow in Vienna and throughout the European continent as a completely private practice activity outside of academia and outside of organized medicine, and in its early days in the face of medical and public opposition. When the first organized psychoanalytic training institute was created by Eitingon in Berlin in 1920, it was, again, a private night school carried on the tired energies of part-time men and women, after daytimes of full clinical practice. To this psychoanalytic activity Freud welcomed all those who came, a majority of them physicians drawn mostly from a sterile diagnostic neurology to the new field of psychoanalysis with its heady promise of treatment and cure at least for the psychogenically ill.

But would-be psychoanalysts also came from a great array of nonmedical fields. Among the early students of the new science, Victor Tausk came from law, Robert Waelder from theoretical physics, Ernst Kris was an art historian, and Ella Sharpe an English professor. And we are all familiar with how many of those who created child analysis came from pedagogy, starting with Anna Freud, or had even less formal education, like Erik Erikson who had been an itinerant artist. To Freud, once immersed in their own analyses and once they participated in his Wednesday evening meetings, they all became psychoanalysts; Freud did not differentiate between those medically trained or not. It was those who were not analytically equipped in this way that Freud considered laymen to analysis, whether or not they were physicians.

The dormant issue in this development erupted into public controversy when Theodor Reik, one of Freud's most gifted non-medical colleagues, was charged with a breach of an Austrian law against "quackery," a law which made it illegal for a person without a medical degree to treat patients. Freud intervened energetically in this case. He argued the issue with a high official and went on to write the book *The Question of Lay Analysis* over a three-month span in 1926(b). Partly because of these endeavors, and also because the evidence seemed inconclusive, the public prosecutor stopped the proceedings after the preliminary investigation.

It is worth detailing Freud's central argument in this book because it is critical to the discussion I am building toward, of the implications of this controversy for the nature and identity of our field. The centerpiece is an oft-repeated quotation: "I have assumed . . . that psycho-analysis is not a specialized branch of medicine. I cannot see how it is possible to dispute this. Psycho-analysis is a part of psychology, not of medical psychology in the old sense, not of the psychology of morbid processes, but simply of psychology. It is certainly not the whole of psychology, but its substructure and perhaps even its entire foundation. The possibility of its application to medical purposes must not lead us astray" (1926b, p. 252).

For the therapeutic practice of this psychoanalysis one of course needed rigorous training. Freud put it thus:

> Preparation for analytic activity is by no means so easy and simple. The work is hard, the responsibility great. But anyone who has passed through such a course of instruction, who has been analyzed himself, who has mastered what can be taught to-day of the psychology of the unconscious, who is at home in the science of sexual life, who has learned the delicate technique of psycho-analysis, the art of interpretation, of fighting resistances and of handling the transference—anyone who has accomplished all this is *no longer a layman in the field of psychoanalysis* [p. 228].

Put most succinctly, Freud declared; "I lay stress on the demand that *no one shall practice analysis who has not acquired the right to do so by a particular training.* Whether such a person is a doctor or not seems to me immaterial" (p. 233). On the other hand, those not so trained are the true laymen, or in Freud's harsher language, quacks. He said; "A quack is anyone who undertakes a treatment without possessing the knowledge and capacities first" (p. 230), and somewhat snidely, "doctors form a preponderating contingent of quacks in analysis. They very frequently practice analytic treatment without having learnt it and without understanding it" (p. 230).

But Freud was never as fanatically one-sided as some of those who advocated alongside him. He did provide a threefold special place for the physician analyst. The first was on issues of proper differential diagnosis: "I allow—no, I insist—that in every case which is under consideration for analysis the diagnosis shall be established by a doctor. For the greater number of neuroses which occupy us are fortunately of a psychogenic nature.... Once the doctor has established this, he can confidently hand over the treatment to a lay analyst" (p. 243). The second place was in regard to supervening somatic symptoms: "There is a further contingency ... in which the analyst has to ask the doctor's help. In the course of an analytic treatment, symptoms—most often physical symptoms—may appear about which one is doubtful whether they should be regarded as belonging to the neurosis or whether they should be related to an independent organic illness that has intervened. The decision on this point must once again be left to a doctor" (p. 243). And the third place was in the arena we today call psychosomatic: "I also share the view that all those problems which relate to the connection between psychical phenomena and their organic, anatomical and chemical foundations can be approached only by those who have studied both, that is, by medical analysts. It should not be forgotten, however, that this is not the whole of psychoanalysis ... " (p. 257). The last phrase of course relates to Freud's constant fear lest psychoanalysis, with all its ramifying vistas for the understanding of the human condition, be simply "swallowed up by medicine ... to find its last resting-place in a textbook of psychiatry under the heading 'Methods of Treatment' ... " (p. 248).

By 1926, however, the elderly Freud was not an unchallenged voice on this subject even with the considerable majority of the European analysts who did support his overall position. In 1927, Ernest Jones, the editor of the *International Journal of Psycho-Analysis*, and on this issue, a somewhat ambivalent supporter of Freud, published twenty-six solicited statements in response to Freud's book, from every major center of organized analytic activity. The four Americans among them all adamantly took the opposing position, and overall there seemed a roughly even balance pro and con, with a significant middle group which accorded a preferential place to the medical analyst, including totally in regard to matters of initial diagnosis and referral, with, however, a protected position for the nonmedical analyst within this framework.

Matters meanwhile had taken a quite different course in America. The American analysts, spearheaded by Brill and Oberndorf, were equally as mindful as Freud and his confreres that psychoanalysis should be in the hands of the properly trained, but mindful also of the morass of pseudomedical charlatanism from which the Flexner report had aroused the nation into long overdue corrective action. They took the opposite view from Freud, that the integrity of analysis could only be safeguarded within the now increasingly respectable and scientific medical orbit. The historian Nathan Hale has chronicled the free-wheeling and irresponsible atmosphere in which analytic ideas were taking hold at that time on the West Coast, as follows:

> You must remember that psychoanalysis was introduced to America partly on the wave of a craze for religious sponsored healing in 1908 and 1909, a development that unnerved Freud on his American visit. In the 1920s Americans enthusiastically repeated to themselves the formula of the French therapist Coué: that every day and in every way they were getting better and better. In Los Angeles, a Mrs. Wilshire, clothed in Grecian robes, plied a self-taught psychoanalysis. In 1923, André Tridon, the most notorious American lay analyst, who gilded his toenails for cocktail parties, wrote an introduction to some writings of Freud's he had pirated and published, to Freud's intense irritation [1993, p. 2].

This is the scene against which the medical analysts in America were reacting in tightening orthodoxy.

Still another powerful determination fed this American intention to keep analysis in this country in medical hands. This was that psychoanalysis should follow a different path in America than the proud and lonely isolation that marked it in Europe. It was, in effect, to capture American psychiatry and its formal training centers and become its prevailing psychological theory under the banner of psychodynamics, and thus to be firmly planted in the midst of medicine, the medical school, and at least via this route, the university as well. Here I speak not of the university-based institute, which was a much later development in time, but of the more basic effort to transform the departments of psychiatry in the leading medical schools of our nation into bulwarks of psychodynamic thinking and practice.

This effort was actually brilliantly successful, leading to a radical transformation of American psychiatry that reached its high watermark in the decade of the 1950s in which, in one after another of the major departments of psychiatry in the country, the retiring chairman, characteristically an Adolf Meyer-trained psychobiological psychiatrist, was replaced by a psychoanalytically trained psychiatrist. In its broad outline that story is well enough known and I have described it in chapter 8 (and also in Wallerstein, 1974). I will here mention only one concomitant of that effort, and one central to the theme of this address, that it was as if to strengthen its claim to hegemony within psychiatry that American psychoanalysis felt it had to divest itself of its nonmedical cohorts, so prominently in place in Europe, no matter how glorious the contributions from these nonmedical sources may have been. Whether it was a sacrifice that was necessary to the waging of what turned out to be so successful a campaign, and whether the campaign would have been more difficult or less successful if this sacrifice had not been made, it is hard to know in hindsight. Certainly, the American analysts of the time felt it to be necessary.

I have not mentioned to this point the so-called baser economic motives that may have played some role in the adamant opposition of the American analysts to allowing nonphysicians to share the analytic marketplace. It is not that such motives are ever nonexistent. Certainly there was a tidal wave of refugee analysts inundating mainly the United States as the spreading Nazi hegemony in Europe depopulated the major analytic centers during the decade of the 1930s. This came during the years of the Great Depression when doctors everywhere were increasingly fearful for their livelihood, and concerned medical voices were being raised about the economic threat that would be posed by an additional pool of nonmedical psychoanalytic providers, crowding an already difficult economic arena. But my principal point here is that the more powerful currents fueling the contending positions were deeply principled convictions about what place psychoanalysis should occupy in our intellectual and professional worldview, and what it should mean to be a psychoanalyst. Certainly, one sees from this accounting, thus far, the clash of apparent irreconcilables building up on the two sides of the Atlantic.

The clash came over the organization of the International Training Commission (ITC) established by the IPA at its ninth international congress in 1925 with Max Eitingon as its chair. The laudable intent was to establish and monitor internationally agreed standards for training, modeled primarily on the first organized analytic institute established in Berlin five years earlier in 1920. This was also intended to ensure the portability of psychoanalytic credentials as analysts emigrated from their countries of origin, which at the time meant mainly to the United States. What this raised for the Americans was the specter of the immigration into the United States of nonmedical (i.e., lay) analysts with credentials from European training centers, all of which accepted nonmedical applicants on the same basis as physicians. This possibility led Oberndorf, the leader of the American contingent, to declare; "The strict American law against quackery, and certain disagreeable observations concerning American candidates for membership who thereby wish to attain to an illegitimate practice, make it necessary to exclude nonphysicians" (Leupold-Lowenthal, 1984). The Americans offered a counterproposal asking exemption from the authority of the ITC with the right to set their own training standards, the admissions criteria for training in the United States, and the acceptance criteria to American societies covering their own graduates and also immigrant analysts from Europe.

Strenuous efforts were made over the next six international congresses through to the fifteenth in Paris in 1938 to reconcile these differences so that a viable ITC could function across the analytic world, but these were each time unsuccessful or just resulted in temporary patchworks that promptly broke down. The matter came to a head at the 1938 Paris Congress where the Americans brought a resolution calling for the dismantling of the ITC and the abrogation of any training authority of the IPA over analysis in the United States, with the voiced threat of secession from the IPA and a split of the analytic world into separate American and European hegemonies. The threat was indeed ominous because of the vastly altered balance in the IPA over the immediately preceding five years subsequent to Hitler's accession to power in 1933. Where the Americans were only 20 percent of the total IPA membership at the beginning of the decade, they were now fast becoming the majority, as Hitler's march across Europe systematically depopulated the major analytic training centers in Central Europe, sending the tide of refugees mainly to the United States.

The secession threat was therefore portentous: the IPA would have been split asunder with the American part much the larger, and the European part, such as still existed in 1938, under close threat of the gathering war clouds. The IPA president, Ernest Jones, therefore proposed deferring the definitive vote until the next Congress, scheduled in 1940, with the injunction to deliberate the issues more intensively in the various component societies, with the hope that some viable compromise might yet emerge. But two years later, in 1940, we were in the midst of World War II and the Congress was cancelled, not to reconvene in fact until 1949 in Zurich, eleven years after the near split of 1938.

In the meantime, directly after the Paris Congress the American Psychoanalytic Association ("the American") passed what became known as the 1938 rule asserting full autonomy concerning training standards in the United States, including the limitation of training to physicians, and barring admission to the American of all nonphysicians except for a grandfathered handful of leaders like Erikson, Kris, and Waelder, all of them trained before 1938. But coming to the 1949 Congress, eleven years later, there was still no agreement between the Americans and the Europeans. In anticipation of that Congress, Ernest Jones, still the IPA president, engineered the resolution of the impending crisis. He arranged a series of meetings prior to the Congress, attended by leaders of the British Society together with the American emissaries, and it was agreed to proceed as if the American resolution of 1938 had been approved at that Congress and was now in effect. The ITC had anyway ceased functioning and the agreement keeping the Americans within the IPA fold had two main components: (1) that the American would have total autonomy in regard to training standards in the United States with no IPA oversight; and (2) the American would have an "exclusive franchise" within the United States, meaning that the IPA would recognize no training bodies in the United States other than those under the auspices of the American. It was not until 1963, however, that this 1949 de facto recognition of the American proposal of 1938 was codified in the IPA Constitution, according the American a special Regional Association status with the two special privileges, total internal autonomy and the exclusive franchise, agreed upon in 1949.

Thus, as of 1938, and for a succeeding period of fifty years, psychoanalytic training under the auspices of the IPA was bifurcated, with all the European institutes open for training by physicians and nonphysicians alike, as against the American institutes where full clinical training was available only to psychiatrists. As institutes arose across Latin America in the post-World War II years, their training programs at first were mostly limited to physicians, emulating the United States model, but over the decade of the 1980s, during the period of overthrow of the ruling military juntas in major Latin American nations, the Latin American institutes were at the same time opening their doors to nonmedical applicants on the European model, so that by the latter half of the decade, of the thirty-nine component IPA societies on five continents, only one Latin American nation followed the exclusionary policy of the American, and that one was in the throes of change.

However, just as the Europeans were never monolithically behind Freud's assertions that psychoanalysis was simply a psychology and not intrinsically related to medicine, so the Americans were never completely of one mind on taking the contrary stand. During the period of rapid expansion in the United States in the postwar years, insistent voices were being raised in the American that the sacrifice of the potential contributions to analysis, especially in the area of analytic research, that was the consequence of the rigid barriers against the training of nonmedical candidates, was indeed a heavy, and an unnecessarily heavy, price to pay. This continuing agitation proved persuasive enough so that in 1958, twenty years after the exclusion act of 1938, the American opened its first breach in this barrier by creating the Committee on Training for Research (CTR) under its Board on Professional Standards, a committee authorized to recommend waivers of the medical requirement for the training of established scholars and researchers, committed to academic careers, whose scholarly and research work would be enhanced by being more solidly psychoanalytic. Such individuals could receive full analytic training with the understanding that they would be free to do ongoing clinical work thereafter so long as it was in the context of their major scholarly and research interests. The CTR did not, of course, come into being without opposition, which was focused on the fear that this would become a back door for otherwise unavailable analytic training for nonphysicians, and that this back door might well prove an opening of the floodgates to a tide of academics becoming full-time practitioners.

It was at this point that I became personally involved in this saga. I had had my psychoanalytic training at the Topeka Institute during the 1950s, becoming a member of the American (and the International) in 1960. Early in that decade, in 1954, I, together with a group of colleagues, created the Psychotherapy Research Project of The Menninger Foundation, an intensive study of the processes and outcomes of psychoanalysis and the psychoanalytic psychotherapies which lasted over a thirty-year span. I was the Principal Investigator of that project and by 1960 had achieved recognition as one of the handful of serious investigators in the then embryonic field of psychotherapy research. This led to an invitation to join the American's just recently established Committee on Training for Research directly upon becoming a member of the organization. I served on that committee for a decade until I became President-Elect of the American, and for the second half of that decade I was Chair of the Committee, guiding the vehicle through which analytic training in the American was available to a particular cadre of gifted scholars and researchers.

From that vantage point I can attest both to the success of that program in the contributions to analysis made by its graduates, but also to its very limited quantitative impact. The great flood of applicants that had been feared by the opponents of the program never materialized; the pattern was two to three approved per year, an insignificant number among the hundred and fifty or so new psychiatrist candidates. The reasons for this paucity seemed clear enough; the requirements of analytic training on top of the demands of an academic career, with its teaching and research pressures, were very heavy and the financial incentives of a subsequent full-time practitioner career were not present.

This program did not still the voices in the American, and I was by then one, who, on the basis of the enrichment brought to our activities by the talents of the small handful of research candidates and graduates, agitated for a wider opening of the doors to full training, for future clinical practice, for individuals from the whole array of helping disciplines—clinical psychologists, of course (nonexistent as a profession in Freud's day, it was in the 1970s an influential and largely psychoanalytically oriented discipline), but also members of other mental health professional disciplines as well. It was under these growing pressures that the American, in 1975, established a Committee on the Prerequisites for Training, with Homer Curtis as Chair, with the charge to explore what the proper prerequisites should be for learning to be a psychoanalyst. By that time, I and my colleagues at Mt. Zion Hospital in San Francisco had already developed our own experimental five-year doctoral program

(Wallerstein, 1991) to create a new kind of mental health professional, drawing on the most relevant aspects of training in the three
major mental health disciplines—psychiatry, clinical psychology,
and psychiatric social work—and equipped upon graduation as a
Doctor of Mental Health (DMH) (see chapter 2). At that time I was
able to influence the formation of the Curtis committee to have
included in its charge the consideration of DMH graduates along
with clinical psychologists and psychiatric social workers.

The Committee on Prerequisites for Training labored over a
six-year span before bringing its final recommendations to the
American in 1981. In addition to the personal attributes expected
of all candidates in analytic training, three specific prerequisite experiences at the graduate level were outlined: (1) the study of science and the scientific method; (2) social and humanistic studies;
and (3) socialization into the professional identity of the caretaker
with full acceptance of clinical responsibility and standards of ethical behavior. Opinion within the American over this recommended
departure from the ban on the analytic training for full clinical work
of any but psychiatrists, was still so divided, however, that three
successor committees were sequentially appointed over the next
four years, a Committee on the *Feasibility* of Non-Medical Training
(now that the proper prerequisites had been outlined) chaired by
Kenneth Calder; a subsequent Committee on the *Desirability* of Non-
Medical Training, chaired by Richard Isay; and, finally, a joint committee of the Board on Professional Standards and the Executive
Council of the American, chaired by Vann Spruiell, and charged to
bring in a plan for such training that would not alter the basic
structure and ambience of the American, for Board, Council, and
then the entire membership, to vote upon.

The Spruiell Committee brought three alternative plans to the
meeting of the American in May 1984 in San Diego and reported
that a straw vote amongst the affiliated institutes and societies had
failed to reach any consensus in favor of one over the others; the
membership seemed hopelessly split. In their turn, the Board and
the Council then failed to vote favorably on any of the three, and
in effect, sent the entire matter back to the drawing board, after
the ten years of intense deliberation on whether and how to take
such a major step of reversing the 1938 rule adopted 46 years earlier.

It was this action, which was the culmination of a decade-long
process of consideration, being watched intently and with growing

impatience by the outside community of psychoanalytically interested mental health professionals, that precipitated the sequence of
events that by 1988 would fundamentally alter the nature and structure of the American, bringing it into line with the organization of
analysis in the rest of the world, and bringing with it the realignment
within the American of the conceptions of the identity of analysis
that constitute the philosophic issues that I am bringing to the attention of the American Academy of Psychoanalysis for its own possible
reconsideration.

But here I must first go backwards in time to pick up another
major developmental strand. The action by the American in 1938
to bar analytic training under its auspices to all but psychiatrists in
no way stilled the clamor of nonmedical mental health professionals
for access to high quality analytic training. In fact, Theodor Reik,
the figure around whom Freud (1926b) had written *The Question of
Lay Analysis,* when he was denied an equal and honored position
in the New York Psychoanalytic Society upon his immigration to the
United States in the 1930s, angrily withdrew and created his own
Society, the National Psychological Association for Psychoanalysis
(NPAP) for psychologist practitioners of analysis like himself and
for the analytic training of generations of successors. Over the years
various other nonmedical societies sprang up, first in New York,
either by splits from NPAP, like the New York Freudian Society and
the Institute for Psychoanalytic Training and Research (IPTAR), or
independently, like the William Alanson White Institute. By the
1980s there were some thirty such psychoanalytic training centers
in the New York area alone. There was a cluster in Los Angeles and
scattered training groups in other cities across the nation. By then
the American Psychological Association had created its thirty-ninth
and fastest growing Division, already numbering several thousand
members interested in psychoanalysis, which vigorously promoted
this development of psychologist-run analytic training institutions.

A major aspect of these psychologist psychoanalyst training centers, starting in New York, was the unofficial support of major figures
in the New York Psychoanalytic Society, mostly but not entirely,
immigrant European analysts who were out of sympathy with the
prevailing regulations of the American, and who enacted this opposition by training the psychologist candidates in the nonmedical
institutes outside the American—simply ignoring the American's
strictures which declared such activities improper for its members.
Until these "outside" training centers had been in existence over

a long enough time to have generated their own classes of graduates who had matured to become new generations of teachers and training analysts, they had in fact depended for their very existence upon this covert participation in training of these highly respected members of the American, often just with the stipulation that the analyzing or supervising role not be publicly revealed.

By the 1980s, the numbers in these groups were substantial enough, and Division 39 of the American Psychological Association politically active enough, that they were putting their own pressures on the American to open the doors to its network of high-standard analytic training centers across the country and far beyond the boundaries of New York and Los Angeles. As the decade from 1975 to 1984 progressed, these watching psychologists were becoming increasingly impatient with what they saw as snaillike progress and were gathering their resources for a lawsuit against the American, to force open its doors if it failed itself to take action in that direction. At the time of the San Diego vote, returning all activity on this issue to the starting post after the ten years of deliberation, we had heard of four such possible lawsuits in the watchful waiting stage. It was this knowledge, in fact, that impelled the American in December 1984 to create yet another Committee, this one chaired by Herbert Gaskill, an Advisory Committee to the Executive of the American, with an urgent charge to bring an agreed plan for extending clinical training in psychoanalysis to nonphysicians, and to do so within the shortest possible time frame.

This action by the American, reopening the issue, did not, however, forestall the lawsuit, entered in March 1985 against the American and two of its affiliated institutes in New York by four psychologists acting on behalf of a declared class of several thousand, and with the accumulated several hundred thousand dollar war chest of a new entity, the Group for the Advancement of Psychotherapy and Psychoanalysis in Psychology (GAPPP) created under the umbrella of Division 39. The lawsuit was on Sherman Anti-Trust grounds, that the American unfairly monopolized the quality analytic training market across the nation, and thereby deprived psychologists of proper access to training for this lucrative means of earning a livelihood. The International was named a codefendant in this suit for allowing its American component to do these improper things, contrary to the practice of all its other component organizations around the world.

I became President of the International for a four-year period at the Hamburg Congress that July, four months after the filing of the lawsuit, and was a principal party to all the negotiations and court actions that occurred over its course through the signing of the settlement agreement in October 1988, three-and-a-half years after the initial filing. I cannot recount here the intricate ebb-and-flow of that long process of correspondence, of negotiating meetings, of discovery and depositions, of court arguments over a motion by the defendants for dismissal of the suit which the judge denied, and the subsequent court arguments over the pros and cons of the class action certification upon which the judge had not yet ruled at the time of the settlement.

At this point I will only summarize the major legal–political positions of the three main protagonists in this drama. The position of the psychologist plaintiffs has already been indicated: that organized psychoanalysis as represented by the American, and under the auspices of the International, was exercising an unfair monopoly in restraint of trade on behalf of its psychiatrist members by denying equal access to its training opportunities to qualified psychologists, and that this was in clear violation of the Sherman Anti-Trust Act. Whatever the stated motives for maintaining these policies, the American was, according to the plaintiffs, clearly economically motivated to monopolize quality analytic training and practice and avoid competition.

In response, the legal contention of the American was that, like all other academic, scholarly, and professional organizations, it had a right to set what it regarded as proper admission, training, and graduation standards; that the issue of lay analysis had been a controversial one over a seventy-year span, with major analytic voices divided over its appropriateness over all those years, and that this scientific–professional controversy was not one in which any court would be competent to render judgment; and further that any economic advantage that thereby might accrue to psychiatrist psychoanalysts was only incidental if it existed at all.

The position of the International, for which I had the leading responsibility, was the most complex. The American demanded that the International support it fully in its defense of the lawsuit, on the grounds that the International was obligated to support all its component organizations operating in accord with its Constitution, and the practices of the American were indeed in accord with its prerogatives under the Regional Association status codified in 1963.

On the other hand, the component organizations in the rest of the world, who all did allow psychologists access to training on an equal basis with psychiatrists, were not eager to help defend a lawsuit over a position that was anathema to them, and were unwilling that their dues dollars be used in that defense. And they numbered two thirds of the world membership to the one third in the American. The International, caught between these contending pressures in its own ranks, tried to play the honest broker, fashioning proposals for the compromise settlement of the suit in a manner maximally responsive to the interests of each of the contending parties.

One such settlement proposal by the International actually seemed agreed upon as early as the spring of 1986, only one year into the litigation process. But when this tentative agreement was put into writing by the attorney for the plaintiffs and then responded to in quite a different version by the attorney for the American, it was apparent that neither the plaintiffs nor the American were ready to settle on that basis. *Each* believed, on the advice of their attorneys, that if they allowed the suit—the discovery process, the depositions, etc.—to go on longer, they would acquire enough additional information helpful to their own cause that they could get a better settlement, or even victory, down the line. Obviously, only one of the opposed sets of attorneys could be correct in this prediction.

Matters became more complicated yet, when in the summer of 1986, ten of the leading members of the British Society, among them some of the leading figures in analysis in the world, submitted a resolution, to be brought to the Business Meeting at the next International Congress in Montreal a year later. This resolution, if it were to pass, would hold the International harmless if any component organization was in a situation of litigation under the laws of its own country, stating that the International would accept no legal or financial responsibility for the failure of that component to take adequate steps to have protected itself against such litigation. The meaning was clear: if the suit were to continue, the full legal expenses of the International, already considerable, though far from the several hundred thousand dollars spent to that point by both the plaintiffs and the American, would have to be reimbursed to the International by the American.

Such a confrontation, still a year off, between the American and the rest of the analytic world, would, if it had come to a head in Montreal, quite possibly have led to the rupture that had been avoided almost fifty years earlier in Paris. Yet, under the International's regulations, any altered arrangement between the American and the International that would effect some resolution of this impasse would need to be posted to the membership by the end of December—six months before the Congress—in order to be eligible for vote at the Congress in July. This created a narrow window of six months, between July and December 1986, for the American and the International to iron out their very disparate perspectives so as both to avoid the risk of a split the next summer in Montreal, and also of course to maintain a united front as codefendants in the lawsuit.

Fortunately, much had happened by this time that signified a vastly altered climate on these issues within the American. The Gaskill Committee, created in December 1984, three months before the filing of the lawsuit, had already brought to the May 1985 meeting the draft of a plan for the full clinical training of psychologists, and other qualified mental health professionals, within the institutes of the American, to be monitored by a national waiver committee. After incorporating some of the suggestions from the very favorable discussions in May, a final draft was available by October, and after strong endorsement by the Executive of the American was scheduled for vote by the Board and Council in December, just one year after the appointment of the committee. This vote was in turn overwhelmingly positive and the matter was then sent for vote by the entire membership, with the stipulation that the proposed plan would not be implemented unless that vote was decisive. The fear was that the membership at large would be much more reluctant to accept so major a change than was the leadership represented by the Board and Council. The surprise was that the Gaskill plan won a very decisive 68 percent vote in the ballot count of March 1986. It was directly implemented with a national waiver committee appointed immediately and the processing of applications starting that very fall. Within a few years there were very substantial numbers of nonmedical candidates in the institutes of the American, and the national waiver proviso itself was dropped, so that full autonomy was accorded the affiliated institutes in their admission processes, putting the selection of nonmedical candidates on a complete par with that of medical candidates.

Though the passage of the Gaskill report had no immediate impact on the lawsuit, and was indeed scorned by the plaintiffs as but a forced token, too little and too late, it did profoundly alter the climate between the American and the International, bringing the two bodies much closer into accord, philosophically and organizationally. What still stood as a divisive barrier between them was the Regional Association status, according the American two special privileges enjoyed by no other component of the International: (1) complete control of its training standards with no authority over this by the International; and (2) an "exclusive franchise" in the United States, so that the International could not accord recognition to groups outside the American under its usual arrangements existing everywhere else in the world, which precluded any of the psychologist-run independent training centers now flourishing, certainly in the New York and Los Angeles areas, from any possibility of affiliation with the International—though many of their members published in the psychoanalytic journals and regularly attended the International Congresses. At least one or the other of the American's special privileges would have to be surrendered before the kind of rapprochement could be reached in our international house of psychoanalysis that would induce the British Society members to withdraw their resolution from the agenda of the coming Business Meeting.

The time to work all this out was, as I have indicated, but six months, and the pace of meetings between the officers of the American and the International was intense. Agreement was finally reached in New York in December. The American, more concerned to maintain control over its own standard setting, opted to surrender the "exclusive franchise" in the knowledge that this would allow the various unrecognized, independent, nonmedical institutes, especially the already well-established ones in New York and Los Angeles, to be accepted as component societies of the International alongside the American, so long as they could meet the standards of the International—which in no way differed from those of the American now that the Gaskill plan for nonmedical training had been adopted. This alteration of the Regional Association agreement was to be proposed by ten members of the American, including all the officers. An ancillary agreement was that, in view of the unwillingness of the rest of the world to see their International dues used in the defense of a lawsuit that they felt should never have been gotten into, the American undertook to reimburse the International the percentage of its continuing legal expenses that represented the percent of the overall dues by all the component organizations other than the American. All this was effected before the December 31 deadline, and in response, the British Society members notified the International that they were withdrawing their proposed resolution.

Events marched swiftly after that. At the Montreal Congress in July 1987, the proposed alteration in the Regional Association agreement passed overwhelmingly, and now two channels were open for IPA membership by nonphysicians in the United States. Such individuals could apply for full analytic training within the institutes of the American, which already a goodly number were doing, or they could seek International membership outside the American, through affiliation with one of the established independent societies which were now free to make application for component status within the International. Three such societies, two in New York and one in Los Angeles, were admitted to the International at the Rome Congress in 1989, and a fourth, in Los Angeles, was admitted at the subsequent Buenos Aires Congress in 1991.

Progress was also taking place on the lawsuit front. There seemed to be intense discussion and clear division within the plaintiff camp. Voices were being raised that now that the American had effected such a change, the Gaskill plan, and the relationship between the American and the International had been so altered in the renunciation of the exclusive franchise that the major goals of the lawsuit had been achieved and the continuing great expense of its further pursuit could no longer be justified. Nonetheless, the legal process of depositions and further discovery went on, and in October 1987 (note, *after* the Montreal Congress) the class-action certification motion did go to the court, and in February, 1988, a defense memorandum objecting to the motion was entered in response. But then shortly thereafter, in April 1988, a serious settlement offer came from the plaintiffs, basically proposing a court-approved codification of the changes already embodied in the actions of the American and the International, and in its essence, and this is the sad part, not different from what had been proposed two years earlier by the International, trying to play its honest broker role between the plaintiffs and the American, and anticipating then the changes later effected in the agreed alterations of the Regional Association agreement (remember, that at that time, two years earlier, the Gaskill proposal had already been passed decisively by the American).

In any case, it was now the plaintiffs' turn, in April 1988, to propose, in essence, this self-same agreement. After intensive negotiations amongst all the involved parties with their somewhat different interests—the plaintiffs, the American, the International, and also the two defendant Institutes of the American in New York—the agreement was finally signed in October 1988, and subsequently ratified by the court the following April 1989, just a bit over four years since the suit had been initially filed in March 1985.

The remainder of the account is, for our purposes, anticlimactic. The enforcement of the settlement is being monitored by the court for a ten-year period. Division 39 has set up its own Settlement Enforcement Committee, and there have been dialogues between it and both the American and the International over the years since having to do with the degree of "good faith" with which the requirements of the settlement have been implemented, mostly around the credentials of various applicant groups to the International. But none of that will have any enduring impact on a history that has already been made—the transformation of analysis in our country, as represented by the American and by the independent International-affiliated institutes, into a total body, open in each channel to both medical and nonmedical applicants to training, all under the auspices of the International. The breach between the United States and the rest of the world, created de facto, if not yet de jure, by the American ultimatum in Paris in 1938, had been completely overcome, by the alteration of the Regional Association agreement in Montreal in 1987 and the settlement of the lawsuit in 1988—exactly half a century later.

The issue in all this that I wish to pose for the American Academy of Psychoanalysis, itself traditionally committed to the same conception as had prevailed in the American, of the limitation of analytic practice to the medically trained, is what it all means for the nature of our discipline, for what I have called, in my title, the identity of psychoanalysis. I can pose the essential question directly. Is psychoanalysis fundamentally a branch of the healing arts dealing with the range of emotional disorders, as a subspecialty of psychiatry, itself a specialty of medicine? In this conception it should of course be limited to the medically trained, the fate that Freud foresaw to his distress as the American path. Or is psychoanalysis a general theory of the mind, with ramifications for all the cognate disciplines that bear on mental functioning more narrowly, and for the entirety of the human condition more broadly? In that sense psychoanalysis would have its interface with human biology, of course, and thereby with medicine, in all its concerns with health and disease. But psychoanalysis would also have its interface with all the rest of psychology, and also with the whole array of social and behavioral sciences, sociology, anthropology, and the like, as they deal with the meanings of the organized behaviors of humankind. And as a third aspect, psychoanalysis would also have an impact on all of the humanities, philosophy, literature, religious studies, and the arts, as they each express the functioning and the reach of the human mind in all its manifold meanings and complexities.

If this be the vision of psychoanalysis, its fundamental identity as a human achievement, pioneered by Freud, but now the collective responsibility of all of us who are its adherents, then it would need to be open to individuals whose originating discipline is in any of the major interfaces that I have postulated for it, biological science, behavioral and social science, and even the humanities, so that psychoanalysis can truly reflect the interaction of all its component influences, all then refracted through the particular psychoanalytic way of looking at things bequeathed to us by Freud.

My thesis in all of this is that it is these two counterposed visions of what psychoanalysis is all about that has been at stake in the fifty-year separation between the American and the worldwide position about analysis, although, as I have indicated, both points of view have been held within each of these separated camps. It has only been the preponderant majority and the political power that has tipped, and not always stably, in the two opposed directions over the half-century span, until the final accommodation in the direction that Freud initially posed for us, of psychoanalysis as a psychology, with all of its interfaces as I have spelled them out, rather than in the opposed direction of simply being an arm of medicine. Put graphically, what has altered profoundly for American psychoanalysis over the course of these events has been the change in identity, from, "I am a physician who has specialized in psychiatry and, within that, psychoanalysis, as a way of understanding and trying to ameliorate human emotional distress" (i.e., I am in the first instance a physician, and secondarily a psychoanalyst) to, "I am a psychoanalyst, devoted to understanding the human mind psychoanalytically, in all its dimensions and activities, who has come to this endeavor by way of prior training in medicine, or in psychology, or in whatever; I am in the first instance a psychoanalyst, and secondarily come to it by way of any of the variety of routes indicated."

This is the issue that I have undertaken to pose to the American Academy of Psychoanalysis in this address. The American Psychoanalytic Association has made a choice, not entirely voluntarily on the part of all its members, but to my mind irrevocably, in reversing a fifty-year-long stance, and joining now in the long-time historical position of its colleagues from all the other countries represented in the International. Its members have in effect taken on an altered psychoanalytic identity. This was not an easy process. It is, after all, a fundamental shift and that is why it has been so contested and took so long in coming. My plea to you in the light of this history and this understanding is that you also as an organization—free of the external pressures that beset the American during its course—likewise undertake your own reconsideration of this major issue for our discipline, what we stand for in our minds and in the world culture in which we play our part. I trust, in closing, that I have taken seriously the responsibility of the keynote address to your meeting, to raise an important issue for your collective consideration.

References

Alexander, F. (1937), *Five Year Report of the Chicago Institute for Psychoanalysis: 1932–1937.* Chicago: Chicago Institute for Psychoanalysis.

———— French, T. M. (1946), *Psychoanalytic Therapy: Principles and Application.* New York: Ronald Press.

———— ———— (1948), *Studies in Psychosomatic Medicine.* New York: Ronald Press.

Altshuler, K. Z. (1990), Whatever happened to intensive psychotherapy? *Amer. J. Psychiatry,* 147:428–430.

Appelbaum, S. A. (1977), *The Anatomy of Change.* New York: Plenum Press.

Applegarth, A. (1971), Comments on aspects of the theory of psychic energy. *J. Amer. Psychoanal. Assn.,* 19:379–416.

Arlow, J. A. (1982), Psychoanalytic education: A psychoanalytic perspective. *Annual of Psychoanalysis,* 10:5–20. New York: International Universities Press.

———— Brenner, C. C. (1988), The future of psychoanalysis. *Psychoanal. Quart.,* 57:1–14.

Auden, W. H. (1940), In memory of Sigmund Freud. In: *Collected Poems.* New York: Vintage, 1991, pp. 273–276.

Bachrach, H. M., Galatzer-Levy, R., Skolnikoff, A., & Waldron, S., Jr. (1991), On the efficacy of psychoanalysis. *J. Amer. Psychoanal. Assn.,* 39:871–916.

———— Weber, J. J., & Solomon, M. (1985), Factors associated with the outcome of psychoanalysis (clinical and methodological considerations): Report of the Columbia Psychoanalytic Center Research Project (IV). *Internat. Rev. Psycho-Anal.*, 12:379–388.

Bak, R. (1970), Psychoanalysis today. *J. Amer. Psychoanal. Assn.*, 18:3–23.

Beres, D., Kanzer, M., Wallerstein, R. S., & Zetzel, E. R. (1968), Discussion of G. F. Engel's "Some obstacles to the development of research in psychoanalysis." *J. Amer. Psychoanal. Assn.*, 16:205–229.

Bibring, E. (1937), Symposium on the theory of the therapeutic results of psychoanalysis. *Internat. J. Psycho-Anal.*, 18:170–189.

Bibring, G. L., Dwyer, T. F., Huntington, D. S., & Valenstein, A. F. (1961), A study of the psychological processes in pregnancy and of the earliest mother–child relationship. *The Psychoanalytic Study of the Child*, 16:9–72. New York: International Universities Press.

Blight, J. G. (1981), Must psychoanalysis retreat to hermeneutics? Psychoanalytic theory in the light of Popper's evolutionary epistemology. *Psychoanal. & Contemp. Thought*, 4:147–206.

Brenner, C. C. (1968), Psychoanalysis and science. *J. Amer. Psychoanal. Assn.*, 16:675–696.

Breuer, J., & Freud, S. (1893–1895), Studies on Hysteria. *Standard Edition*, 2. London: Hogarth Press, 1955.

Brown, B. S. (1977), The NIMH manpower training program. Presented to the National Advisory Mental Health Council, January 24.

Burnham, J. C. (1967), Psychoanalysis and American Medicine, 1894–1918: Medicine, Science, and Culture. *Psychological Issues*, Monogr. 20. New York: International Universities Press.

Calef, V. (1972), A report of the 4th Pre-Congress on Training, Vienna 1971, to the 17th International Psycho-Analytical Congress. *Internat. J. Psycho-Anal.*, 53:37–43.

Coriat, I. (1917), Some statistical results of the psychoanalytic treatment of the psychoneuroses. *Psychoanal. Rev.*, 4:209–216.

Dahl, H., Kaechele, H., & Thomae, H. (1988), *Psychoanalytic Process Research Strategies*. New York: Springer.

DeWitt, K. N., Hartley, D. E., Rosenberg, S. E., Zilberg, N. J., & Wallerstein, R. S. (1991), Scales of Psychological Capacities: Development of an assessment approach. *Psychoanal. & Contemp. Thought*, 14:343–361.

Eagle, M. N. (1973), Sherwood on the logic of explanation in psychoanalysis. *Psychoanal. & Contemp. Sci.*, 2:331–337.
—— (1980), A critical examination of motivational explanation in psychoanalysis. *Psychoanal. & Contemp.Thought*, 3:329–380.
—— (1984), *Recent Developments in Psychoanalysis: A Critical Evaluation.* New York: McGraw-Hill.
Edelson, M. (1983), Is testing psychoanalytic hypotheses in the psychoanalytic situation really impossible? *The Psychoanalytic Study of the Child*, 38:61–109. New Haven, CT: Yale University Press.
—— (1984), *Hypothesis and Evidence in Psychoanalysis.* Chicago: University of Chicago Press.
—— (1988), *Psychoanalysis: A Theory in Crisis.* Chicago: University of Chicago Press.
Eissler, K. R. (1969), Irreverent remarks about the present and the future of psychoanalysis. *Internat. J. Psycho-Anal.*, 50:461–471.
Engel, G. L. (1968), Some obstacles to the development of research in psychoanalysis. *J. Amer. Psychoanal. Assn.*, 16:195–204.
Erdelyi, M. H. (1985), *Psychoanalysis: Freud's Cognitive Psychology.* New York: W. H. Freeman.
Erikson, E. H. (1958), The nature of clinical evidence. *Daedalus*, 87:65–87.
Erle, J. B. (1979), An approach to the study of analyzability and analysis: The course of forty consecutive cases selected for supervised analysis. *Psychoanal. Quart.*, 48:198–228.
—— Goldberg, D. A. (1979), Problems in the assessment of analyzability. *Psychoanal. Quart.*, 48:48–84.
—— —— (1984), Observations on assessment of analyzability by experienced analysts. *J. Amer. Psychoanal. Assn.*, 32:715–737.
Feldman, F. (1968), Results of psychoanalysis in clinic case assignments. *J. Amer. Psychoanal. Assn.*, 16:274–300.
Fenichel, O. (1930), Statistischer Bericht über die Therapeutische Tätigkeit, 1920–1930. In: *Zehn Jahre Berliner Psychoanalytisches Institut.* Berlin: Internationale Psychoanalytisches Verlag, pp. 13–19.
Frank, J. D. (1961), *Persuasion and Healing: A Comparative Study of Psychotherapy.* Baltimore: Johns Hopkins University Press.
Freud, A. (1936), *The Ego and the Mechanisms of Defense.* New York: International Universities Press, 1946.
—— (1954), The widening scope of indications for psychoanalysis: Discussion. *J. Amer. Psychoanal. Assn.*, 2:607–620.

—— (1971), The ideal psychoanalytic institute: A utopia. *Bull. Menn. Clin.,* 35:226–239.

—— (1976), Changes in psychoanalytic practice and experience. *Internat. J. Psycho-Anal.,* 57:257–260.

Freud, S. (1895), Project for a Scientific Psychology. *Standard Edition,* 1:281–397. London: Hogarth Press, 1966.

—— (1900), The Interpretation of Dreams. *Standard Edition,* 4& 5. London: Hogarth Press, 1953.

—— (1910), "Wild" psycho-analysis. *Standard Edition,* 11:219–227. London: Hogarth Press, 1957.

—— (1915), A case of paranoia running counter to the psychoanalytic theory of the disease. *Standard Edition,* 14:261–272. London: Hogarth Press, 1957.

—— (1916–1917), Introductory Lectures on Psycho-Analysis. *Standard Edition,* 16:448–463. London: Hogarth Press, 1963.

—— (1919), On the teaching of psycho-analysis in universities. *Standard Edition,* 17:169–173. London: Hogarth Press, 1955.

—— (1923), The Ego and the Id. *Standard Edition,* 19:1–66. London: Hogarth Press, 1961.

—— (1926a), Inhibitions, Symptoms and Anxiety. *Standard Edition,* 20:75–175. London: Hogarth Press, 1959.

—— (1926b), The Question of Lay Analysis. *Standard Edition,* 20:177–258. London: Hogarth Press, 1959.

—— (1933), New Introductory Lectures on Psycho-Analysis. *Standard Edition,* 22:1–182. London: Hogarth Press, 1964.

—— (1937), Analysis terminable and interminable. *Standard Edition,* 23:209–253. London: Hogarth Press, 1964.

—— Pfister, O. (1963), *Psychoanalysis and Faith.* London: Hogarth Press.

Fromm-Reichmann, F. (1950), *Principles of Intensive Psychotherapy.* Chicago: University of Chicago Press.

Gadamer, H. G. (1975), *Truth and Method.* New York: Seabury Press.

Gill, M. M. (1954), Psychoanalysis and exploratory psychotherapy. *J. Amer. Psychoanal. Assn.,* 2:771–797.

—— (1963), Topography and Systems in Psychoanalytic Theory. *Psychological Issues,* Monogr. 10. New York: International Universities Press.

—— (1976), Metapsychology is not psychology. In: Psychology versus Metapsychology: Psychoanalytic Essays in Memory of George S. Klein, ed. M. M. Gill & P. S. Holzman. *Psychological*

Issues, Monogr. 36. New York: International Universities Press, pp. 71–105.

———— (1983), The point of view of psychoanalysis: Energy discharge or person? *Psychoanal. & Contemp. Thought,* 6:523–551.

———— (1984), Psychoanalysis and psychotherapy: A revision. *Internat. Rev. Psycho-Anal.,* 11:161–179.

———— Simon, J., Fink, G., Endicott, N. A., & Paul, I. H. (1968), Studies in audio-recorded psychoanalysis. I: General considerations. *J. Amer. Psychoanal. Assn.,* 16:230–244.

Gitelson, M. (1964), On the identity crisis in American Psychoanalysis. *J. Amer. Psychoanal. Assn.,* 12:451–476.

Glover, E. (1952), Research methods in psycho-analysis. *Internat. J. Psycho-Anal.,* 33:403–409.

———— (1954), The indications for psycho-analysis. *J. Ment. Sci.,* 100:393–401.

Glymour, C. (1974), Freud, Kepler, and the clinical evidence. In: *Philosophical Essays on Freud,* ed. R. Wollheim & J. Hopkins. Cambridge, U.K.: Cambridge University Press, 1982, pp. 12–31.

Goodman, S., Ed. (1977), *Psychoanalytic Education and Research: The Current Situation and Future Possibilities.* New York: International Universities Press.

Grünbaum, A. (1979a), Is Freudian psychoanalytic theory pseudoscientific by Karl Popper's criterion of demarcation? *Amer. Philosoph. Quart.,* 16:131–141.

———— (1979b), Epistemological liabilities of the clinical appraisal of psychoanalytic theory. *Psychoanal. & Contemp. Thought,* 2:451–526.

———— (1980a), The role of psychological explanations of the rejection or acceptance of scientific theories. *Trans. NY Acad. Sci., Series II,* 39:75–90.

———— (1980b), Epistemological liabilities of the clinical appraisal of psychoanalytic theory. *NOUS,* 14:307–385.

———— (1982), Can psychoanalytic theory be cogently tested "on the couch"? *Psychoanal. & Contemp. Thought,* 5:155–250, 311–346.

———— (1983a), Retrospective versus prospective testing of aetiological hypotheses in Freudian theory. In: Testing Scientific Theories. *Minnesota Studies in Philosophy of Science,* Vol. 10, ed. J. Earman. Minneapolis: University of Minnesota Press, pp. 315–347.

―――― (1983b), Freud's theory: The perspective of a philosopher of science. *Proc. & Addresses Amer. Philosoph. Assn.*, 57:5–31.

―――― (1983c), Logical foundations of psychological theory. *Erkenntnis*, 19:109–152.

―――― (1984), *The Foundations of Psychoanalysis: A Philosophical Critique.* Berkeley: University of California Press.

Habermas, J. (1968), *Knowledge and Human Interests*, tr. J. J. Shapiro. Boston: Beacon Press, 1971.

Hale, N. (1993), Lay analysis: San Francisco and national policy. An oral history workshop presented at the Annual Meeting of the American Psychoanalytic Association, San Francisco.

Hamburg, D. A., Bibring, G. L., Fisher, C., Stanton, A. H., Wallerstein, R. S., Weinstock, H. I., & Haggard, E. (1967), Report of Ad Hoc Committee on Central Fact-Gathering Data of the American Psychoanalytic Association. *J. Amer. Psychoanal. Assn.*, 15:841–861.

Harrison, S. I. (1970), Is psychoanalysis "our science"? Reflections on the scientific status of psychoanalysis. *J. Amer. Psychoanal. Assn.*, 18:125–149.

Hartmann, H. (1939), *Ego Psychology and the Problem of Adaptation.* New York: International Universities Press, 1958.

―――― (1964), *Essays on Ego Psychology.* New York: International Universities Press.

―――― Kris, E., & Loewenstein, R. M. (1964), Papers on Psychoanalytic Psychology. *Psychological Issues*, Monogr. 14. New York: International Universities Press.

Henry, W. E., Sims, J. H., & Spray, S. L. (1971), *The Fifth Profession: Becoming a Psychotherapist.* San Francisco: Jossey-Bass.

Holland, N. N. (1968), *The Dynamics of Library Response.* New York: Oxford University Press.

Holt, R. R. (1961), Clinical judgment as a disciplined inquiry. In: *Methods in Clinical Psychology*, Vol. 2. New York: Plenum Press, 1978, pp. 38–54.

―――― (1962), Individuality and generalization in the psychology of personality. In: *Methods in Clinical Psychology*, Vol. 1. New York: Plenum Press, 1978, pp. 5–29.

―――― Ed. (1971), *New Horizon for Psychotherapy: Autonomy as a Profession.* New York: International Universities Press.

―――― (1972), Freud's mechanistic and humanistic images of man. *Psychoanal. & Contemp. Sci.*, 1:3–24.

———— (1976), Drive or wish? A reconsideration of the psychoanalytic theory of motivation. In: Psychology versus Metapsychology: Psychoanalytic Essays in Memory of George S. Klein, ed. M. M. Gill & P. S. Holzman. *Psychological Issues,* Monogr. 36. New York: International Universities Press, pp. 158–197.

———— (1981), The death and transfiguration of metapsychology. *Internat. Rev. Psycho-Anal.,* 8:129–143.

———— (1984), The current status of psychoanalytic theory. Presented at the American Psychological Meeting, August.

Holzman, P. S. (1985), Psychoanalysis: Is the therapy destroying the science? *J. Amer. Psychoanal. Assn.,* 33:725–770.

Home, H. J. (1966), The concept of mind. *Internat. J. Psycho-Anal.,* 47:42–49.

Hook, S., Ed. (1959), *Psychoanalysis, Scientific Method and Philosophy: A Symposium.* New York: International Universities Press.

Hopkins, J. (1982), Introduction: Philosophy and psychoanalysis. In: *Philosophical Essays on Freud,* ed. R. Wollheim & J. Hopkins. Cambridge, U.K.: Cambridge University Press, pp. vii-xiv.

Horwitz, L. (1974), *Clinical Prediction in Psychotherapy.* New York: Jason Aronson.

Jones, E., et al. (1927), Discussion on lay analysis. *Internat. J. Psycho-Anal.,* 8:174–283, 392–401.

———— (1936), *Decannual Report of the London Clinic of Psychoanalysis, 1926–1936.* Typescript.

Kantrowitz, J. L. (1986), The role of the patient–analyst "match" in the outcome of psychoanalysis. *Annual of Psychoanalysis,* 14:273–297. Madison, CT: International Universities Press.

———— Katz, A. L., Greenman, D. A., Morris, H., Paolitto, F., Sashin, J., & Solomon, L. (1989), The patient–analyst match and the outcome of psychoanalysis: A pilot study. *J. Amer. Psychoanal. Assn.,* 37:893–919.

———— ———— Paolitto, F. (1990a), Follow-up of psychoanalysis five to ten years after termination: I. Stability of change. *J. Amer. Psychoanal. Assn.,* 38:471–496.

———— ———— ———— (1990b), Follow-up of psychoanalysis five to ten years after termination: II. Development of the self-analytic function. *J. Amer. Psychoanal. Assn.,* 38:637–654.

———— ———— ———— (1990c), Follow-up of psychoanalysis five to ten years after termination: III. The relation between resolution of the transference and the patient–analyst match. *J. Amer. Psychoanal. Assn.,* 38:655–678.

———— ———— ———— Sashin, J., & Solomon, L. (1987a), Changes in the level and quality of object relations in psychoanalysis: Follow-up of a longitudinal prospective study. *J. Amer. Psychoanal. Assn.*, 35:23–46.

———— ———— ———— ———— ———— (1987b), The role of reality testing in psychoanalysis: Follow-up of 22 cases. *J. Amer. Psychoanal. Assn.*, 35:367–385.

———— Paolitto, F., Sashin, J., Solomon, L. & Katz, A. L. (1986), Affect availability, tolerance, complexity and modulation in psychoanalysis: Follow-up of a longitudinal, prospective study. *J. Amer. Psychoanal. Assn.*, 34:529–559.

Kernberg, O. F. (1975), *Borderline Conditions and Pathological Narcissism.* New York: Jason Aronson.

———— (1984a), From the Menninger project to a research strategy for long-term psychotherapy of borderline personality disorders. In: *Psychotherapy Research: Where Are We and Where Should We Go?* ed. J. W. B. Williams & R. L. Spitzer. New York: Guilford Press, pp. 247–259.

———— (1984b), *Severe Personality Disorders: Psychotherapeutic Strategies.* New Haven, CT: Yale University Press.

———— Burstein, E. D., Coyne, L., Appelbaum, A., Horwitz, L., & Voth, H. (1972), Psychotherapy and psychoanalysis: Final report of The Menninger Foundation's Psychotherapy Research Project. *Bull. Menn. Clin.*, 36:1–275.

Kessel, L., & Hyman, H. (1933), The value of psychoanalysis as a therapeutic procedure. *J. Amer. Med. Assn.*, 101:1612–1615.

Klauber, J. (1968), On the dual use of historical and scientific method in psychoanalysis. *Internat. J. Psycho-Anal.*, 49:80–88.

Klein, G. S. (1973), Is psychoanalysis relevant? *Psychoanal. & Contemp. Sci.*, 2:3–21.

———— (1976), *Psychoanalytic Theory: An Exploration of Essentials.* New York: International Universities Press.

Knapp, P. H., Levin, S., McCarter, R. H., Wermer, H., & Zetzel, E. (1960), Suitability for psychoanalysis: A review of one hundred supervised analytic cases. *Psychoanal. Quart.*, 29:459–477.

Knight, R. P. (1941), Evaluation of the results of psychoanalytic therapy. *Amer. J. Psychiatry*, 98:434–446.

Kohut, H. (1970), Scientific activities of the American Psychoanalytic Association: An inquiry. *J. Amer. Psychoanal. Assn.*, 18:462–484.

————— (1971), *The Analysis of the Self.* New York: International Universities Press.

————— (1972), Thoughts on narcissism and narcissistic rage. *The Psychoanalytic Study of the Child,* 27:360–400. Chicago: Quadrangle.

————— (1973), The future of psychoanalysis. Presentation following Chicago Symposium on "Psychoanalysis and History."

————— (1984), *How Does Analysis Cure?* ed. A. Goldberg & P. E. Stepansky. Chicago: University of Chicago Press.

Kramer, M. K. (1959), On the continuation of the analytic process after psychoanalysis (A self-observation). *Internat. J. Psycho-Anal.,* 40:17–25.

Kris, E. (1947), The nature of psychoanalytic propositions and their validation. In: *Freedom and Experience: Essays Presented to Horace M. Kallen,* ed. S. Hook & M. R. Konvitz. Ithaca, NY: Cornell University Press, pp. 239–259.

Kubie, L. S. (1954), The pros and cons of a new profession: A doctorate in medical psychology. *Tex. Rep. Bio. Med.,* 12:692–737.

————— (1966), A reconsideration of thinking, the dream process, and "the dream." *Psychoanal. Quart.,* 35:191–198.

Kuhn, T. S. (1962), *The Structure of Scientific Revolutions.* Chicago: University of Chicago Press.

Leupold-Lowenthal, H. (1984), On the history of the "Question of Lay Analysis." *Psyche,* 38:97–120.

Lindemann, E. (1944), Symptomatology and management of acute grief. *Amer. J. Psychiatry,* 101:141–148.

Lippman, W. (1966), The university. *New Republic,* May 28.

Loftus, E. (1980), *Memory.* Reading, MA: Addison-Wesley.

Lustman, S. L. (1963), Some issues in contemporary psychoanalytic research. *The Psychoanalytic Study of the Child,* 18:51–74. New York: International Universities Press.

————— (1969), Introduction to panel: The use of the economic viewpoint in clinical analysis: The economic point of view and defense. *Internat. J. Psycho-Anal.,* 50:95–102.

McIntosh, D. (1979), The empirical bearing of psychoanalytic theory. *Internat. J. Psycho-Anal.,* 60:405–431.

Mahler, M. (1968), *On Human Symbiosis and the Vicissitudes of Individuation.* New York: International Universities Press.

Meehl, P. E. (1973), Some methodological reflections on the difficulties of psychoanalytic research. In: Psychoanalytic Research: Three Approaches to the Experimental Study of Subliminal

Processes, ed. M. Mayman. *Psychological Issues,* Monogr. 30. New York: International Universities Press, pp. 104–117.

Mohl, P. C., Lomax, J., Tasman, A., Chan, C., Sledge, W., Summergrad, P., & Norman, M. (1990), Psychotherapy training for the psychiatrist of the future. *Amer. J. Psychiatry,* 147:7–13.

Norman, H. F., Blacker, K. H., Oremland, J. D., & Barrett, W. G. (1976), The fate of the transference neurosis after termination of a satisfactory analysis. *J. Amer. Psychoanal. Assn.,* 24:471–498.

Oremland, J. D., Blacker, K. H., & Norman, H. F. (1975), Incompleteness in "successful" psychoanalysis: A follow-up study. *J. Amer. Psychoanal. Assn.,* 23:819–844.

Ostwald, P.F. (1977), *Communication and Social Interaction.* New York: Grune & Stratton.

Panel (1971), Models of the psychic apparatus. Reporter: S. Abrams. *J. Amer. Psychoanal. Assn.,* 19:131–142.

——— (1989), Evaluation of outcome of psychoanalytic treatment: Should follow-up by the analyst be part of the post-termination phase of analytic treatment? Reporter: M. Johan. *J. Amer. Psychoanal. Assn.,* 37:813–822.

——— (1993), Stability of gains achieved during analytic treatment from a follow-up perspective. Reporter: G. C. Martin. *J. Amer. Psychoanal. Assn.,* 41:209–217.

Panels, (1954), The widening scope of indications for psychoanalysis; The traditional psychoanalytic technique and its variations; Psychoanalysis and dynamic psychotherapy: Similarities and differences. *J. Amer. Psychoanal. Assn.,* 2:565–797.

Parsons, T. (1964), *Social Structure and Personality.* Glencoe, IL: Free Press.

Peterfreund, E., with Schwartz, J. T. (1971), Information Systems and Psychoanalysis: An Evolutionary Biological Approach to Psychoanalytic Theory. *Psychological Issues,* Monogr. 25 & 26. New York: International Universities Press.

Pfeffer, A. Z. (1959), A procedure for evaluating the results of psychoanalysis: A preliminary report. *J. Amer. Psychoanal. Assn.,* 7:418–444.

——— (1961), Follow-up study of a satisfactory analysis. *J. Amer. Psychoanal. Assn.,* 9:698–718.

——— (1963), The meaning of the analyst after analysis: A contribution to the theory of therapeutic results. *J. Amer. Psychoanal. Assn.,* 11:229–244.

Poland, W. S., & Major, R., Eds. (1984), French psychoanalytic voices. *Psychoanal. Inq.*, 4:145–311.

Popper, K. R. (1963), *Conjectures and Refutations: The Growth of Scientific Knowledge*. New York: Basic Books.

Ramzy, I. (1962), Research in psychoanalysis: Contribution to discussion. *Internat. J. Psycho-Anal.*, 43:292–296.

——— (1963), Research aspects of psychoanalysis. *Psychoanal. Quart.*, 32:58–76.

——— Shevrin, H. (1976), The nature of the inference process in psychoanalytic interpretation: A critical review of the literature. *Internat. J. Psycho-Anal.*, 57:151–159.

Rangell, L. (1966), An overview of the ending of an analysis. In: *The Human Core: The Intrapsychic Base of Behavior*, Vol. 2. Madison, CT: International Universities Press, 1990, pp. 703–725.

——— (1981), Psychoanalysis and dynamic psychotherapy: Similarities and differences twenty-five years later. *Psychoanal. Quart.*, 50:665–693.

Rapaport, D. (1960), The Structure of Psychoanalytic Theory: A Systematizing Attempt. *Psychological Issues*, Monogr. 6. New York: International Universities Press.

——— (1967), *Collected Papers*, ed. M. M. Gill. New York: Basic Books.

Reik, T. (1937), *Surprise and the Psycho-Analyst*. New York: E. P. Dutton.

Reiser, M. F. (1984), *Mind, Brain, Body: Toward a Convergence of Psychoanalysis and Neurobiology*. New York: Basic Books.

Ricoeur, P. (1970), *Freud and Philosophy: An Essay on Interpretation*, tr. D. Savage. New Haven, CT: Yale University Press.

——— (1977), The question of proof in Freud's psychoanalytic writings. *J. Amer. Psychoanal. Assn.*, 25:835–871.

Ritvo, S. (1971), Psychoanalysis as science and profession: Prospects and challenges. *J. Amer. Psychoanal. Assn.*, 19:3–21.

Rosenblatt, A. D., & Thickstun, J. T. (1970), A study of the concept of psychic energy. *Internat. J. Psycho-Anal.*, 51:265–278.

——— ——— (1977), Modern Psychoanalytic Concepts in General Psychology. *Psychological Issues*, Monogr. 42/43. New York: International Universities Press.

——— ——— (1984), The psychoanalytic process: A systems and information processing model. *Psychoanal. Inq.*, 4:59–86.

Rubinstein, B. B. (1973), On the logic of explanation in psychoanalysis. *Psychoanal. & Contemp. Sci.*, 2:338–358.

———— (1975), On the clinical psychoanalytic theory and its role in the inference and confirmation of particular clinical hypotheses. *Psychoanal. & Contemp. Sci.*, 4:3–58.

———— (1976), On the possibility of a strictly clinical psychoanalytic theory: An essay in the philosophy of psychoanalysis. In: Psychology versus Metapsychology: Psychoanalytic Essays in Memory of George S. Klein, ed. M. M. Gill & P. S. Holzman. *Psychological Issues*, Monogr. 36. New York: International Universities Press, pp. 229–264.

———— (1980a), On the psychoanalytic theory of unconscious motivation and the problem of its confirmation. *Psychoanal. & Contemp. Thought*, 3:3–20.

———— (1980b), The problem of confirmation in clinical psychoanalysis. *J. Amer. Psychoanal. Assn.*, 28:397–417.

Rycroft, C. (1966), Causes and meanings. In: *Psychoanalysis Observed*, ed. C. Rycroft. London: Constable, pp. 7–22.

Sandler, J., & Joffe, W. G. (1969), Towards a basic psychoanalytic model. *Internat. J. Psycho-Anal.*, 50:79–90.

San Francisco School of Medicine, Department of Psychiatry (1975), Proposal for a Doctoral Degree in Mental Health; submitted for consideration to the Graduate Council of the University of California, San Francisco. Typescript.

Sargent, H. D., Coyne, L., Wallerstein, R. S., & Holtzman, W. (1967), An approach to the quantitative problems of psychoanalytic research. *J. Clin. Psychol.*, 23:243–291.

———— Horwitz, L., Wallerstein, R. S. , & Appelbaum, A. (1968), Prediction in Psychotherapy Research: A Method for the Transformation of Clinical Judgments into Testable Hypotheses. *Psychological Issues*, Monogr. 21. New York: International Universities Press.

Sashin, J. I., Eldred, S. H., & van Amerongen, S. T. (1975), A search for predictive factors in institute supervised cases: A retrospective study of 183 cases from 1959–1966 at the Boston Psychoanalytic Society and Institute. *Internat. J. Psycho-Anal.*, 56:343–359.

Schacter, J. (1990a), Does a panel discussion on analytic technique have any effect on an audience of analysis? *J. Amer. Psychoanal. Assn.*, 38:733–741.

———— (1990b), Post-termination patient–analyst contact. I. Analyst's attitudes and experience. II. Impact on patients. *Internat. J. Psycho-Anal.*, 71:475–486.

Schafer, R. (1970), An overview of Heinz Hartmann's contributions to psychoanalysis. *Internat. J. Psycho-Anal.*, 51:425–446.

———— (1972), Internalization: Process or fantasy? *The Psychoanalytic Study of the Child*, 27:411–436. Chicago: Quadrangle.

———— (1973a), Action: Its place in psychoanalytic interpretation and theory. *Annual of Psychoanalysis*, 1:159–196. New York: International Universities Press.

———— (1973b), The idea of resistance. *Internat. J. Psycho-Anal.*, 54:259–285.

———— (1975), Psychoanalysis without psychodynamics. *Internat. J. Psycho-Anal.*, 56:41–55.

———— (1976), *A New Language for Psychoanalysis*. New Haven, CT: Yale University Press.

———— (1981), Presentation at Rapaport-Klein Forum, Austen Riggs Center, Stockbridge, MA, June.

———— (1985), Wild analysis. *J. Amer. Psychoanal. Assn.*, 33:275–299.

Schlessinger, N., & Robbins, F. P. (1974), Assessment and follow-up in psychoanalysis. *J. Amer. Psychoanal. Assn.*, 22:542–567.

———— ———— (1975), The psychoanalytic process: Recurrent patterns of conflict and changes in ego functions. *J. Amer. Psychoanal. Assn.*, 23:761–782.

———— ———— (1983), *A Developmental View of the Psychoanalytic Process: Follow-Up Studies and Their Consequences*. New York: International Universities Press.

Schmidl, F. (1955), The problem of scientific validation in psychoanalytic interpretation. *Internat. J. Psycho-Anal.*, 36:105–113.

Schur, M. (1966), *The Id and the Regulatory Principles of Mental Functioning*. New York: International Universities Press.

Schwartz, F. (1981), Psychic structure. *Internat. J. Psycho-Anal.*, 62:61–72.

Searles, H. F. (1965), *Collected Papers on Schizophrenia and Related Subjects*. New York: International Universities Press.

Segel, N. P. (1981), Narcissism and adaptation to indignity. *Internat. J. Psycho-Anal.*, 62:465–476.

Seitz, P. F. D. (1966), The consensus problem in psychoanalytic research. In: *Methods of Research in Psychotherapy*, ed. L. A. Gottschalk & A. H. Auerbach. New York: Appleton-Century-Crofts, pp. 209–225.

Shakow, D. (1962), Psychoanalytic education of behavioral and social scientists for research. In: *Science and Psychoanalysis*, Vol. 5. New York: Grune & Stratton, pp. 146–161.

Sherwood, M. (1969), *The Logic of Explanation in Psychoanalysis.* New York: Academic Press.

Smith, M. L., Glass, G. V., & Miller, T. I. (1980), *The Benefits of Psychotherapy.* Baltimore: Johns Hopkins University Press.

Spence, D. P. (1982), *Narrative Truth and Historical Truth: Meaning and Interpretation in Psychoanalysis.* New York: W. W. Norton.

Spruiell, V. (1983), Kuhn's "paradigm" and psychoanalysis. *Psychoanal. Quart.,* 52:353–363.

Steele, R. S. (1979), Psychoanalysis and hermeneutics. *Internat. Rev. Psycho-Anal.,* 6:389–412.

Stone, L. (1954), The widening scope of indications for psychoanalysis. *J. Amer. Psychoanal. Assn.,* 2:567–594.

———— (1982), The influence of the practice and theory of psychotherapy on education in psychoanalysis. In: *Psychotherapy: Impact on Psychoanalytic Training,* ed. E. D. Joseph & R. S. Wallerstein. New York: International Universities Press, pp. 75–118.

Strupp, H. (1960), Some comments on the future of research in psychotherapy. *Behav. Sci.,* 5:60–70.

———— Schacht, T. E., & Henry, W. P. (1988), Problem-treatment-outcome congruence—A principle whose time has come. In: *Psychoanalytic Process Research Strategies,* ed. H. Dahl, H. Kaechele, & H. Thomae. New York: Springer, pp. 1–14.

Szasz, T. S. (1961), *The Myth of Mental Illness.* New York: Hoeber.

Thomä, H., & Kächele, H. (1975), Problems of metascience and methodology in clinical psychoanalytic research. *Annual of Psychoanalysis,* 3:49–119. New York: International Universities Press.

Ticho, G. (1967), On self-analysis. *Internat. J. Psycho-Anal.,* 48:308–318.

Treurniet, N. (1980), On the relation between the concepts of self and ego in Kohut's Psychology of the Self. *Internat. J. Psycho-Anal.,* 61:325–333.

Voth, H. M., & Orth, M. H. (1973), *Psychotherapy and the Role of the Environment.* New York: Behavioral Publications.

Wachtel, P. L. (1977), *Psychoanalysis and Behavior Therapy: Toward an Integration.* New York: Basic Books.

Waelder, R. (1962), Psychoanalysis, scientific method, and philosophy. *J. Amer. Psychoanal. Assn.,* 10:617–637.

Wallerstein, R. S. (1963), The problem of the assessment of change in psychotherapy. *Internat. J. Psycho-Anal.,* 44:31–41.

——— (1964), The role of prediction in theory building in psychoanalysis. *J. Amer. Psychoanal. Assn.*, 12:675–691.

——— (1968), The Psychotherapy Research Project of The Menninger Foundation: A semi-final view. In: *Research in Psychotherapy*, Vol. 3, ed. J. M. Shlien. Washington, DC: American Psychological Association, pp. 584–605.

——— (1972), The futures of psychoanalytic education. *J. Amer. Psychoanal. Assn.*, 20:591–606.

——— (1974), Herbert S. Gaskill and the history of American psychoanalysis in American psychiatry. *Denver Psychoanal. Soc. Newsletter*, 1(3):1–9.

——— (1975), *Psychotherapy and Psychoanalysis: Theory, Practice, Research.* New York: International Universities Press.

——— (1983a), Self psychology and "classical" psychoanalytic psychology: The nature of their relationship. In: *The Future of Psychoanalysis*, ed. A. Goldberg. New York: International Universities Press, pp. 19–63.

——— (1983b), Defenses, defense mechanisms and the structure of the mind. In: *Defense and Resistance: Historical Perspective and Current Concepts*, ed. H. P. Blum. New York: International Universities Press, 1985, pp. 201–225.

——— (1983c), The Topeka Institute and the future of psychoanalysis. *Bull. Menninger Clinic*, 47:497–518.

——— (1985), Review: *Mind, Brain, Body: Toward a Convergence of Psychoanalysis and Neurobiology*, by M. F. Reiser. *Internat. J. Psycho-Anal.*, 66:518–521.

——— (1986), *Forty-Two Lives in Treatment: A Study of Psychoanalysis and Psychotherapy.* New York: Guilford Press.

——— (1988a), One psychoanalysis or many? *Internat. J. Psycho-Anal.*, 69:5–21.

——— (1988b), Psychoanalysis and psychotherapy: Relative roles reconsidered. *Annual of Psychoanalysis*, 16:129–151. Madison, CT: International Universities Press.

——— (1988c), Psychoanalysis, psychoanalytic science, and psychoanalytic research—1986. *J. Amer. Psychoanal. Assn.*, 36:3–30.

——— (1989a), Psychoanalysis and psychotherapy: An historical perspective. *Internat. J. Psycho-Anal.*, 70:563–591.

——— (1989b), Follow-up in psychoanalysis: Clinical and research values. *J. Amer. Psychoanal. Assn.*, 37:921–942.

——— (1991), *The Doctorate in Mental Health: An Experiment in Mental Health Professional Education.* New York: University Press of America.

——— (1992), Follow-up in psychoanalysis: What happens to treatment gains? *J. Amer. Psychoanal. Assn.*, 40:665–690.

——— (1994), Psychotherapy research and its implications for a theory of therapeutic change: A forty-year overview. *The Psychoanalytic Study of the Child*, 49:120–141. New Haven, CT: Yale University Press.

——— (1998), *Lay Analysis: Life Inside the Controversy*. Mahwah, NJ: Analytic Press.

——— (1999), *Psychoanalysis: Clinical and Theoretical*. Madison, CT: International Universities Press.

——— Robbins, L. L. (1958), The Psychotherapy Research Project of The Menninger Foundation: Second report. Further notes on design concepts. *Bull. Menn. Clin.*, 22:117–125.

——— ——— Sargent, H. D., & Luborsky, L. (1956), The Psychotherapy Research Project of The Menninger Foundation. *Bull. Menn. Clin.*, 20:221–278.

——— Sampson, H. (1971), Issues in research in the psychoanalytic process. *Internat. J. Psycho-Anal.*, 52:11–50.

——— Smelser, N. J. (1969), Psychoanalysis and sociology: Articulations and applications. *Internat. J. Psycho-Anal.*, 50:693–710.

Weber, J. J., Bachrach, H. M., & Solomon, M. (1985a), Factors associated with the outcome of psychoanalysis: Report of the Columbia Psychoanalytic Center Research Project (II). *Internat. Rev. Psycho-Anal.*, 12:127–141.

——— ——— ——— (1985b), Factors associated with the outcome of psychoanalysis: Report of the Columbia Psychoanalytic Center Research Project (III). *Internat. Rev. Psycho-Anal.*, 12:251–262.

——— Solomon, M., & Bachrach, H. M. (1985), Characteristics of psychoanalytic clinic patients: Report of the Columbia Psychoanalytic Center Research Project (I). *Internat. Rev. Psycho-Anal.*, 12:13–26.

Weinshel, E. M. (1979), Message from a past president—Maxwell Gitelson, M.D. In: *The Identity of the Psychoanalyst*, ed. E. D. Joseph & D. Widlocher. New York: International Universities Press, pp. 67–83.

——— (1990), How wide is the widening scope of psychoanalysis and how solid is its structural model? Some concerns and obligations. *J. Amer. Psychoanal. Assn.*, 38:275–296.

Weinstein, F., & Platt, G. M. (1973), *Psychoanalytic Sociology*. Baltimore: Johns Hopkins University Press.

Whitehorn, J. C., Braceland, F. J., Lippard, V. W., & Malamud, W. (1953), *The Psychiatrist, His Training and Development.* Washington, DC: American Psychiatric Association.

Wolff, P. H. (1960), The Developmental Psychologies of Jean Piaget and Psychoanalysis. *Psychological Issues,* Monogr. 5. New York: International Universities Press.

Scientific Bibliography: Robert S. Wallerstein, M.D.

1946

The possible relationship of the pleuropneumonia-like organisms to Reiter's disease, rheumatoid arthritis and ulcerative colitis (with B. Vallee & L. Turner). *J. Infect. Dis.*, 79:134–140.

1949

Longevity of Schistosoma Mansoni: Observations based on a case. *Amer. J. Tropical Med.*, 29:717–722.

Polymyxin effective in the treatment of pyocyaneus sepsis: Report of a case (with E. B. Schoenbach). *J. Mt. Sinai Hosp.*, 16:190–196.

Hepatosplenomegaly and liver damage in Graves' disease (with W. J. Walker). *Annals Internal Med.*, 31:904–912.

1950

Infectious mononucleosis: With hepatic dysfunction, thrombocytopenic purpura, and isolated peripheral nerve palsy (with L. Madison). *Amer. Practitioner*, 1:624–629.

The role of antibodies in insulin resistance: Report of a case (with R. M. Berne). *J. Mt. Sinai Hosp.*, 17:102–111.

Thrombophlebitis secondary to acute respiratory infection. *J. Mt. Sinai Hosp.*, 17:176–182.

1951

Multiple myeloma without demonstrable bone lesions. *Amer. J. Med.*, 10:325–333.

Treatment of the psychosis of general paresis with combined sodium amytal and psychotherapy: Report of a case. *Psychiatry*, 14:307–317. Reprinted in *Case Studies in Psychopathology*, ed. L. Diamant. Columbus, OH: Charles E. Merrill, 1971, pp. 34–49.

1954

Some psychosomatic considerations in Addison's disease: Report of a case (with R. L. Sutherland & J. Lyons). *Psychosom. Med.*, 16:67–76.

Some psychosomatic considerations in dystrophia myotonica: Report of a case (with S. Rubin). *J. Nerv. Ment. Dis.*, 120:277–281.

Unusual wheal reaction in a tattoo: Psychosomatic aspects (with N. I. Graff). *Psychosom. Med.*, 16:505–515.

Perspectives of the Research Department of The Menninger Foundation (with G. Murphy). *Bull. Menn. Clin.*, 18:223–231.

1956

Comparative study of treatment methods for chronic alcoholism—The alcoholism research project at Winter VA Hospital. *Amer. J. Psychiatry*, 113:228–233.

The Psychotherapy Research Project of The Menninger Foundation (with L. L. Robbins, H. D. Sargeant, & L. Luborsky). *Bull. Menn. Clin.*, 20:221–278.

1957

Hospital Treatment of Alcoholism: A Comparative Experimental Study (with J. W. Chotlos, M. B. Friend, D. W. Hammersley, E. A. Perlswig, & G. M. Winship. Menninger Monogr. 11. New York: Basic Books. pp. 212.

1958

The Teaching and Learning of Psychotherapy, by R. Ekstein & R. S. Wallerstein. New York: Basic Books. Revised and reprinted, International Universities Press, 1972. pp. 334.

Psychologic factors in chronic alcoholism. *Annals Internal Med.*, 48:114–122.

The Psychotherapy Research Project of The Menninger Foundation: Second report. Further notes on design concepts (with L. L. Robbins). *Bull. Menn. Clin.*, 22:117–125.

Pain, fear and anxiety: A study of their interrelationships (with I. Ramzy). *The Psychoanalytic Study of the Child*, 13:147–189. New York: International Universities Press.

1959

The research strategy and tactics of the Psychotherapy Research Project of The Menninger Foundation and the problems of controls (with L. L. Robbins), ed. E. A. Rubinstein & B. Parloff. In: *Research in Psychotherapy*. Washington, DC: American Psychological Association, pp. 27–43.

GAP Report 42. Some observations on controls in psychiatric research. Formulated by the Committee on Research, pp. 533–623. R. S. Wallerstein, Member.

1960

The Psychotherapy Research Project of The Menninger Foundation: Third Report. Helen D. Sargent and the Psychotherapy Research Project. *Bull. Menn. Clin.*, 24:159–163.

The Psychotherapy Research Project of The Menninger Foundation: Third Report. Initial studies (with L. L. Robbins). *Bull. Menn. Clin.*, 24:164–189.

Psychotherapy Research Project of The Menninger Foundation: Third Report. Termination studies (with B. H. Hall). *Bull. Menn. Clin.*, 24:190–214.

1961

Report of the Psychotherapy Research Project of The Menninger Foundation, January 1954–July 1961. *Internat. Ment. Health Res. Newsletter*, 3:12–15.

A estrategia e a tatica de investigacao o projeto de pesquisa em Psicoterapia da Menninger Foundation e o problema de controles (with L. L. Robbins). *Arquivos da Clinica Pinel*, 1:166–186. (Portuguese)

1963

The problem of the assessment of change in psychotherapy. *Internat. J. Psycho-Anal.*, 44:31–41.

1964

Therapist and patient (with R. Ekstein). In: *Child Psychotherapy*, ed. M. R. Haworth. New York: Basic Books, 1964, pp. 437–445. Reprinted from *The Teaching and Learning of Psychotherapy*. New York: Basic Books, 1958.

The role of prediction in theory building in psychoanalysis. *J. Amer. Psychoanal. Assn.*, 12:675–691.

1965

The goals of psychoanalysis: A survey of analytic viewpoints. *J. Amer. Psychoanal. Assn.*, 13:748–770.

Thyroid "hot spots": A psychophysiological study (with P. S. Holzman, H. M. Voth, & N. Uhr). *Psychosom. Med.*, 27:508–523.

1966

The Psychotherapy Research Project of The Menninger Foundation—An overview at the midway point. In: *Methods of Research in Psychotherapy,* ed. A. Gottschalk & A. H. Auerbach. New York: Appleton-Century-Crofts, pp. 500–516.

The Current state of psychotherapy: Theory, practice, research. *J. Amer. Psychoanal. Assn.* 14:183–225.

GAP Report 63. Psychiatric research and the assessment of change. Formulated by the Committee on Research, pp. 347–479. R. S. Wallerstein, Chairman.

Review *Mind and Destiny: A Social Approach to Psychoanalytic Theory,* by R. Seidenberg & H. S. Cochrane. *Psychoanal. Quart.,* 35:437–441.

1967

Development and metapsychology of the defense organization of the ego: Panel report. *J. Amer. Psychoanal. Assn.,* 15:130–149.

An approach to quantitative problems of psychoanalytic research (with H. D. Sargent, L. Coyne, & W. H. Holtzman). *J. Clin. Psychology,* 23:243–291. Also published as a separate Monograph Supplement, No. 23.

Reconstruction and mastery in the transference psychosis. *J. Amer. Psychoanal. Assn.,* 15:551–583. Reprinted in *Survivors of Suicide,* ed. A. C. Cain. Springfield: Charles C Thomas, 1972, pp. 242–255. Reprinted in condensed form.

Report of Ad Hoc Committee on Central Fact-Gathering Data of the American Psychoanalytic Association (with D. A. Hamburg, G. L. Bibring, C. Fisher, A. H. Stanton, H. I. Weinstock, & E. Haggard). *J. Amer. Psychoanal. Assn.,* 15:841–861.

Terapeuta e paziente: Probleme di apprendimento (with R. Ekstein). In: *Psicoterapia Infantile,* ed. M. R. Haworth. Rome: Armando Armando Editore, pp. 559–571. (Italian)

1968

Prediction in psychotherapy research: A method for the transformation of clinical judgments into testable hypotheses (with H. D. Sargent, L. Horwitz, & A. Appelbaum). *Psychological Issues,* Monogr. 21. New York: International Universities Press, p. 146.

The challenge of the community mental health movement to psychoanalysis. *Amer. J. Psychiatry,* 124:1049–1056.

A talk about the Psychotherapy Research Project of The Menninger Foundation. *Nederlands Nijdschrift voor de Psychologie en haar Grensgebieden,* 23:137–164.

The Psychotherapy Research Project of The Menninger Foundation: A semi-final view, ed. J. M. Schlien. *Research in Psychotherapy,*

Vol. 3, Washington, DC: American Psychological Association, pp. 584–605.

Alcoholism: Symptom or disease? Discussion of "A multidisciplinary approach to the treatment of alcoholism," by R. Fox. *Internat. J. Psychiatry*, 5:59–65.

Discussion: "Some obstacles to the development of research in psychoanalysis," by G. Engel. *J. Amer. Psychoanal. Assn.*, 16:215–222.

Discussion: "On affect control," by A. Peto. *Internat. J. Psycho-Anal.*, 49:474–476.

1969

Introduction to Panel on psychoanalysis and psychotherapy; The relationship of psychoanalysis to psychotherapy—Current issues. *Internat. J. Psycho-Anal.*, 50:117–126.

Psychoanalysis and sociology: Articulations and applications (with N. J. Smelser). *Internat. J. Psycho-Anal.*, 50:693–710. Reprinted in *The Social Edges of Psychoanalysis* by N. J. Smelser. Berkeley, Los Angeles, London: University of California Press, 1998, pp. 3–35.

Introduzione al "Panel" su psicoanalisi e psicoterapia: Rapporti fra psicoanalisis e psicoterapia—Problemes attuali. *Riv. Psicoanalisi*, 15:213–230. (Italian)

1970

Thyroid "hot spots": Their relationship to life stress (with H. M. Voth, P. S. Holzman, & J. B. Katz). *Psychosom. Med.*, 32:561–568.

1971

Issues in research in the psychoanalytic process (with H. Sampson). *Internat. J. Psycho-Anal.*, 52:11–50, Reprinted in *Psychotherapy*, ed. J. O. Matarazzo, A. E. Bergin, J. D. Frank, P. J. Lang, I. M. Marks, & H. H. Strupp. Chicago: Aldine-Atherton, 1972, pp. 26–63. Also reprinted in *The Challenge to Psychoanalysis and Psychotherapy*, ed. S. de Schill & S. Lebovici. London: Jessica Kingsley, 1999, pp. 154–178.

The role of research training: How much, what kind, how? In: *New Horizon for Psychotherapy: Autonomy as a Profession*, ed. R. R. Holt. New York: International Universities Press, pp. 241–260.

Issues in research in the psychoanalytic process (condensation) (with H. Sampson). In: *Currents in Psychoanalysis*, ed. I. M. Marcus. New York: International Universities Press, pp. 265–302.

Introduccion a la mesa redonda sobre psicoanalisis y psicoterapia. La relacion entre el psicoanalisis y la psicoterapia. Problemas actuales. *Revista de Psicoanalisis,* 28:25–49. (Spanish)

1972

Transactional psychotherapy. In: *Modern Psychiatry and Clinical Research,* ed. D. Offer & D. X. Freedman. New York: Basic Books, pp. 120–135.

The futures of psychoanalytic education. *J. Amer. Psychoanal. Assn.,* 20:591–606.

Discussion (with H. Sampson): Some empirical and conceptual bases for coordinated research in psychotherapy. In: *Changing Frontiers in the Science of Psychotherapy,* ed. A. E. Bergin & H. H. Strupp. Chicago: Aldine-Atherton, pp. 292–300, 444–446.

Preface. Psychotherapy and psychoanalysis: Final report of The Menninger Foundation's Psychotherapy Research Project, by O. F. Kernberg, E. D. Burstein, L. Coyne, A. Appelbaum, L. Horwitz & H. Voth. *Bull. Menn. Clin.,* 36(1/2):vii–x.

Discussion: "Radical and militant youth: A study of Columbia undergraduates," by R. S. Liebert. *Psychoanal. Forum,* 4:52–58.

Discussion: "Supervision by tape: A new method of case supervision," by J. A. Lindon. *Psychoanal. Forum,* 4:436–442.

Las Nuevas Direcciones de la Psicoterapia: Teoria, Practica, Investigacion. Buenos Aires: Paidos. pp. 85 (Spanish)

1973

Psychoanalytic perspectives on the problem of reality. *J. Amer. Psychoanal. Assn.,* 21:5–33.

Discussion: "On being sane in insane places," by D. L. Rosenhan. *Bull. Menn. Clin.,* 37:526–530. Reprinted in *Psychotherapy and Behavior Change,* ed. H. H. Strupp, A. E. Bergin, P. J. Lang, I. M. Marks, J. O. Matarazzo, & G. R. Patterson. Chicago: Aldine, 1974, pp. 48–52.

Discussion: "Psychoanalytic implications of reactions of soldiers to the Six-Day War," by R. Jaffe. In: *Psychological Bases of War,* ed. H. Z. Winnik, R. Moses, & M. Ostow. New York: Quadrangle Books; Jerusalem: Jerusalem Academic Press, pp. 103–110.

Insegnamento e apprendimento della psicoterapia (with R. Ekstein). Presentazione de Enzo Codignola. Turin: Editore Boringhieri. pp. 400. (Italian)

1974

Herbert S. Gaskill and the history of American psychoanalysis in American psychiatry. *Denver Psychoanal. Soc. Newsletter,* 1(3): 1–9.

Foreword. In: *The Fear of Looking: Or Scopophilic–Exhibitionistic Conflicts*, by D. W. Allen. Charlottesville, VA: University Press of Virginia, pp. vii–viii.

Foreword. In: *Clinical Prediction in Psychotherapy*, by L. Horwitz. New York: Jason Aronson, pp. xiii–xviii.

Perspectivas Psicanaliticas Quanto ao Problema da Realidade. *Rev. Brasileira de Psicanalise*, 8:223–253. (Portuguese)

1975

Psychotherapy and Psychoanalysis: Theory, Practice, Research. New York: International Universities Press. pp. 475.

Shirley Cooper, M. S., President, American Orthopsychiatric Association. *Amer. J. Orthopsychiatry*, 45:324–327.

1976

Psychoanalysis as a science: Its present status and its future tasks. In: Psychology versus Metapsychology: Psychoanalytic Essays in Memory of George S. Klein, ed. M. M. Gill & P. S. Holzman. *Psychological Issues*, Monogr. 36, Vol. 9. New York: International Universities Press, pp. 198–228.

Summary of the 6th Pre-Congress Conference on "Training: The contribution of child analysis to the training in adult analysis." *Internat. J. Psycho-Anal.*, 57:198–205.

Introduction. Symposium on "Ethics, moral values and psychological interventions." *Internat. Rev. Psycho-Anal.*, 3:369–372.

Foreword. In: *Stress Response Syndromes*, by M. J. Horowitz. New York: Jason Aronson, pp. xiii–xvi.

1977

Psychoanalysis as a profession and psychoanalysis as a science: A stocktaking. In: *Psychoanalytic Education and Research: The Current Situation and Future Possibilities*, ed. S. Goodman. New York: International Universities Press, pp. 307–326.

Psychic energy reconsidered: Introduction. *J. Amer. Psychoanal. Assn.*, 25:529–535.

Psychotherapy research: One paradigm. In: *Communication and Social Interaction*, ed. P. Ostwald. New York: Grune & Stratton, pp. 189–202.

Foreword (with H. S. Gaskill). In: *Psychoanalytic Education and Research: The Current Situation and Future Possibilities.* New York: International Universities Press, pp. ix–xvi.

Handledning och utbildning i psykoterapi (with R. Ekstein). Svensk upplaga Bokforlaget Natur och Kultur. Borås, Sweden: Centraltrycheriet AB. pp. 288. (Swedish)

A contribuicao de analise de criencas para o treino de analise de adultos. *Rev. Brasileira de Psicanalise,* 11:225–242. (Portuguese)

1978

Perspectives on psychoanalytic training around the world. *Internat. J. Psycho-Anal.,* 59:477–503.

The mental health professions: Conceptualization and reconceptualization of a new discipline. *Internat. Rev. Psycho-Anal.,* 5:377–392.

1979

Review: "Toward the Validation of Dynamic Psychotherapy, by D. H. Malan. *J. Amer. Psychoanal. Assn.,* 27:276–279.

Reflexions sur le symposium. In: *L'Identité du Psychanalyste,* ed. E. D. Joseph & D. Widlocher. Paris: Presses Universitaires de France, pp. 273–284. (French)

1980

Psychoanalysis and academic psychiatry–Bridges. *The Psychoanalytic Study of the Child,* 35:419–448. New Haven, CT: Yale University Press.

International scientific colloquium on the significance of insight in psychoanalytic theory and practice. *Bull. Hampstead Clin.,* 3:153–156, 181–183, 186–187, 192–193.

Doctorat en Santé Mentale: Une creation de l'Université de Californie. *Psychoanalyse a l'Université,* 5(18):343–364. (French)

Diagnosis revisited (and revisited): The case of hysteria and the hysterical personality. *Internat. J. Psychoanal. Psychother.,* 8:533–547. 1980–1981.

1981

Becoming a Psychoanalyst: A Study of Psychoanalytic Supervision. (Editor) New York: International Universities Press. pp. 351.

The bipolar self: Discussion of alternative perspectives. *J. Amer. Psychoanal. Assn.,* 29:377–394.

The psychoanalyst's life: Expectations, vicissitudes, and reflections. *Internat. Rev. Psycho-Anal.,* 8:285–298.

International scientific colloquium on the superego: Its early roots and the road from outer to inner conflict as seen in psychoanalysis. *Bull. Hampstead Clin.,* 4:99–101, 108–110.

L'étude psychanalytique de la realité. In: *Dix Ans de Psychanalyse en Amerique*—(Papers from the *Journal of the American Psychoanalytic Association*). Paris: Presses Universitaires de France, pp. 263–286. (French)

1982

Psychotherapy: Impact on Psychoanalytic Training. (Editor, with E. D. Joseph) New York: International Universities Press. pp. 174.

Analyse d'enfants et analyse d'adultes: possibilités d'integration. In: *La Formation du psychanalyste*, ed. S. Lebovici & A. Solnit. Paris: Presses Universitaires de France, pp. 239–245. (French)

Review: *The Psychoanalytic Vision: A Controversial Reappraisal of the Freudian Revolution*, by R. Fine. *Internat. Rev. Psycho-Anal.*, 9:360–363.

Report of the Fund for Psychoanalytic Research's first five years: Accomplishments, problems and prospects. *J. Amer. Psychoanal. Assn.*, 30:539–549.

Foreword. In: *Narrative Truth and Historical Truth: Meaning and Interpretation in Psychoanalysis*, by D. P. Spence. New York: W. W. Norton, pp. 9–14.

1983

Reality and its attributes as psychoanalytic concepts: An historical overview. *Internat. Rev. Psycho-Anal.*, 10:125–144.

Self psychology and "classical" psychoanalytic psychology: The nature of their relationship. In: *The Future of Psychoanalysis*, ed. A. Goldberg. New York: International Universities Press, pp. 19–63. Reprinted in *Psychoanal. & Contemp. Thought*, 6:553–595.

Some thoughts about insight and psychoanalysis. *Israel J. Psychiatry & Allied Professions*, 20:33–43.

The Topeka Institute and the future of psychoanalysis. *Bull. Menn. Clin.*, 47:497–518.

Self psychology and "classical" psychoanalytic psychology—The nature of their relationship: A review and overview (condensation). In: *Reflections on Self Psychology*, ed. J. D. Lichtenberg & S. Kaplan. Hillsdale, NJ: Analytic Press, pp. 313–337.

Defenses, defense mechanisms and the structure of the mind. *J. Amer. Psychoanal. Assn.*, 31(Suppl.):201–225. Reprinted in *Defense and Resistance: Historical Perspective and Current Concepts*, ed. H. P. Blum. New York: International Universities Press, 1985, pp. 201–225.

Reflections on the identity of the psychoanalyst. In: *The Identity of the Psychoanalyst*, ed. E. D. Joseph & D. Widlocher. New York: International Universities Press, pp. 265–276.

Review: *Basic Principles and Techniques in Short-Term Dynamic Psychotherapy*, by H. Davanloo. *J. Amer. Psychoanal. Assn.*, 31:780–784.

Personal tribute to Anna Freud. *Bull. Hampstead Clin.*, 6:95–98.
Historical perspective. In: *Emotions in Health and Illness: Theoretical and Research Foundations,* ed. L. Temoshok, C. Van Dyke, & L. S. Zegans. New York: Grune & Stratton, pp. 3–5.
Tribute to Selma Fraiberg. *Dialogue: J. Psychoanal. Perspect.*, 6:5.
International scientific colloquium on fantasy and reality in the organisation of the oedipal situation. *Bull. Hampstead Clin.*, 6:147–218.

1984
Personality and Brief Psychotherapy (with M. Horowitz, C. Marmar, J. Krupnick, N. Wilner, & N. Kaltreider). New York: Basic Books. pp. 349.
Psychoanalysis and long-term dynamic psychotherapy. In: *Review of General Psychiatry,* ed. H. H. Goldman. Los Altos, CA: Lange Medical Publications, pp. 514–522. Reprinted in *Review of General Psychiatry,* ed. H. H. Goldman. Singapore: Lange Medical Publications/Maruzen Asian Edition, pp. 514–522.
Anna Freud: Radical innovator and staunch conservative. *The Psychoanalytic Study of the Child,* 39:65–80. New Haven, CT: Yale University Press.
The analysis of transference: A matter of emphasis or of theory reformulation? *Psychoanal. Inq.*, 4:325–354.
Review: *The Standing of Psychoanalysis,* by B. A. Farrell. *NOUS,* 18:534–541.
International scientific colloquium on the role of fantasy in the adaptive process. *Bull. Hampstead Clin.*, 7:166–211.

1985
The concept of psychic reality: Its meaning and value. *J. Amer. Psychoanal. Assn.*, 33:555–569.
Changes in Analysts and in Their Training. (Editor) International Psychoanalytical Association, Monograph Series No. 4. pp. 90.
How does self psychology differ in practice? *Internat. J. Psycho-Anal.*, 66:391–404. Reprinted in *Progress in Self Psychology,* ed. A. Goldberg. New York: Guilford Press, 1986, pp. 63–83.
Review: *Mind, Brain, Body: Toward a Convergence of Psychoanalysis and Neurobiology,* by M. F. Reiser. *Internat. J. Psycho-Anal.*, 66:518–521.
The role of transference in the doctor–patient relationship. *Western J. Med.*, 142:681–682.
International scientific colloquium on fantasy and body representation in physical disturbances. *Bull. Anna Freud Centre,* 8:111–149.

Change and integration in psychoanalysis as a profession: Discussion. In: *New Ideas in Psychoanalysis: The Process of Change in a Humanistic Science*, ed. C. F. Settlage & R. Brockbank. Hillsdale, NJ: Analytic Press, pp. 167–176.

Les Changements intervenus chez les analystes et dans leur formation, ed. R. S. Wallerstein. *Association Psychanalytique Internationale.* Monogr. 4. (French)

Cambios en los analistas y en su formacion, ed. R. S. Wallerstein. *Asociacion Psicoanalitica Internacional.* Mongr. 4. (Spanish)

Veranderungen bei Analytikern und in der Analytikerausbildung, ed. R. S. Wallerstein. *Internationalen Psychoanalytischen Vereinigung.* Mongr. 4. (German)

1986

Forty-Two Lives in Treatment: A Study of Psychoanalysis and Psychotherapy. New York: Guilford Press. pp. 784.

Psychoanalysis as a science: A response to the new challenges. *Psychoanal. Quart.*, 55:414–451.

The termination of the training analysis: The institute's view. In: *The Termination of the Training Analysis: Process, Expectations, Achievements*, ed. A. M. Cooper. International Psychoanalytical Association. Monogr. 5, pp. 35–52.

The transformation of thought that the nuclear age requires: Can we achieve it? *Psychoanal. Inq.*, 6:303–312.

Review: *Psychoanalysis and Its Discontents*, by J. E. Gedo. *Psychoanal. Quart.*, 55:323–334.

Review: *Severe Personality Disorders: Psychotherapeutic Strategies* by O. F. Kernberg. *J. Amer. Psychoanal. Assn.*, 34:711–712.

International scientific colloquium on repeating, reenactment and verbalization in different stages of development. *Bull. Anna Freud Centre*, 9:119–152.

La fin de l'analyse didactique: Le point de vue de l'institut. In: *La Fin de l'Analyse Didactique: Le Processus, Les Previsions, Les Realisations*, ed. A. M. Cooper. Association Psychanalytique Internationale. Monogr. 5, pp. 37–56. (French)

La terminacion del analisis didactico: El punto de vista del instituto. In: *La Terminacion del Analisis Didactico: El Proceso, Las Expectativas, Los Logros*, ed. A. M. Cooper. Associacion Psicoanalitica Internacional. Mongr. 5, pp. 39–58. (Spanish)

Die Beendigung der Lehranalyse: Die Sicht des Instituts. In: *Die Beendigung der Lehranalyse: Prozess, Erwartungen, was erreicht wurde*, ed. A. M. Cooper. Internationalen Psychoanalytischen Vereinigung. Mongr. 5, pp. 36–53. (German)

1987

Maintenance of the psychoanalytic identity and functioning in a world in flux: The terms of the dialectic. In: *Maintenance of the Psychoanalytic Identity and Functioning in a World in Flux*, ed. J. Chasseguet-Smirgel. International Psychoanalytical Association. Mongr. 6, pp. 21–61.

The assessment of analyzability and of analytic outcomes. In: *The Yearbook of Psychoanalysis and Psychotherapy*, Vol. 2, ed. R. Langs & Editorial Board. New York: Gardner Press, pp. 416–426.

Review: *The Psychoanalytic Process: Theory, Clinical Observation, and Empirical Research*, by J. Weiss, H. Sampson, & the Mt. Zion Psychotherapy Research Group. *Internat. J. Psycho-Anal.*, 68:565–567.

Foreword. In: *The Teaching and Learning of Psychoanalysis: Selected Papers of Joan Fleming, M.D.*, by S. S. Weiss. New York: Guilford Press, pp. vii–xii.

Foreword. In: *Psychoanalytic Practice I. Principles*, by H. Thomae & H. Kaechele. New York: Springer, pp. v–viii.

Foreword. In: *From Safety to Superego*, by J. Sandler. New York: Guilford Press, pp. x–xiv.

International scientific colloquium on sexual and gender identity in childhood, adolescence and adulthood. *Bull. Anna Freud Centre*, 10:215–241.

El psicoanalisis como ciencia: Una respuesta a las nuevas criticas. *Revista de Psicoanalisis*, 44:9–40. (Spanish)

1988

Psychoanalysis, psychoanalytic science, and psychoanalytic research—1986. *J. Amer. Psychoanal. Assn.*, 36:3–30. Reprinted in *Medelelingenblad, Nederlandse Vereniging voor psychoanalyse*, January 1987, pp. 11–26.

One psychoanalysis or many? *Internat. J. Psycho-Anal.*, 69:5–21.

Commentary on *Psychoanalytic Models of History: Freud and After*. In: *Psychology and Historical Interpretation*, ed. W. Mck. Runyan. New York: Oxford University Press, pp. 157–165.

The continuum of reality, inner and outer. In: *Fantasy, Myth, and Reality: Essays in Honor of Jacob A. Arlow, M.D.*, ed. H. P. Blum, Y. Kramer, A. K. Richards, & A. D. Richards. Madison, CT: International Universities Press, pp. 305–321.

Psychoanalysis in Nazi Germany: Historical and psychoanalytic lessons. *Psychoanal. & Contemp. Thought*, 11:351–370.

Psychoanalysis and psychotherapy: Relative roles reconsidered. *Annual of Psychoanalysis*, 16:129–151. Madison, CT: International Universities Press.

Assessment of structural change in psychoanalytic therapy and research. *J. Amer. Psychoanal. Assn.*, 36(Suppl.):241–261. Reprinted in *The Concept of Structure in Psychoanalysis*, ed. T. Shapiro. Madison, CT: International Universities Press, 1991, pp. 241–261.

International scientific colloquium on playing: Its role in child and adult psychoanalysis. *Bull. Anna Freud Centre*, 11:168–182.

Une psychanalyse ou plusieurs? (Compte rendu de l'expose de R. S. Wallerstein). *Rev. Française de Psychanalyse*, 52:1035–1039. (French)

Matter over mind (with D. W. Allen and I. Philips). *San Francisco Med.*, December: 24–25.

1989

The Psychotherapy Research Project of The Menninger Foundation: An overview. *J. Consult. & Clin. Psychol.*, 57:195–205.

The future of psychoanalysis (with E. M. Weinshel). *Psychoanal. Quart.*, 58:341–373.

Psychoanalysis and psychotherapy: An historical perspective (condensed version). In: *The Psychoanalytic Core: Essays in Honor of Leo Rangell, M.D.*, ed. H. P. Blum, E. M. Weinshel & F. R. Rodman. Madison, CT: International Universities Press, pp. 109–146.

Psychoanalysis and psychotherapy: An historical perspective. *Internat. J. Psycho-Anal.*, 70:563–591.

Follow-up in psychoanalysis: Clinical and research values. *J. Amer. Psychoanal. Assn.*, 37:921–942.

Review: *Psychoanalysis: A Theory in Crisis*, by M. Edelson (condensed version). *New York Times Book Rev.*, February 26, p. 36.

Preface and greetings from the International Psychoanalytical Association. In: *Italy in Psychoanalysis*, ed. A. Novelletto. Institute of the Enciclopedia Italiana, pp. 11–13.

International scientific colloquium on self-esteem and shame: A psychoanalytic approach. *Bull. Anna Freud Centre*, 12:226–259.

Foreword. In: *Supportive Therapy: A Psychodynamic Approach*, by L. H. Rockland. New York: Basic Books, pp. vii–x.

Un Psicoanalisis o muchos? *Libro Anual de Psicoanalisis 1988*, 1–15. (Spanish)

Introduzione e saluto della Associazione Psicoanalitica Internazionale. In: *L'Italia Nella Psicoanalisi*, ed. A. Novelletto. Instituto della Enciclopedia Italiana, pp. 11–13. (Italian)

Eine Psychoanalyse—oder viele? *Zeitschr. für psychoanalytische Theorie und Praxis*, Jahrgang, 4:126–153. (German)

El self bipolar: un examen de perspectivas alternativas. *Psico-analisis: Rev. de la Asociacion Psicoanalitica de Buenos Aires*, 11:219–234. (Spanish)

Uno o molte psicoanalisi. *Gli Argonauti*, 43:253–277. (Italian)

Psychoanalysis and psychotherapy: An historical perspective. *Japan. J. Psycho-Anal.*, 33:71–86. (Japanese)

Psychoanalysis and psychotherapy: Relative roles reconsidered. *Japan. J. Psycho-Anal.*, 33:141–153. (Japanese)

1990

Psychoanalysis: The common ground. *Internat. J. Psycho-Anal.*, 71:3–20.

The corrective emotional experience: Is reconsideration due? *Psychoanal. Inq.*, 10:288–324.

Karl Menninger and Arthur Marshall: Comments on the early years of the Menninger School of Psychiatry. *Psychohist. Rev.*, 19:123–135.

Review: *Freud Reappraised: A Fresh Look at Psychoanalytic Theory*, by R. R. Holt. *J. Amer. Psychoanal. Assn.*, 38:836–839.

Review: *The Anatomy of Psychotherapy*, by L. Friedman. *Internat. Rev. Psycho-Anal.*, 17:510–513.

Foreword. In: *Understanding Transference: The CCRT Method*, by L. Luborsky & P. Crits-Cristoph. New York: Basic Books, pp. vii–x.

Foreword. In: *Psychodynamic Psychiatry in Clinical Practice*, by G. O. Gabbard. Washington, DC: American Psychiatric Press, pp. ix–xi.

International scientific colloquium on the impact of developmental considerations on the aims of child and adult psychoanalysis. *Bull. Anna Freud Centre*, 13:123–162.

Foreword. In: *Learning from the Patient*, by P. Casement. New York: Guilford Press, pp. xi–xiv.

Foreword. In: *Psychoanalytic Theories of Development: An Integration*, by P. Tyson & R. L. Tyson. New Haven, CT: Yale University Press, pp. ix–xiv.

Zum Verhaltnis von Psychoanalyse und Psychotherapie. Wiederaufnahme einer Diskussion. *Psyche,* 44:967–994. (German)

1991

The Doctorate in Mental Health: An Experiment in Mental Health Professional Education. (Editor) Lanham, MD: University Press of America. pp. 287.

Psychoanalytic education and research: A transformative proposal. *Psychoanal. Inq.,* 11:196–226.

A conceptual analysis and strategy for assessing structural change (with N. J. Zilberg, K. N. DeWitt, D. E. Hartley, & S. E. Rosenberg). *Psychoanal. & Contemp. Thought,* 14:317–342.

Scales of psychological capacities: Development of an assessment approach (with K. N. DeWitt, D. E. Hartley, S. E. Rosenberg, & N. J. Zilberg). *Psychoanal. & Contemp. Thought,* 14:343–361.

Psychoanalytic psychotherapies. In: *Encyclopedia of Human Biology,* 6:293–303. San Diego, CA: Academic Press.

The future of psychotherapy. *Bull. Menn. Clin.,* 55:421–443. Reprinted in *The Challenge to Psychoanalysis and Psychotherapy,* ed. S. de Schill & S. Lebovici. London: Jessica Kingsley, pp. 69–86.

Review: *Psychoanalysis: A Theory in Crisis,* by M. Edelson. *J. Amer. Psychoanal. Assn.,* 39:810–814.

Psychiatry, psychoanalysis and psychotherapy. *Psychodynamic Newsletter: Master Clinician Series,* 1:3–7.

Foreword. In: *The Fundamentals of Psychoanalytic Technique,* by H. Etchegoyen. London: Karnac Books, pp. xxvii–xxxii.

International scientific colloquium on maturational and experiential components in character formation. *Bull. Anna Freud Centre,* 14:213–250.

Observations on the personal myth and on theoretical perspectives in psychoanalysis. In: *The Personal Myth in Psychoanalysis,* ed. P. Hartocollis & I. D. Graham. Madison, CT: International Universities Press, pp. 357–372.

Psychoanalysis and psychotherapy. Exchange of Letters with Merton Gill. *Internat. J. Psycho-Anal,* 72:161–164, 165–166.

Psychoanalysis: The common ground. Exchange of Letters with Sidney and Esther Fine. *Internat. J. Psycho-Anal.,* 72:166–167.

1992

The Common Ground of Psychoanalysis. (Editor) Northvale, NJ: Jason Aronson. pp. 320.

The goals of psychoanalysis reconsidered. In: *The Technique and Practice of Psychoanalysis,* Vol. 2, *A Memorial Volume to Ralph R.*

Greenson, ed. A. Sugarman, R. A. Nemiroff, & D. P. Greenson. Madison, CT: International Universities Press, pp. 63–90.

Comments on psychoanalysis, pure and applied. *Internat. Rev. Psycho-Anal.,* (Special Issue)19:1–6.

The Menninger Project. In: *History of Psychology: A Century of Change,* ed. D. K. Freedheim. Washington, DC: American Psychological Association, pp. 401–408.

International scientific colloquium on therapeutic process in child and adult psychoanalysis. *Bull. Anna Freud Centre,* 15:173–182.

Los Tratamientos Psicoanalitocos: Una Perspectiva Historica. Hogar del Libro. Colecion-PDU / 13: Barcelona. pp. 88. (Spanish)

Follow-up in psychoanalysis: What happens to treatment gains? *J. Amer. Psychoanal. Assn.,* 40:665–690.

Foreword. In: *A Psychoanalytic Theory of Infantile Experience: Conceptual and Clinical Reflections,* by E. Gaddini; ed. A. Limentani. London: Tavistock/Routledge, pp. vii–x.

Psychoanalytic research. *Newsletter of the Internat. Psycho-Anal. Assn.,* Summer:20–21.

Psychoanalytic research. *Newsletter of the Internat. Psycho-Anal. Assn.,* Winter:29–31.

1993

Manutencao da identidade psicanalitica e functionamento num mundo em mutacao: os termos da dialetica. *Boletim Informativo: Publicacao da Associacao Brasileira de Psycianalise,* 2:65–90. (Portuguese)

Foreword. In: *Mind and Its Treatment: A Psychoanalytic Approach,* by V. Tahka. Madison, CT: International Universities Press, pp. xiii–xix.

Between chaos and petrification: A summary of the fifth IPA conference of training analysts. *Internat. J. Psycho-Anal.,* 74:165–178.

On transference love: Revisiting Freud. In: *On Freud's "Observations on Transference Love,"* ed. E. S. Person, A. Hagelin, & P. Fonagy. International Psychoanalytical Association Monogr. 3. New Haven, CT: Yale University Press, pp. 57–74.

Psicoanalisi e Psicoterapia, ed. M. Lang. Milano: FrancoAngeli. p. 240. (Italian)

International scientific colloquium on regression and progression in adult and child psychoanalysis. *Bull. Anna Freud Centre,* 16:254–264.

Psychoanalysis as science: Challenge to the data of psychoanalytic research. In: *Psychodynamic Treatment Research: A Handbook for*

Clinical Practice, ed. N. E. Miller, L. Luborsky, J. B. Barber, & J. P. Docherty. New York: Basic Books, pp. 96–106.

Vyucba a Vycvik v Psychoterapii (with R. Ekstein). Bratislava, Slovakia: Veda Vydavatelstvo Slovenskej Akademie Vied. pp. 324. (Slovak)

The effectiveness of psychotherapy and psychoanalysis: Conceptual issues and empirical work. *J. Amer. Psychoanal. Assn.,* 41 (Suppl.):299–312. Reprinted in *Research in Psychoanalysis: Process, Development, Outcome,* ed. T. Shapiro & R. N. Emde. Madison, CT: International Universities Press, 1995, pp. 299–312.

Psychoanalytic research. *Newsletter of the Internat. Psycho-Anal. Assn.,* 2(1):30–31.

The history of lay analysis in the United States. *Newsletter of the Internat. Psycho-Anal. Assn.,* 2(2):19–21.

Psychoanalytic research. *Newsletter of the Internat. Psycho-Anal. Assn.,* 2(2):35–36.

1994

Psicoanalisis y Psicoterapia dinamica prolongada. In: *Psychiatria General,* ed. H. H. Goldman. Mexico, DF: El Manual Moderno, SA de CV, pp. 503–513. (Spanish)

International scientific colloquium on aims and criteria for termination of adult and child psychoanalysis. *Bull. Anna Freud Centre,* 17:173–182.

Borderline disorders: Report on the 4th IPA research conference. *Internat. J. Psycho-Anal.,* 75:763–774.

Psychotherapy research and its implications for a theory of therapeutic change: A forty-year overview. *The Psychoanalytic Study of the Child,* 49:120–141. New Haven, CT: Yale University Press. Reprinted in *Samiksa* (J. Indian Psychoanal. Soc.), 49:13–32, 1995.

The ambivalence about research. *Newsletter of the Internat. Psycho-Anal. Assn.,* 3(2):45–46.

Sull'amore di transfert. Freud rivisitato. In: *Studi Critici su L'Amore Di Transfert,* ed. E. S. Person, A. Hagelin, & P. Fonagy. Milan: Raffaello Cortina Editore, pp. 41–58. (Italian)

1995

Obituary: Erik Erikson (1902–1994). *Internat. J. Psycho-Anal.,* 76:173–175.

Obituary: Merton Max Gill (1914–1994). *Internat. J. Psycho-Anal.,* 76:399–402. Reprinted in *The Annual of Psychoanalysis,* 24:13–17, 1996.

348 SCIENTIFIC BIBLIOGRAPHY

Research in psychodynamic therapy. In: *Psychodynamic Concepts in General Psychiatry*, ed. H. J. Schwartz, E. Bleiberg, & S. H. Weissman. Washington, DC: American Psychiatric Press, pp. 431–456.
The Talking Cures: The Psychoanalyses and the Psychotherapies. New Haven, CT: Yale University Press. pp. 587.
Review: *Psychoanalysis in Transition: A Personal View*, by M. M. Gill. *J. Amer. Psychoanal. Assn.*, 43:595–600.
Reality. In: *Psychoanalysis: The Major Concepts*, ed. B. E. Moore & B. D. Fine. New Haven, CT: Yale University Press, pp. 293–305.
Locating Erikson in contemporary psychoanalysis. *Psychoanal. Dial.*, 5:567–577.
The relation of theory to technique. *J. Clin. Psychoanal.*, 4:527–542.
Entre el caos y la petrificacion: Resumen de la quinta conferencia de analistas didacticas de API. *Libro Anual de Psicoanalisis, 9* (1993):239–251. (Spanish)
Psychoanalytic research. *Newsletter of the Internat. Psycho-Anal. Assn.*, 4(2):34–35.
1996
Outcomes of psychoanalysis and psychotherapy at termination and at follow-up. In: *Textbook of Psychoanalysis*, ed. E. Nersessian & R. G. Kopff, Jr. Washington, DC: American Psychiatric Press, pp. 531–573.
Continuation of Limentani history of the IPA. *Internat. J. Psycho-Anal.*, 77:156–158.
Ideas and identities: The life and work of Erik Erikson. (Editor) *Psychoanal. & Contemp. Thought*, 19:161–365.
Commentary: Common ground or not? In: *The British Schools of Psychoanalysis: Pluralism and Convergence in the Clinical Setting*, ed. D. Hill & C. Grand. Northvale, NJ: Jason Aronson, pp. 91–114.
Research in psychodynamic psychotherapy. *Mt. Sinai J. Med.*, 63:167–177.
The relation of theory to therapy: An alternative vision. *Psychoanal. Inq.*, 16:491–507.
The Psychotherapy Research Project of The Menninger Foundation: An overview. (Russian) In: *Foreign Psychology*, 6:44–53. Institute of Psychology, Russian Academy of Sciences). Reprinted from *J. Consult. & Clin. Psychology*, 57:195–205, 1989.
The identity of psychoanalysis: The question of lay analysis. *Bull. Menn. Clin.*, 60:514–535.

Review: *The Supervisory Encounter: A Guide for Teachers of Psychodynamic Psychotherapy and Psychoanalysis*, by D. Jacobs, P. David, & D. J. Meyer. *Bull. Menn. Clin.*, 60:548–551.

Psychoanalysis and psychotherapy: An historical perspective (with summaries in Portuguese and Spanish). *Arquivos de Psiquiatria, Psicoterapia e Psicanalise*, 3:123–158. Reprinted from *Internat. J. Psycho-Anal.*, 70:563–591, 1989.

Psychoanalytic research: Where do we disagree? *Newsletter of the Internat. Psycho-Anal. Assn.*, 5(1):15–17.

1997

Merton Gill, psychotherapy and psychoanalysis: A personal dialogue. *J. Amer. Psychoanal. Assn.*, 45:233–256.

Commentary on Samuel Arbiser's *Psychoanalysis in Argentina. Fort Da* (Journal of the N. Calif. Soc. for Psychoanalytic Psychology), 3:10–12.

Die Zukunft der Psychotherapie. In: *Psychoanalyse und Psychotherapie: Herausforderung und Losungen fur die Zukunft*, ed. S. de Schill, S. Lebovici, & H. Kaechele. Stuttgart: Georg Thieme Verlag, pp. 48–63. (German). Translated from *Bull. Menn. Clin.*, 55:421–443, 1991.

Wichtige Fragen der Psychoanalytischen Prozessforschung (with H. Sampson). In: *Psychoanalyse und Psychotherapie: Herausforderung und Losungen für die Zukunft*, ed. S. de Schill, S. Lebovici, & H. Kaechele. Stuttgart: Georg Thieme, pp. 132–154. (German). Translated from *Internat. J. Psycho-Anal.*, 52:11–50, 1971.

El Psicoanalisis como ciencia: Una respuesta a los nuevos desafios. In: *Psicoanalisis y Ciencia*, ed. A. M. Wagner. Buenos Aires: Ediciones Dunken, pp. 45–79. (Spanish). Translated from *Psychoanal. Quart.*, 55:414–451, 1986.

Resultados del psicoanalisis y de la psicoterapia en la terminacion y en el desarrollo. In: *Psicoanalisis y Ciencia*, ed. A. M. Wagner. Buenos Aires: Ediciones Dunken, pp. 85–124. (Spanish). Translated from *Textbook of Psychoanalysis*, ed. E. Nersessian & R. G. Kopff, 1996, pp. 531–573.

Foreword. In: *Freud's Models of the Mind: An Introduction*, by J. Sandler, A. Holder, C. Dare, & A. U. Dreher. London: Karnac Books, pp. xiii–xvi.

Foreword. In: *Supervision and Its Vicissitudes*, ed. B. Martindale, M. Morner, M. E. Cid Rodriguez, & J.-P. Videt. London: Karnac Books, pp. xiii–xviii.

Intervention modes in psychoanalysis and in psychotherapies: A revised classification (with K. N. DeWitt). In: *The Perverse Transference and Other Matters: Essays in Honor of R. Horacio Etchegoyen*, ed. J. Ahumada, J. Olagaray, A. K. Richards, & A. D. Richards. Northvale, NJ: Jason Aronson, pp. 87–114. Reprinted in *J. Psychother. Integration*, 7:129–150, 1997.

Katamnesen in der Psychoanalyse: Zu ihrem klinischen und empirischen Wert. In: *Psychoanalysen im Ruckblick*, ed. M. Leuzinger-Bohleber & U. Stuhr. Giessen, Germany: Psychosozial-Verlag, pp. 46–60. (German). Translated from *J. Amer. Psychoanal. Assn.*, 37:921–1942, 1989.

La ricerca psicoanalitica: Su cosa non siamo d'accordo? *Richard e Piggle*, 5:296–298. (Italian)

1998

Erikson's concept of ego identity reconsidered. *J. Amer. Psychoanal. Assn.*, 46:229–247.

Ideas and Identities: The Life and Work of Erik Erikson. (Editor, with L. Goldberger) Madison, CT: International Universities Press, pp. 411.

A Cura Pela Fala: As Psicanalises e as Psicoterapias (*The Talking Cures*), tr. M. A. Verissima Veronese. Porto Alegre, Brazil: Artmed. pp. 404. (Portuguese)

The IPA and the American Psychoanalytic Association: A perspective on the Regional Association agreement. *Internat. J. Psycho-Anal.*, 79:553–564.

Psychoanalysis: The future of an illusion? *Newsletter of the Internat. Psycho-Anal. Assn.*, 7(1):43–45.

Lay Analysis: Life Inside the Controversy. Mahwah, NJ: Analytic Press, pp. 511.

The New American psychoanalysis: A commentary. *J. Amer. Psychoanal. Assn.*, 46:1021–1043.

Sobre el Amor de Transferencia: Consideraciones sobre Freud. In: *En Torno a Freud: "Observaciones Sobre el Amor de Transferencia,"* ed E. S. Person, A. Hagelin, & P. Fonagy. Madrid: Biblioteca Nueva, pp. 35–51. (Spanish)

1999

Discussion: "The Cabernite Affair," by P. Hildebrand. *Bull. Brit. Psychoanal. Soc.*, 35(1):35–39.

Psychoanalytic research and the IPA: History, present status and future potential (with P. Fonagy). *Internat. J. Psycho-Anal.*, 80:91–109.

"The Cabernite affair." *Bull. Brit. Psychoanal. Soc.*, 35(3):22–24.

A half-century perspective on psychoanalysis and psychotherapy: The historical context of Joseph Sandler's contributions. In: *Psychoanalysis on the Move: The Work of Joseph Sandler*, ed. P. Fonagy, A. M. Cooper, & R. S. Wallerstein. London: Routledge, pp. 30–50.

Psychoanalysis: Clinical and Theoretical. Madison, CT: International Universities Press. pp. 430.

Freud and culture in our fin de siècle revisited. In: *Psychoanalysis and Culture at the Millennium*, ed. N. Ginsburg & R. Ginsburg. New Haven, CT: Yale University Press, pp. 355–379.

Obituary: Joseph J. Sandler (1927–1998). *Newsletter of the Internat. Psycho-Anal. Assn.*, 8(1):44–45.

Diagnosi riveduta (E ancora riveduta): Il caso dell'isteria e la personalita isterica. In: *Perche L'Isteria? Attualita di una Malattia Ontologica*, ed. F. Scalzone & G. Zontini. Naples: Liguori Editori, pp. 177–193 (Italian). Reprinted from *Internat. J. Psychoanal. Psychother.*, 8:533–547, 1980–1981.

L'Avenir de la psychotherapie. In: *A la Recherche de l'Avenir*, ed. S. de Schill & S. Lebovici. Paris: Presses Universitaires de France, pp. 111–148. (French). Translated from *Bull. Menn. Clinic*, 55:421–443, 1991.

La recherche dans le domaine du processus psychoanalytique: Questions. In: *A la Recherche de l'Avenir*, ed. S. de Schill & S. Lebovici. Paris: Presses Universitaires de France, pp. 291–337. (French). Translated from *Internat. J. Psycho-Anal.*, 52:11–50, 1971.

La identidad del psicoanalisis. *Imagen Psicoanalitica*, 7:33–59. (Spanish) Translated from *Bull. Menn. Clin.*, 60:514–535, 1996.

Commentary: "Making the case for psychoanalytic therapies in the current psychiatric environment," by J. G. Gunderson & G. O. Gabbard. *J. Amer. Psychoanal. Assn.*, 47:728–735.

Commentary on review of H. B. Vianna, *Psychoanalysis, Dictatorship, and Torture: Don't Talk About It*, by J. Puget. *J. Amer. Psychoanal. Assn.*, 47:965–973.

Scales of Psychological Capacities: Support for a measure of structural change (with K. N. DeWitt & C. Milbrath). *Psychoanal. & Contemp. Thought*, 22:453–480.

La psicologia del *self* y la psicologia psicoanalitica "clasica": La naturaleza de su relacion. In: *El self en la Teoria y en la Practica*, ed. G. Lancelle. Buenos Aires: Paidos, pp. 115–164. (Spanish)

2000

Response to Young-Bruehl (1999), *Psychoanal. Psychol.*, 17:160–163.

The question of lay analysis. *The Affiliate Council Newsletters*, 2(1):10–11.

Psychoanalysis and long-term dynamic psychotherapy (with M. D. Wilson). *Review of General Psychiatry*, 5th ed. New York: Lange Medical Books/McGraw-Hill, pp. 453–462.

Forty-Two Lives in Treatment: A Study of Psychoanalysis and Psychotherapy, paperback ed. New York: Other Press.

Where have all the patients gone? They're still here. *Psychoanal. Inq.*, 20:503–526.

Review: *Does Psychoanalysis Work?* by R. M. Galatzer-Levy, H. Bachrach, A. Skolnikoff, & S. Waldron, Jr. *J. Amer. Med. Assn.*, 284:1712–1713.

Psychoanalytic research: Where do we disagree? In: *Clinical and Observational Psychoanalytic Research: Roots of a Controversy, André Green and Daniel Stern*. ed. J. Sandler, A. M. Sandler, & R. Davies. London: Karnac Books, pp. 27–31.

Introduction. In: *Proceedings of the first Latin American Conference on Psychoanalytic Research*. (Introduccion a los Procidimientos de la Primera Conferencia Latino Americana de Investigacion Psicoanalitica.) London: International Psycho-Analytical Association, pp. 411–416, English; pp. 417–423, Spanish.

Letters: The Lobo-Cabernite affair. *J. Amer. Psychoanal. Assn.*, 48:1030–1036.

Merton Max Gill, M.D. & Merton Gill, psychotherapy and psychoanalysis: A personal dialogue. In: *Changing Conceptions of Psychoanalysis: The Legacy of Merton M. Gill*, ed. D. K. Silverman & D. L. Wolitzky. Mahwah, NJ: Analytic Press, pp. 15–19; 198–219.

Ko-Refarat: Discussion of Ronald Britton's *A Post-Kleinian Approach to the Ego*. In: *Das Ich—eine vernachlässigte Instanz*, ed. G. Weidenfeller. Frankfurt am Main: Deutsche Psychoanalytische Vereinigung (DPV), pp. 38–48.

Die Entwicklung und moderne Umgestaltung der (amerikanischen) Ich-Psychologie. In: *Das Ich–eine vernachlässigte Instanz*, ed. G. Weidenfeller. Frankfurt am Main: Deutsche Psychoanalytische Vereinigung (DPV), pp. 49–74. (German)

The trajectory of psychoanalysis: Past and future. *Samiksa*, 54:17–28.

Modus de interpretacion en psicoanalisis y en psicoterapias psicoanaliticas: una clasificacion revisada (with K. N. DeWitt). ed. J. Ahumada, J. Olagaray, A. K. Richards, and A. D. Richards. *Las*

Tareas del psicoanalisis: Ensayos en honor R. Horacio Etchegoyen. Buenes Aires: Polemos, pp. 114–143. (Spanish)

2001

Die Generationen der Psychotherapieforschung: Ein Uberblick. In: *Langzeit-Psychotherapie: Perspektiven für Therapeuten und Wissenschaftler,* ed. U. Stuhr, M. Leuzinger-Bohleber, & M. Beutel. Stuttgart: Verlag W. Kohlhammer, pp. 38–60. (German)

Review: *Countertransference and Regression,* by L. B. Boyer. *Newsletter of San Francisco Psychoanalytic Institute and Society,* March:3–4.

The generations of psychotherapy research: An overview. *Psychoanal. Psychology,* 18:243–267.

Foreword. *Psychoanalysis and Psychotherapy: The Controversies and the Future,* ed. S. Frisch. London, Karnac Books, pp. xiii–xix.

Entwicklung und moderne Transformation der (amerikanischen) Ich-Psychologie. *Psyche,* 55:649–684. (German)

La Trajectoire de la Psychanalyse: Ou en somme-nous Aujourd'hui? *Rev. Française de Psychanalyse,* Numero Hors Serie: 81–92. Erratum p. 679, Tome 66, 2002. (French)

Psychotherapy research and psychoanalytic practice: Commentary on papers by Lester Luborsky and Hans H. Strupp. *Psychoanal. Dial.,* 11:621–634.

Book Review of Joseph Schwartz *Cassandra's Daughter: A History of Psychoanalysis. Amer. Imago,* 58:723–737.

Letter to the Editor, Contemporary psychoanalysis. *Cont. Psychoanal.,* 37:505–509.

Zur Ubertragungsliebe: Wiederbegegnung mit Freud. In: *Uber Freud's "Bemerkungen uber die Ubertragungsliebe,* ed. E. Person, A. Hagelin, P. Fonagy. Stuttgart: Frommann-Holzboog Press, pp. 73–94.

Transference in psychoanalysis. In: *International Encyclopedia of the Social and Behavioral Sciences,* ed. N. Smelser & P. Baltes. Oxford, UK: Elsevier, 23: pp. 15851–15856.

2002

The generations of psychotherapy research: An overview. In: *Outcomes of Psychoanalytic Treatment: Perspectives for Therapists and Researchers,* ed. M. Leuzinger-Bohleber & M. Target. London: Whurr, pp. 30–52.

Association Psychoanalytique Internationale. In: *Dictionnaire International de la Psychoanalyse,* ed. A. de Mijolla. Paris: Calmann-Levy, pp. 140–147. (French)

Psychoanalytic therapy research: An overview. *Amer. Psychoanalyst,* 36 (1):10,13.

Obituary: William Gillespie (1905–2001). *Internat. J. Psycho-Anal.,* 83:277–281.

APsaA—IPA history: Determinants of the certification and training analyst issues. *Amer. Psychoanalyst,* 36, (2):14.

The growth and transformation of American ego psychology. *J. Amer. Psychoanal. Assn.,* 50:135–169.

The Common Ground. *The Affiliate Council Newsletter,* 4 Issue (1):1, 6–7.

Psychoanalytic treatments within psychiatry: An expanded view. *Arch. Gen. Psychiat.,* 59:499–500.

The organizational maturation of the IPA. *Newsletter of the Intern. Psycho-Anal. Assn.,* 11 Issue (1):24–26.

Psychotherapy research: The issue of structural change. *Newsletter of the San Francisco Psychoanal. Instit. & Soc.,* Sept. p. 8

Letter to the editor. *J. Amer. Psychoanal. Assn.* Wallerstein on lay analysis and the lawsuit. *J. Amer. Psychoanal. Assn.* 50:639–642.

LaRicerca Psicoanalytica: su cosa non siamo d'Accordo? In: *Quale Ricerca per la Psicoanalisi?* ed. Vincenzo Bonaminio & Paolo Fabozzi. Milano, Italy: Franco Angeli, pp. 36–38. (Italian)

LeQuestioni della Ricerca nel Processo Psicoanalitico (with Harold Sampson), In: *Quale Ricerca per la Psicoanalisi?* ed. Vincenzo Bonaminio & Paolo Fabozzi. Milano, Italy: Franco Angeli, pp. 168–231. (Italian)

LeQuestioni della Ricerca Psicoanalitica: Aggiornamenti, In: *Quale Ricerca per la Psicoanalisi?* ed. Vincenzo Bonaminio & Paulo Fabozzi. Milano, Italy: Franco Angeli, pp. 232–241. (Italian)

Name Index

Adler, A., 292
Alexander, F., 120, 230, 260
Altshuler, K. Z., 279
Appelbaum, A., 92, 94n, 95
Applegarth, A., 171n, 181n
Arlow, J. A., 212, 252
Auden, W. H., 250

Bachrach, H. M., 119n, 124, 126–128,
    132, 134, 150
Bak, R., 162, 167
Barrett, W. G., 131, 132
Beres, D., 255
Bibring, E., 109, 270
Bibring, G. L., 109–110, 120–121
Bini, 259n
Blacker, K. H., 131, 132
Blight, J. G., 193, 197
Braceland, F. J., 224, 267
Brenner, C. C., 160, 164, 167, 175, 252n
Breuer, J., 205, 216
Brill, 296
Brown, B. S., 67
Bryant, M., 56n
Burke, E., 10n
Burnham, J., 160
Burnstein, E. D., 94n

Calder, K., 302
Calef, V., 7–8
Cameron, D. E., 227, 273
Cerletti, 259n
Coriat, I., 119, 120n
Coyne, L., 92, 94n
Curtis, H., 301

Dahl, H., 145–146
Detre, 281–282
DeWitt, K. N., 114n
Diamond, B., 56n
Dilthey, W., 190, 197
Dunkel, L., 10n
Dwyer, T. F., 109–110

Eagle, M. N., 197, 198, 200–201
Edelson, M., 208–209, 256–257
Eissler, K., 162, 163, 167
Eitingon, M., 1, 241, 247, 293, 298
Eldred, S. H., 123–124, 132
Elson, R., 56n
Endicott, N. A., 163
Engel, G., 255, 284
Erdelyi, M. H., 210
Erikson, E. H., 165, 246, 293, 299
Erle, J. B., 127, 128–129, 132, 134

355

Subject Index